Register Now fo
to Your

Your print purchase of *Emotion-Centered Problem-Solving Therapy: Treatment Guidelines,* **includes online access to the contents of your book**—increasing accessibility, portability, and searchability!

Access today at:

http://connect.springerpub.com/content/book/978-0-8261-4316-7 or scan the QR code at the right with your smartphone and enter the access code below.

75GAE3SJ

Scan here for quick access.

SPRINGER / PUBLISHING COMPANY
View all our products at springerpub.com

Arthur M. Nezu, PhD, DHL, ABPP, is a distinguished professor of psychology, medicine, and public health at Drexel University. He is a licensed psychologist, a fellow of multiple psychological associations, and certified by the American Board of Professional Psychology (ABPP). He is a past president of both the Association of Behavioral and Cognitive Therapies and the American Board of Behavioral and Cognitive Psychology. Dr. Nezu is editor-in-chief of *Clinical Psychology: Science and Practice*, past editor of both the *Journal of Consulting and Clinical Psychology* and *the Behavior Therapist*, past associate editor of both *American Psychologist* and *Archives of Scientific Psychology*, and past chair of American Psychological Association's (APA's) Council of Editors. He was a member of APA's working group to develop the *Journal Article Reporting Standards for Quantitative Research* and a current member of the committee to revise the APA *Publication Manual*. He was also a member of the APA expert panel that developed the clinical practice guidelines for the treatment of depression and is a recipient of multiple awards for his research and professional contributions, including an honorary doctoral degree. Dr. Nezu has published over 225 journal articles and book chapters and 25 books. His research and program development activities have been funded by the National Cancer Institute, the National Institute of Mental Health, the Department of Veterans Affairs (VA), the Department of Defense, the U.S. Air Force, and the Pew Charitable Trusts. He is the codeveloper of numerous problem-solving–based treatment programs, including an intervention known as Moving Forward that is currently being implemented in VA medical centers across the United States.

Christine Maguth Nezu, PhD, ABPP, is a professor of psychology and medicine at Drexel University. She is a past president of the American Board of Professional Psychology (ABPP); a Fellow of the American Psychological Association; coprincipal of Nezu Psychological Associates' clinical and consulting practice; and a member of numerous journal editorial boards, including the *American Psychologist* and the *Journal of Consulting and Clinical Psychology*. She is the recipient of numerous awards, including the Russell J. Bent Distinguished Service and Contributions to the American Board of Professional Psychology Award and the Outstanding Contribution by an Individual for Education and Training Activities Award from the Association of Behavioral and Cognitive Therapies. She is also certified by ABPP. She codeveloped a problem-solving–based therapy program for the Department of Veterans Affairs (VA) and the Department of Defense (DoD), which is currently being implemented across the United States. As a consultant to the U.S. Air Force, she recently codeveloped a problem-solving–skills training program. She has published more than 150 journal articles and book chapters, and coauthored 21 books. Dr. Maguth Nezu's clinical research collaboration and program development activities have been funded by the National Cancer Institute, the National Institute of Mental Health, the Department of Justice, VA, DoD, the U.S. Air Force, and the Pew Charitable Trusts. She has held honorary and visiting faculty appointments in Japan and the United Kingdom and has presented numerous invited workshops around the world. Her current clinical and research interests include suicide treatment and prevention and integrative psychotherapy.

EMOTION-CENTERED PROBLEM-SOLVING THERAPY

Treatment Guidelines

Arthur M. Nezu, PhD, DHL, ABPP
Christine Maguth Nezu, PhD, ABPP

SPRINGER PUBLISHING COMPANY

Springer Publishing Company, LLC
11 West 42nd Street
New York, NY 10036
www.springerpub.com

Acquisitions Editor: Sheri W. Sussman
Compositor: Graphic World

ISBN: 978-0-8261-4314-3
ebook ISBN: 978-0-8261-4316-7
DOI: 10.1891/9780826143167

18 19 20 21 22 / 5 4 3 2 1

The author and the publisher of this Work have made every effort to use sources believed to be reliable to provide information that is accurate and compatible with the standards generally accepted at the time of publication. The author and publisher shall not be liable for any special, consequential, or exemplary damages resulting, in whole or in part, from the readers' use of, or reliance on, the information contained in this book. The publisher has no responsibility for the persistence or accuracy of URLs for external or third-party Internet websites referred to in this publication and does not guarantee that any content on such websites is, or will remain, accurate or appropriate.

Library of Congress Cataloging-in-Publication Data

Names: Nezu, Arthur M., author. | Nezu, Christine M., author.
Title: Emotion-centered problem-solving therapy : treatment guidelines /
    Arthur M. Nezu, PhD, DHL, ABPP, Christine Maguth Nezu, PhD, ABPP.
Description: New York, NY : Springer Publishing Company, LLC, [2019] | Includes
    bibliographical references and index.
Identifiers: LCCN 2018046844 (print) | LCCN 2018047794 (ebook) |
    ISBN 9780826143167 | ISBN 9780826143143 (pbk.)
Subjects: LCSH: Emotion-focused therapy. | Emotions.
Classification: LCC RC489.F62 (ebook) | LCC RC489.F62 N49 2019 (print) | DDC
    616.89/1425—dc23
LC record available at https://lccn.loc.gov/2018046844

Contact us to receive discount rates on bulk purchases.
We can also customize our books to meet your needs.
For more information please contact: sales@springerpub.com

Arthur M. Nezu: https://orcid.org/0000-0002-1651-2102
Christine Maguth Nezu: https://orcid.org/0000-0003-3324-9729

Publisher's Note: **New and used products purchased from third-party sellers are not guaranteed for quality, authenticity, or access to any included digital components.**

Printed in the United States of America.

This book is dedicated to all who suffer and struggle.

CONTENTS

PREFACE

This book represents the culmination of decades of research and clinical experience regarding various problem-solving–based interventions. These interventions, primarily known as *problem-solving therapy (PST)*, have been in existence (ostensibly as a type of cognitive-behavioral approach) since the 1970s. More specifically, on the basis of an extensive review of the literature, psychologists Thomas D'Zurilla and Marvin Goldfried developed a training model geared to foster positive mental health and adaptive functioning via problem-solving skills (D'Zurilla & Goldfried, 1971). Note that the title of this seminal paper was "Problem Solving and Behavior Modification," which to some extent may appear to represent an anomaly. Historically, the "first wave" of behavior therapy or modification was based very heavily on principles of respondent learning and operant learning. This focus on a more cognitive approach to treatment, that is, problem solving, was part of the "cognitive revolution" in psychology in general (Greenwood, 1999), and within behavior therapy/modification in particular (Bandura, 1969; Mahoney, 1977). Other cognitive approaches that were gaining popularity at that time included rational emotive therapy, cognitive behavior modification, self-control therapy, and cognitive therapy (Kendall & Hollon, 1979). Such attempts posited that traditional behavior therapy and modification did not take into account various cognitive factors that were empirically shown to be involved in the etiology and maintenance of psychological disorders and behavior problems.

It is within this context that PST continued to flourish (even to this day). However, one of the basic tenets of this approach was to be more on the side of the fence that maintained that cognitions (in the form of problem-solving variables) took precedence over affective or emotional factors in understanding the etiopathogenesis of psychopathology as well as designated primary targets of change. The role of emotions in the problem-solving process of our earlier models was predominately viewed as either facilitator (e.g., positive emotions enhance motivation) or inhibitor (e.g., negative emotions interfere with making effective decisions; D'Zurilla & Nezu, 1999). Although in general such processes continue to be valid, the interplay between cognition, albeit of all forms, and emotion is substantially more complex than originally thought. Of particular relevance are recent major advances in affective neuroscience, which have provided a deeper understanding, for example, of how stress impacts the brain and subsequently affects emotions and cognitions (Korb, 2015).

Because of the tendency by many in the field to view cognitive factors as antecedents of emotions, many researchers considered PST solely as a tool for training individuals in various rational problem-solving activities (i.e., defining a problem, generating solutions, decision-making, solution verification). However, the original model espoused by D'Zurilla and Goldfried, as well as by us, included a "problem orientation" component that involved the manner in which individuals view problems, their problem-solving abilities, and the role emotions play in problem solving. Although many clinical trials of PST did include a focus on orientation variables, many others did not. This exclusion of orientation variables unfortunately continues to this day, despite two meta-analyses (Bell & D'Zurilla, 2009; Malouff, Thorsteinsson, & Schutte, 2007) and a direct assessment of the question (Nezu & Perri, 1989), "Does including training to foster a positive orientation and attenuate a negative orientation foster better outcome?" that indicate such variables do improve outcomes. Such differences in what constitutes the important treatment ingredients of PST may have led to meta-analyses of PST interventions that point to the wide variability in outcome effect sizes (Cuijpers, de Wit, Kleiboer, Karyotaki, & Ebert, 2018).

This is all to indicate that the term *emotion-centered problem-solving therapy* or *EC-PST* does not represent a revolution of ideas, but rather an evolutionary process. In other words, it is to highlight the importance of focusing on emotional factors, in addition to cognitive variables, especially in light of how neuroscience research has led to an improved understanding of their complex relationships (Lai, Hagoort, & Casasanto, 2012; Okon-Singer, Hendler, Pessoa, & Shackman, 2015). For example, as noted in Chapter 2, research by Damasio (1999) indicates that we may have feelings without knowing that we have feelings. Such nonconscious processes are important to acknowledge when developing meaningful treatment strategies (e.g., our "Stop and Slow Down" approach to better emotion regulation). In addition, we wish to remind our colleagues that PST is not simply rational problem-solving training; EC-PST is more complex and able to adequately address complex psychological problems. For example, the cases of the three patients we highlight and follow throughout the book are quite complicated—EC-PST is not simply geared to helping people find better jobs or manage minor stressors. As the wide variety of clinical trials that have found this approach to be effective attests (see

Chapter 3), it has been efficacious for very complex and difficult problems and populations. So, we urge future researchers interested in PST to be more interested in EC-PST, as we posit that outcomes will be better. We also urge clinicians to apply this approach because it has been found to be well received, user-friendly, and effective.

So this edition represents an update of relevant research and theory as well as changes in the treatment. It should be of interest to researchers, therapists, counselors, and instructors. These same groups will also be interested in our Client Workbook, which is meant to be used in conjunction with this therapy manual and provides material that can be used as handouts for clients engaged in EC-PST. **To purchase the Client Workbook, please visit: http://connect.springerpub .com/content/book/978-0-8261-3523-0**

We thank all of our colleagues and students who have helped us during the past several decades in various research and program development activities. In particular, we thank Tom D'Zurilla, who served as an inspiration and mentor throughout the years. We also thank the thousands of patients and clients who have trusted our programs and undergone treatment. Last, we offer much appreciation to Sheri Sussman of Springer Publishing Company, who has had continued faith in us over many years.

Arthur M. Nezu
Christine Maguth Nezu

REFERENCES

Bandura, A. (1969). *Principles of behavior modification*. Oxford, England: Holt, Rinehart, & Winston.

Bell, A. C., & D'Zurilla, T. J. (2009). Problem-solving therapy for depression: A meta-analysis. *Clinical Psychology Review, 29,* 348–353. doi:10.1016/j.cpr.2009.02.003

Cuijpers, P., de Wit, L., Kleiboer, A., Karyotaki, E., & Ebert, D. D. (2018). Problem-solving therapy for adult depression: An updated meta-analysis. *European Psychiatry, 48,* 27–37. doi:10.1016/ j.eurpsy.2017.11.006

D'Zurilla, T. J., & Goldfried, M. R. (1971). Problem solving and behavior modification. *Journal of Abnormal Psychology, 78,* 107–126. doi:10.1037/h0031360

D'Zurilla, T. J., & Nezu, A. M. (1999). *Problem-solving therapy: A social competence approach to clinical intervention* (2nd ed.). New York, NY: Springer Publishing.

Damasio, A. R. (1999). *The feeling of what happens*. New York, NY: Harcourt & Brace.

Greenwood, J. D. (1999). Understanding the "cognitive revolution" in psychology. *Journal of the History of the Behavioral Sciences, 35,* 1–22. doi:10.1002/(SICI)1520-6696(199924)35:1<1::AID-JHBS1>3.0.CO;2-4

Kendall, P. C., & Hollon, S. D. (1979). *Cognitive-behavioral interventions*. New York, NY: Academic Press.

Korb, A. (2015). *The upward spiral: Using neuroscience to reverse the course of depression, one small change at a time*. Oakland, CA: New Harbinger Publications.

Lai, V. T., Hagoort, P., & Casasanto, D. (2012). Affective primacy vs. cognitive primacy: Dissolving the debate. *Frontiers in Psychology, 3*, 243. doi:10.3389/fpsyg.2012.00243

Mahoney, M. J. (1977). Reflections on the cognitive-learning trend in psychotherapy. *American Psychologist, 32*, 5–13. doi:10.1037/0003-066X.32.1.5

Malouff, J. M., Thorsteinsson, E. B., & Schutte, N. S. (2007). The efficacy of problem solving therapy in reducing mental and physical health problems: A meta-analysis. *Clinical Psychology Review, 27*, 46–57. doi:10.1016/j.cpr.2005.12.005

Nezu, A. M., & Perri, M. G. (1989). Social problem-solving therapy for unipolar depression: An initial dismantling investigation. *Journal of Consulting and Clinical Psychology, 57*, 408–413. doi:10.1037/0022-006X.57.3.408

Okon-Singer, H., Hendler, T., Pessoa, L., & Shackman, A. J. (2015). The neurobiology of emotion–cognition interactions: Fundamental questions and strategies for future research. *Frontiers in Human Neuroscience, 9*, 58. doi:10.3389/fnhum.2015.00058

CONCEPTUAL AND EMPIRICAL
CONSIDERATIONS

WHAT IS EMOTION-CENTERED PROBLEM-SOLVING THERAPY?

We begin this chapter by asking the reader to solve the following problem:

> *A young boy turned off the lights in his bedroom and managed to get into bed before the room was dark. If the bed is 10 feet from the light switch and the lamp, and he did not use any wires, strings, or other contraptions to actually turn off the light, how did he do it?*

How *did* he do it? This type of problem is generally referred to as an "insight problem." An *insight* involves a sudden recognition of a solution or a straightforward path to a solution. For example, while pondering the preceding question about the lights, one may look at the problem from a different perspective and suddenly realize the answer. If you continue to have difficulty with the question, note that the answer is provided at the end of this chapter.

Other types of problems can involve mathematical calculations. For example, once again, try to solve the following problem:

> *If a baseball and a bat cost $1.10 together, and the bat costs $1.00 more than the ball. How much does the ball cost?*

If you answered "10 cents," although this is the answer most people provide, unfortunately, it is incorrect. Intuitively, the answer would *appear* to be 10 cents as $1.00 plus $0.10 does equal $1.10. However, that was not the question, nor was that the problem. Consider that if one subtracts $0.10 from $1.00, the remainder is $0.90, and not $1.00. Remember that the problem requires that the bat costs $1.00 *more* than the ball, *not* $0.90 more. Once again, the answer is at the end of this chapter.

© Springer Publishing Company DOI: 10/1891/9780826143167.0001

Problems like those just posed have often been the focus of the fields of experimental and cognitive psychology. Within this context, the construct of problem solving has traditionally been conceptualized as a major component of executive functioning involving higher order mental or cognitive processes. *Problem solving* has generally been defined as the process by which one attempts to reach a goal by overcoming barriers that block the path to a solution. Thus, this area of psychological inquiry basically addresses the question of how humans solve problems of a cognitive or intellectual nature, such as those provided earlier in the text.

Now think about the types of problems that your clients come to you for assistance with or the types of problems that your research is geared to better understand or ameliorate. For example, the following problem would not be one uncommonly encountered by most therapists or clinical researchers. As you scan this problem, consider how you might "solve" it (or help the client solve it).

> *Steve Johnson has been experiencing sleep difficulties for the past several weeks, and is having problems concentrating at work. This all started when he began to hear rumors about layoffs. Due to a history of depression, he knows that he has a strong tendency to "jump to conclusions," but he is very afraid of getting fired, especially when he and his wife just learned that she is pregnant with a third child. Upon learning of the pregnancy, he began to question the desirability of a new family member, which led to major arguments with his wife, who was thinking that another child would improve their marriage. The fear of getting laid off while expecting a new baby has increased Steve's anxiety and worry. Plus, his migraine headaches have come back and have intensified. What should Steve do?*

Of course, this represents a much different type of problem than the two described earlier. As we have argued, insight, logic, and mathematical problems do not reflect the complexity of dilemmas that people like Steve (and all of us) face in the real world (Nezu, Greenfield, & Nezu, 2016). In essence, we suggest that "real-life" problems are different in that:

- They are more complicated.
- They are often stressful.
- They are caused by or engender emotional difficulties.
- They frequently involve other individuals.
- They have real-life consequences.

- They usually have more than one "correct" solution, and because of different goals, values, and personal variables, whether a given solution to a real-life problem is successful or effective depends *heavily* on the people involved and the specific nature of the circumstances that characterize the problem.

Although the construct of problem solving has a rich history of research within the fields of experimental psychology, cognitive psychology, and cognitive neuroscience, the question of whether social and behavioral adjustment is actually related to one's ability to successfully solve *everyday problems* did not receive serious scientific study until the second half of the 20th century (D'Zurilla & Nezu, 2007). Similarly, the issue of whether training individuals to become better problem solvers may be appropriate as a psychosocial intervention to reduce psychopathology, enhance effective coping, and prevent psychopathology from developing received little attention prior to the 1970s. Thus, the focus of this book is *emotion-centered problem-solving therapy* (EC-PST).

EC-PST: AN OVERVIEW

EC-PST is the reformulated and updated version of *problem-solving therapy* or PST. This newer approach puts more emphasis on teaching individuals to better understand and manage their emotional reactions to stressful events than those previously included in our PST protocols. EC-PST essentially is a psychosocial intervention developed within a social learning framework that is based on a biopsychosocial, diathesis–stress model of psychopathology (see Chapter 2). In general, this intervention involves training individuals in a set of skills aimed at enhancing their ability to cope effectively with a variety of life stressors that have the potential to generate negative health and mental health outcomes, such as chronic medical conditions, depression, and anxiety. Life stressors can include major negative life events (e.g., death of a loved one, diagnosis and treatment of a chronic illness, loss of a job, incarceration, military combat), chronic daily problems (e.g., continuous tension with coworkers, reduced financial resources, discrimination, marital difficulties), and traumatic events (e.g., victim of rape/sexual assault, witnessing death, significant vehicular accident).

The theoretical underpinnings of EC-PST assume that much of what is conceptualized as psychopathology and behavioral difficulties, including significant emotional problems, is a function of continuous ineffective coping with such life stress, in part, because of ineffective problem-solving skills and abilities. As a result, it is hypothesized that teaching individuals to become better problem solvers can serve to reduce extant physical and mental health difficulties. The overarching goal of this approach is to promote the following:

1. Successful adoption of adaptive problem-solving attitudes (e.g., optimism, enhanced self-efficacy, recognition and appreciation of the notion that problems are a normal aspect of living)

2. Effective implementation of certain behaviors (e.g., emotional regulation, planful problem solving) as a means of coping with life stress and thereby attenuating the negative effects of stress on physical and mental well-being

EC-PST TREATMENT COMPONENTS

In essence, EC-PST is based on the notion that four ubiquitous obstacles exist when people attempt to cope with stressful real-life problems. These include:

- Ineffective problem-solving strategies
- Stimulus or "brain overload"
- Poor motivation and/or feelings of hopelessness
- Limited ability to engage in effective emotional regulation

Clinically, EC-PST involves training individuals in four major problem-solving "tool kits" or skill sets that directly address each of the major barriers just mentioned. The following lists the tool kits using the labels provided to clients:

- Planful Problem Solving
- Overcoming "Brain Overload"
- Enhancing Motivation for Action
- "Stop and Slow Down"

It is important to note that the order in which the tool kits are listed and described throughout this book represents the sequence administered in research settings when there is the need to standardize treatment implementation, for example, in a randomized clinical trial. In clinical settings, however, we advocate that therapists develop a case formulation plan to better determine individual client needs and tailor EC-PST accordingly. This is discussed further in Chapter 4. All four tool kits are described in detail as part of the detailed treatment guidelines offered in Section III.

Planful Problem-Solving Tool Kit: Fostering Effective Problem Solving

This first tool kit includes a training module that teaches the four major planful problem-solving tasks, the first being *problem definition*. This initial activity involves having a client separate facts from assumptions when describing a problem, delineate a realistic and attainable set of problem-solving goals and objectives, and identify those obstacles that prevent the client from reaching these goals. Note that we advocate identifying both *problem-focused goals* (i.e., those goals that entail changing the nature of the situation so that it no longer represents a problem) and *emotion-focused goals* (i.e., those goals that involve moderating one's cognitive–emotional reactions to those situations that cannot be changed, such as the death of a loved one). Strategies that can be effective in reaching such emotion-focused goals might include stress management, forgiveness of others, and acceptance that the situation cannot be changed.

The second activity, *generating alternatives*, involves creatively brainstorming a range of possible solution activities aimed at overcoming various identified obstacles to goals. *Decision making*, the third planful problem-solving task, involves predicting the likely consequences of such alternatives, conducting a cost–benefit analysis based on these identified outcomes, and developing a solution plan geared to achieve the articulated problem-solving goal. The last activity, *solution implementation and verification*, entails having individuals optimally carry out the solution plan, monitor and evaluate the consequences of the plan, and determine whether their problem-solving efforts have been successful or need to continue.

Problem-Solving "Multitasking" Tool Kit: Overcoming "Brain Overload"

This set of tools is taught to help clients overcome a ubiquitous human limitation when attempting to cope with stressful situations in real life—"brain overload" or "cognitive overload." Because of basic human limitations in people's ability to manipulate large amounts of information in their working memory while attempting to actually solve complex problems or make effective decisions when under stress, individuals are taught to use three "multitasking enhancement" skills: externalization, visualization, and simplification. These skills are considered foundational to effective problem solving, similar to those skills that may be taught as basic to effective aerobic exercise, such as stretching, breathing, and maintaining a healthy diet.

Externalization involves displaying information "externally" as often as possible. More specifically, clients are taught, for example, to write down ideas, draw diagrams or charts to determine relationships, draw maps, make lists, and to audiotape their ideas. Thus, one's working memory is not overly taxed, and therefore one can concentrate more on other activities, such as creatively thinking of various solutions. The *visualization* tool is presented as using one's "mind's eye," or visual imagery, to help (a) better clarify the nature of a problem, (b) practice carrying out a solution (imaginal rehearsal), and (c) reduce high levels of negative arousal (i.e., a form of guided imagery whereby one is directed imaginally to go on a peaceful vacation). *Simplification* involves "breaking down" or simplifying problems to make them more manageable. Here, clients are taught to break down complex problems into more manageable smaller problems and/or goals, and translate complex, vague, and abstract concepts into more simple, specific, and concrete language.

Enhancing Motivation for Action Tool Kit: Overcoming Low Motivation and Feelings of Hopelessness

This third tool kit is included in EC-PST to specifically address certain motivational issues if relevant to a particular individual, that is, procrastination and/or feelings of hopelessness. The first tool in this skill set would be used if clients are hesitant to move forward at any point in treatment, for example, when they have trepidation at carrying out an action plan to solve a problem. Here, clients are taught to list a series of consequences that can occur if they do not carry out an action plan. In addition, they are directed to delineate a series of outcomes that are potentially possible if the plan is carried out and is somewhat successful in reaching a desired goal. The comparison of these two lists can lead to enhanced motivation to actually implement one's solution plan. Also, it can lead to the potential identification of a deficient or limited action plan that would signal to both the therapist and the client that they need to potentially revise the plan.

A second activity in this tool kit involves the use of visualization to further enhance motivation and specifically to reduce feelings of hopelessness. The application of visualization in this context, which is different than that described within the multitasking tool kit (#2), is to help individuals to sensorially experience what it "feels" like to successfully solve a difficult problem, in other words, to see and experience the light at the end of the tunnel or to cross the finish line at the end of a race. With this strategy, the therapist's goal is to help clients create the experience of success in their "mind's eye," and vicariously experience the potential reinforcement to be gained. They are specifically taught to *not* focus on "how the problem got solved," but rather to focus on the feelings associated with having *already* solved it. The central goal of this strategy is to have individuals create their own positive consequences (in the form of affect, thoughts, physical sensations, and behavior) associated with solving a difficult problem as a major motivational step toward overcoming low motivation and feelings of hopelessness, as well as minimizing the tendency to engage in avoidant problem solving.

"Stop and Slow Down": Overcoming Emotion Dysregulation

This final tool kit becomes especially important to emphasize in situations in which the primary goal of EC-PST for particular individuals involves the decrease of clinically significant emotional distress (e.g., depression, suicidal ideation, generalized anxiety). It is also useful for training individuals as a means of preventing extant emotional concerns from becoming particularly problematic. In essence, clients are taught a series of steps to enhance their ability to modulate (as opposed to "eradicate") negative emotional arousal so as to apply a systematic approach to solving problems more effectively (i.e., to be able to optimally use the various planful problem-solving skills). This tool kit is also presented to individuals as the overarching "map" to follow when attempting to cope with stressful problems that engender strong emotional reactions and is included as the major treatment strategy geared to foster adaptive emotional regulation skills. It is also included in EC-PST as a means of minimizing impulsive/careless attempts at problem solving, as well as avoidance of the problem.

According to this approach, clients are first taught to become "emotionally mindful" by being more aware of, and specifically attentive to, when and how they experience negative emotional arousal. Specifically, they are taught to notice changes in physical (e.g., headache, fatigue, pain), emotional (e.g., sadness, anger, tension), cognitive (e.g., worry, thoughts of negative outcomes), and/or behavioral (e.g., urge to run away, yelling, crying) indicators. For certain individuals, additional training may be necessary to increase the accuracy by which they attempt to identify and label emotional phenomena. Next, they are taught to *stop* and focus on what is happening to become more aware of what is engendering this arousal. More specifically, they are directed to engage in behaviors (e.g., shouting out loud, raising one's hands, holding up a stop sign) that can aid them in "putting on the brakes" to better modulate their emotional arousal (i.e., prevent the initial arousal from evoking a more intense form of the emotion together with its "full blown" concomitant negative thinking, state-dependent negative memories, negative affect, and maladaptive behaviors).

Next, to meaningfully be able to *stop*, clients are further taught to *slow down*; that is, to decrease the accelerated rate at which their negative emotionality can occur. Various specific techniques are provided and practiced with clients to offer them a choice of potentially effective tools used to slow down. These techniques include counting backward from 20 to 1, diaphragmatic breathing, guided imagery or visualization, "fake yawning" (in accord with neuroscience research demonstrating the efficacy of directed yawning as a stress-management strategy and a means to enhance cognitive awareness; Newberg & Waldman, 2009), meditation, exercise, talking to others, and prayer (if relevant). Individuals are also encouraged to identify and use strategies that have been especially helpful to them in the past not included in the slow-down list.

An acronym, *SSTA* (Stop, Slow down, Think, Act), is then taught in which the *T* and *A* refer to *thinking* and *acting*; thus the acronym represents the four planful problem-solving tasks described earlier. In other words, once individuals have "slowed down," they are able to think and act in a rational manner as a means of attempting to cope with the stressful problem situation that initially evoked the negative emotional reaction.

Guided Practice

A major part of the EC-PST intervention involves providing feedback and additional training to individuals through use of the four tool kits as they continue to apply the model to current problems they are experiencing. In addition, EC-PST encourages individuals to "forecast" future stressful situations, whether positive (e.g., getting a promotion and moving to a new city) or negative (e.g., the breakup of a relationship) to anticipate how such tools can be used in the future to minimize potential negative consequences.

EC-PST: HISTORICAL PERSPECTIVE

The genesis of problem-solving–based interventions from a cognitive and behavioral perspective can be traced back to a seminal article written by D'Zurilla and Goldfried (1971), who conducted a comprehensive review of the relevant theory and research literature on problem solving to better understand its "relevance for problem solving in real-life situations, to show how difficulties in problem solving may arise, and to suggest possible training or therapeutic procedures which may be employed to facilitate more effective problem solving" (p. 107). The construct of problem solving that occurs within real-world contexts had been subsequently referred to in the literature as *social problem solving* (SPS) to differentiate it from the types of problems presented earlier, such as logic or mathematical dilemmas (e.g., D'Zurilla & Nezu, 1982; Nezu & D'Zurilla, 1989).

D'Zurilla and Goldfried (1971) also articulated a prescriptive model of problem-solving training geared to enhance one's ability to cope effectively with difficulties encountered in daily living. In essence, their protocol involved training people in a set of skills that encompassed the following three dimensions: (a) the ability to use a variety of alternative pathways or behavioral responses to reach a given goal; (b) the ability to take advantage of various social resources;

and (c) the ability to adopt a positive, broad, and sophisticated understanding of the world (D'Zurilla & Nezu, 1999).

Subsequently, by virtue of being a graduate student in clinical psychology under the mentorship of Professor T. D'Zurilla, one of us (A.M.N.) became especially interested in the clinical applications of this approach. A.M.N.'s initial efforts involved confirming several of the theoretical tenets of the model, including the positive benefits of training individuals to better define social problems (Nezu & D'Zurilla, 1981a, 1981b), generate alternatives (D'Zurilla & Nezu, 1980), and make effective decisions regarding such problems (Nezu & D'Zurilla, 1979). On the basis of research regarding the stress-buffering properties of effective problem-solving coping (e.g., Nezu & Ronan, 1985, 1988), D'Zurilla and Nezu later developed the relational/problem-solving model of stress referred to in Chapter 2, which initially provided for a conceptual framework supporting the broad-based applicability of PST across a wide range of clinical problems and populations (Nezu & D'Zurilla, 1989).

In the 1980s, Nezu and colleagues focused their research activities on the relationship between problem solving and clinical depression, an effort resulting in the development of both a conceptual model of depression (Nezu, 1987) and an adapted version of PST for depression called *social problem-solving therapy (SPST*; Nezu, Nezu, & Perri, 1989). The earlier outcome studies evaluated the efficacy of PST for major depressive disorder (e.g., Nezu, 1986; Nezu & Perri, 1989), so this approach has come to be viewed as an efficacious, evidence-based psychosocial treatment alternative for depression, as supported, for example, by various systematic reviews and meta-analyses of this literature (see Chapter 3). However, the adjective "social" within the title was often dropped by other researchers and the model become more readily known as *PST*.

Since that time, researchers and clinicians have successfully applied variations of this model to a wide range of psychological disorders, medical problems, and clinical populations (Nezu, Nezu, & D'Zurilla, 2013). As new research improves our understanding of the relationship between problem solving and stress, we have continuously revised and updated the basic PST model to incorporate findings from the outcome literature, as well as basic research from the fields of affective neuroscience, cognitive psychology, and clinical psychology. In particular, given advances in our understanding of the important role that stress-related negative emotional arousal plays in engendering psychological difficulties (e.g., LeBlanc, McConnell, & Monteiro, 2015), we refer to the most recent iteration of our approach as *EC-PST* to underscore the important need to focus on attenuating the impact of such arousal on one's ability to engage in rational problem-solving activities when applied as a psychotherapy intervention. In other words, EC-PST underscores the importance of teaching those types of skills that foster one's ability to engage in effective emotion regulation. The importance of focusing on emotions within the problem-solving process is emphasized throughout this book.

Overall, this intervention approach has been effective in helping individuals suffering from a wide variety of health and mental health problems, such as depression, anxiety, emotional distress, suicidal ideation, cancer, heart disease, diabetes, stroke, traumatic brain injury, back pain, hypertension, and posttraumatic stress disorder (see D'Zurilla & Nezu [2007] and Nezu et al. [2013], for detailed overviews of the extant outcome literature at the time these books were written, and Chapter 3 of this book for more recent PST applications). EC-PST has also been used effectively to treat individuals with schizophrenia and functional disability, as well as implemented as a means of preventing emotional difficulties from initially occurring or becoming worse in certain vulnerable populations, such as veterans returning from combat war zones. Problem-solving–based interventions have further been evaluated empirically as an adjunctive strategy to enhance one's adherence to other forms of medical or psychological treatments, as a means of improving the lives of caregivers as well as enhancing their ability to care for a loved one, and as a major treatment component of marital and couples therapy. In addition, PST has been effectively implemented across various venues, including individual therapy, group counseling, and telemedicine protocols (e.g., telephone, Internet).

SOCIAL PROBLEM-SOLVING CONSTRUCTS: DEFINITIONS

In this section, we provide definitions for the following constructs: *real-life problems, real-life solutions, SPS.* We also describe a multidimensional model of SPS that helps guide the treatment process.

"Real-Life" Problems

A *real-life problem* is defined as a life situation, present or anticipated, that requires an adaptive response to prevent negative consequences from occurring, but for which an effective response or solution is not immediately obvious or available to the individual(s) experiencing the situation. Problems can occur externally within a person's social or physical environment, for example, a conflict with a family member or poor living conditions. They can also originate internally or intrapersonally, such as a desire to make more money or being confused about one's life goals.

Such situations are a problem for a given individual because of the presence of various barriers that make it difficult for that person to *automatically* overcome the barriers to reach a desired goal. Such obstacles can include the following:

- Novelty (e.g., beginning a new romantic relationship)
- Ambiguity (e.g., uncertainty about how to obtain a mortgage)
- Unpredictability (e.g., lack of control over one's job stability)
- Conflicting goals (e.g., differences between spouses/partners with regard to child-rearing practices)
- Performance skill deficits (e.g., difficulties communicating)
- Lack of resources (e.g., limited finances)
- Significant emotional arousal (e.g., prolonged grief over the loss of a loved one)
- Long-standing negative schemas or worldviews (e.g., poor self-esteem)

Individuals may recognize that a problem exists almost immediately based on their reactions to a situation. Such reactions can involve physical symptoms (e.g., headaches), negative thoughts (e.g., thoughts of incompetence), or negative emotions (e.g., urge to aggress against someone). Alternatively, they may only identify the problem after repeated initial attempts to cope with the situation have failed. However, for some people, not labeling such situations as "a problem" can serve to inhibit their ability to effectively solve them. Problems can be a *single time-limited event* (e.g., losing one's car keys; being late for an important appointment); a *series of similar or related events* (e.g., repeated disagreements between friends; not having a job that pays well); or a *chronic, ongoing situation* (e.g., parenting a child with a serious medical illness; living in poverty). They can especially be created by the occurrence of a new major life change (e.g., getting fired, getting a divorce) or a traumatic event (e.g., experiencing sexual violence, being in a major vehicular accident).

Problems should not be considered solely the result of either one's environment or the action of the individual himself or herself. Instead, a problem is an interaction between people and their environment that is represented by a real or perceived discrepancy between the demands of the situation and one's coping ability. Thus, problems are by definition idiographic and can change in difficulty or significance over time, depending on changes in the person, environment, or both. In other words, what is thought of as a problem for one individual may not be considered a problem for someone else. Moreover, what is thought of as a problem for a given person at one time may not, in fact, be considered a problem for this same person at a different point in time.

"Real-Life" Solutions

Solutions within real-world contexts involve situation-specific coping responses that are geared to mitigate the problem. However, solutions vary in their ability to successfully achieve an optimal problem-solving goal. Thus, differences between effective and ineffective solutions need to be defined. An *effective* solution is one that not only successfully attains a person's desired objective but also simultaneously further maximizes positive consequences and attenuates negative outcomes. Alternatively, *ineffective solutions* are characterized as attempts that (a) do not reach one's desired goal(s) as a function of being unable to overcome various obstacles, (b) are focused on addressing inappropriate (e.g., avoidance of the problem) or ill-defined goals, and/or (c) create more negative consequences than positive ones. Consequences include the various effects on oneself and others, as well as short- and long-term outcomes. Note that individuals can differ in their evaluation of the efficacy of a given solution as a function of varying norms, values, and goals.

Social Problem Solving

We define *SPS* as the process by which individuals attempt to identify, discover, or create adaptive means of coping with a wide variety of stressful problems, both acute and chronic, encountered during the course of living (D'Zurilla & Nezu, 2007). As argued earlier, this is in contrast to the types of problem solving involved in solving cognitive or intellectual problems, such as insight problems or mathematical problems. SPS reflects the process whereby people direct their coping efforts at altering the problematic nature of a given situation, their reactions to such problems, or both. Rather than representing a singular type of coping behavior or activity, SPS represents the multidimensional metaprocess of ideographically identifying and selecting various coping responses to implement in order to adequately address the unique features of a given problematic situation at a given time (Nezu, 2004).

To minimize confusion often found in the literature, note that the construct of *SPS* should be differentiated from that of *problem-focused coping*. The term *coping* generally refers to the cognitive and behavioral activities that an individual uses to manage stressful situational demands, as well as the emotions they generate. Two major types of coping have been described in the literature: problem-focused coping and emotion-focused coping (Lazarus & Folkman, 1984). *Problem-focused coping* includes those activities that are directed at changing the stressful situation for the better (i.e., meeting, changing, or controlling situational demands), whereas *emotion-focused coping* is represented by activities aimed at managing the negative emotions generated by a stressful situation.

Within this context, SPS has, at times, been misrepresented as equivalent to a form of problem-focused coping, suggesting that SPS goals include only mastery goals or attempts to control the environment (e.g., change another's behavior).

However, we conceive of SPS as being a broader, more versatile coping process that often can include both problem-focused and emotion-focused objectives. Regardless of whether the objective is articulated as problem-focused or emotion-focused, the ultimate goal of SPS is to minimize the negative effects of stressful life events on well-being. Note that it is likely that particularly stressful problems require both problem-focused and emotion-focused activities to be resolved successfully.

A MULTIDIMENSIONAL MODEL OF SOCIAL PROBLEM SOLVING

SPS outcomes are a function of two general, but partially independent, dimensions: (a) problem orientation and (b) problem-solving style (D'Zurilla, Nezu, & Maydeu-Olivares, 2004). *Problem orientation* represents the set of cognitive–affective schemas or worldviews regarding individuals' generalized beliefs, attitudes, and emotional reactions about real-life problems, as well as their ability to successfully cope with such difficulties. Although our original model suggested that there are two types of problem orientations and that they represent opposite ends of the same continuum (e.g., D'Zurilla & Nezu, 1999), subsequent research suggests that they operate somewhat independent of each other and are only minimally correlated (Nezu, 2004). These two orthogonal orientation dimensions include positive problem orientation and negative problem orientation.

A *positive problem orientation* involves the tendency of individuals to

- Perceive problems as challenges rather than major threats to one's well-being
- Be optimistic in believing that problems are solvable
- Have a strong sense of self-efficacy regarding their ability to handle difficult problems
- Believe that successful problem solving usually involves time and effort
- View negative emotions as important sources of information necessary for effective problem solving (e.g., "something is occurring that requires my attention")

A *negative problem orientation* refers to the tendency of individuals to

- View problems as major threats to one's well-being
- Generally perceive problems to be unsolvable or extremely difficult to resolve

- Maintain doubts about their ability to cope with problems successfully
- Become particularly frustrated and upset when faced with problems or when they experience negative emotions

By definition, individuals' problem orientations can have a strong influence on their motivation and ability to engage in focused attempts to solve problems. Thus, the importance of assessing and addressing one's dominant orientation should be considered a key component of any attempt to teach clients to become more effective problem solvers. Unfortunately, some researchers have only included "rational or logical" problem-solving skills when applying such concepts to psychotherapeutic applications and have de-emphasized or ignored problem-orientation variables. However, in doing so, there is a risk that training would be less effective.

Consistent with this view, two meta-analytic reviews of the literature of randomized controlled trials (RCTs) of problem-solving training programs support the notion that excluding a specific focus on problem-orientation variables consistently leads to significantly less efficacious outcomes as compared to protocols that do include such training (Bell & D'Zurilla, 2009; Malouff, Thorsteinsson, & Schutte, 2007). Moreover, a study using a dismantling strategy to evaluate the relative efficacy of such differing protocols (i.e., training in problem orientation and rational problem-solving skills vs. training in problem-solving skills alone) in reducing clinical depression further confirmed this principle directly (Nezu & Perri, 1989).

The second major dimension of SPS, *problem-solving style*, refers to the core cognitive and behavioral activities that people engage in when attempting to solve problems that occur in real life. Three styles have been empirically identified (D'Zurilla et al., 2002, 2004)—planful or rational problem solving, avoidant problem solving, and impulsive/careless problem solving.

Planful problem solving is the constructive approach that involves the systematic and planful application of the following set of specific skills:

- *Problem definition and formulation* (i.e., clarifying the nature of a problem, delineating a realistic set of problem-solving goals and objectives, and identifying those obstacles that prevent one from reaching such goals)
- *Generation of alternatives* (i.e., brainstorming a range of possible solution strategies geared to overcome the identified obstacles)
- *Decision making* (i.e., predicting the likely consequences of these various alternatives, conducting a cost–benefit analysis based on these identified outcomes, and developing a solution plan that is geared to achieve the problem-solving goal)

- *Solution implementation and verification* (i.e., carrying out the solution plan, monitoring and evaluating the consequences of the plan, and determining whether one's problem-solving efforts have been successful or need to continue)

The remaining two problem-solving styles in contrast are generally associated with ineffective outcomes (D'Zurilla et al., 2002, 2004). One maladaptive method, an *impulsive/careless style*, involves the problem-solving approach whereby people tend to engage in impulsive, hurried, and careless attempts at problem resolution. *Avoidant problem solving* is the problem-solving style represented by procrastination, passivity, and overdependence on others to provide solutions. Both these approaches are associated with ineffective or unsuccessful coping, and they are likely to worsen existing problems or create new ones.

This multidimensional model of SPS has been cross-validated numerous times across various populations, ethnic minority cultures, and age groups (D'Zurilla & Nezu, 2007). Note that we are not suggesting that these five dimensions represent "personality traits" through which individuals can be characterized exclusively by either type of orientation or problem-solving style across all problems. Rather, each represents a strong tendency to either view or react toward problems from a particular perspective based on one's learning experiences. For example, in a study we conducted with college students, subjects were found to be more effective in their problem-solving activities when dealing with an academic or work problem as compared to when attempting to cope with a relationship problem (Stern, Lee, Nezu, & Nezu, 2013). This suggests that the nature of problems and the problem-solving process need to be understood contextually.

STRUCTURE OF THIS BOOK

The major purpose of this book is to provide clinicians and researchers a detailed treatment manual of EC-PST. The first section focuses on various conceptual and empirical foundations of this approach, whereas the second section addresses assessment issues, treatment planning, and various "metamessages" that detail crucial aspects of the treatment protocol. The third section contains the actual treatment manual of EC-PST and includes multiple examples of how to conduct the intervention. Throughout these chapters, we provide examples of "scripts" to use to explain important concepts to clients. We also include clinical examples of cases to illustrate certain applications of EC-PST. Our concluding chapter contains descriptions on how to apply EC-PST to certain populations (i.e., military veterans and active service members) and goals (i.e., suicide prevention and treatment; positive functioning). Note that a comprehensive Client Workbook containing material that can be given to a client and used in conjunction with face-to-face treatment is also available (see the Preface of this book for information on obtaining this workbook).

Although a significant portion of this book involves the treatment manual, we believe it is important to offer both the conceptual and empirical underpinnings of this approach for two reasons. First, such information can help the clinician to better understand the fundamental principles inherent in EC-PST and thus be able to apply it more effectively with a variety of individuals and situations. We suggest that the research literature regarding PST-based protocols, similar to *all* other psychotherapy approaches, has not been able to address *every* individual client demographic and characteristic (and combination of these characteristics), such as age, ethnicity, sexual orientation, socioeconomic status, comorbidity, and so forth. Thus, no manual can offer specific guidelines for every individual or contingency. This notion underscores our basic commitment that understanding and using these principles and treatment goals are critical to the success of EC-PST, rather than the specific activities, exercises, scripts, or homework assignments that even we, ourselves, describe and offer in this manual.

Second, we firmly believe that the greater the degree to which our clients and therapy clients understand our approach, the more likely it is that the treatment will be effective. In other words, in most cases, if clients understand (and, we hope, share) our therapeutic worldview (e.g., why EC-PST is important; how problem solving relates to distress; whether it has been previously documented to be effective for problems similar to those experienced by that client), it is more likely that they will "be on the same page," making treatment activities and objectives more understandable and transparent. Thus, we provide the background material in hopes that clinicians have such information in their "back pocket" when providing the purposes of EC-PST, the rationale for why it may be important to engage with a particular client (i.e., why it is relevant to the person or persons requesting treatment), and the evidence showing that EC-PST has been found to be effective in instilling confidence both in this approach and in the therapist providing this treatment.

SUMMARY

We began this chapter by differentiating among logic, insight, and mathematical problems and the stressful difficulties encountered in everyday living. EC-PST is described as a psychosocial intervention geared toward enhancing one's ability to cope effectively with such life stressors as a means of decreasing existing health and mental health difficulties as well as preventing future difficulties from occurring. Four major EC-PST treatment components to address ubiquitous obstacles that exist when people attempt to cope with life problems were outlined. A history of this approach was provided, identifying a seminal article by D'Zurilla and Goldfried (1971) as being the impetus for subsequent decades of problem-solving–based research and program development. It was further noted that the original model has been revised recently in accordance with a better appreciation of the interplay between emotions and the problem-solving process. Definitions of important concepts were provided in this chapter, including *problem solving* (i.e., the self-directed process of putting one's coping efforts toward changing the nature of a situation such that it no longer represents a problem, one's maladaptive reactions to such a situation, or both), *problem* (i.e., a life situation that requires an adaptive response but for which no effective action is immediately apparent), and *solution* (i.e., a coping response that is the outcome of the problem-solving process when applied to a specific situation).

A multidimensional model of SPS was also described that includes two major dimensions: *problem orientation* (i.e., a person's generalized beliefs, attitudes, and emotional reactions to problems in living and his or her ability to effectively cope with them) and *problem-solving style* (i.e., the cognitive and behavioral activities that are applied to solve or cope with problems in living). Research continuously identifies two orthogonal types of orientations—positive and negative—as well as three types of problem-solving styles (i.e., rational or planful problem solving, avoidant problem solving, and impulsive/careless problem solving).

Last, the structure of this book was presented, which includes three major sections: "Conceptual and Empirical Foundations"; "Assessment, Clinical, and Treatment Planning Considerations and EC-PST 'Metamessages'"; and "Emotion-Centered Problem-Solving Therapy: Treatment Guidelines." The final chapter describes the application of EC-PST to various special populations. Last, a comprehensive Client Workbook is available (see the Preface of this book for information on obtaining this workbook).

The next chapter describes the biopsychosocial model on which EC-PST is based.

ANSWERS TO PROBLEMS

1. He turned off the light during the daytime.
2. The ball costs $0.05 (the bat then costs $1.05, which is $1.00 more than the ball).

REFERENCES

Bell, A. C., & D'Zurilla, T. J. (2009). Problem-solving therapy for depression: A meta-analysis. *Clinical Psychology Review, 29*, 348–353. doi:10.1016/j.cpr.2009.02.003

D'Zurilla, T. J., & Goldfried, M. R. (1971). Problem solving and behavior modification. *Journal of Abnormal Psychology, 78*, 107–126. doi:10.1037/h0031360

D'Zurilla, T. J., & Nezu, A. (1980). A study of the generation-of-alternatives process in social problem solving. *Cognitive Therapy and Research, 4*, 67–72. doi:10.1007/BF01173355

D'Zurilla, T. J., & Nezu, A. (1982). Social problem solving in adults. In P. C. Kendall (Ed.), *Advances in cognitive-behavioral research and therapy* (Vol. 1, pp. 202–274). New York, NY: Academic Press.

D'Zurilla, T. J., & Nezu, A. M. (1999). *Problem-solving therapy: A social competence approach to clinical intervention* (2nd ed.). New York, NY: Springer Publishing.

D'Zurilla, T. J., & Nezu, A. M. (2007). *Problem-solving therapy: A positive approach to clinical intervention* (3rd ed.). New York, NY: Springer Publishing.

D'Zurilla, T. J., Nezu, A. M., & Maydeu-Olivares, A. (2002). *Manual for the Social Problem-Solving Inventory–Revised*. North Tonawanda, NY: Multi-Health Systems.

D'Zurilla, T. J., Nezu, A. M., & Maydeu-Olivares, A. (2004). Social problem solving: Theory and assessment. In E. C. Chang, T. J. D'Zurilla, & L. J. Sanna (Eds.), *Social problem solving: Theory, research, and training* (pp. 11–27). Washington, DC: American Psychological Association.

Lazarus, R. S., & Folkman, S. (1984). *Stress, appraisal, and coping*. New York, NY: Springer Publishing.

LeBlanc, V. R., McConnell, M. M., & Monteiro, S. D. (2015). Predictable chaos: A review of the effects of emotions on attention, memory and decision making. *Advances in Health Sciences Education: Theory and Practice, 20*, 265–282. doi:10.1007/s10459-014-9516-6

Malouff, J. M., Thorsteinsson, E. B., & Schutte, N. S. (2007). The efficacy of problem solving therapy in reducing mental and physical health problems: A meta-analysis. *Clinical Psychology Review, 27*, 46–57. doi:10.1016/j.cpr.2005.12.005

Newberg, A., & Waldman, M. R. (2009). *How God changes your brain*. New York, NY: Ballantine Books.

Nezu, A. M. (1986). Efficacy of a social problem-solving therapy approach for unipolar depression. *Journal of Consulting and Clinical Psychology, 54*, 196–202. doi:10.1037/0022-006X.54.2.196

Nezu, A. M. (1987). A problem-solving formulation of depression: A literature review and proposal of a pluralistic model. *Clinical Psychology Review, 7*, 121–144. doi:10.1016/0272-7358(87)90030-4

Nezu, A. M. (2004). Problem solving and behavior therapy revisited. *Behavior Therapy, 35*, 1–33. doi:10.1016/S0005-7894(04)80002-9

Nezu, A., & D'Zurilla, T. J. (1979). An experimental evaluation of the decision-making process in social problem solving. *Cognitive Therapy and Research, 3*, 269–277. doi:10.1007/BF01185967

Nezu, A., & D'Zurilla, T. J. (1981a). Effects of problem definition and formulation on decision making in the social problem-solving process. *Behavior Therapy, 12*, 100–106. doi:10.1016/S0005-7894(81)80110-4

Nezu, A., & D'Zurilla, T. J. (1981b). Effects of problem definition and formulation on the generation of alternatives in the social problem-solving process. *Cognitive Therapy and Research, 5*, 265–271. doi:10.1007/BF01193410

Nezu, A. M., & D'Zurilla, T. J. (1989). Social problem solving and negative affective conditions. In P. C. Kendall & D. Watson (Eds.), *Anxiety and depression: Distinctive and overlapping features* (pp. 285–315). New York, NY: Academic Press.

Nezu, A. M., Greenfield, A. P., & Nezu, C. M. (2016). Contemporary problem-solving therapy: A transdiagnostic intervention. In C. M. Nezu & A. M. Nezu (Eds.), *The Oxford handbook of cognitive and behavioral therapies* (pp. 160–171). New York, NY: Oxford University Press.

Nezu, A. M., Nezu, C. M., & D'Zurilla, T. J. (2013). *Problem-solving therapy: A treatment manual.* New York, NY: Springer Publishing.

Nezu, A. M., Nezu, C. M., & Perri, M. G. (1989). *Problem-solving therapy for depression: Theory, research, and clinical guidelines.* New York, NY: John Wiley.

Nezu, A. M., & Perri, M. G. (1989). Social problem-solving therapy for unipolar depression: An initial dismantling investigation. *Journal of Consulting and Clinical Psychology, 57,* 408–413. doi:10.1037/0022-006X.57.3.408

Nezu, A. M., & Ronan, G. F. (1985). Life stress, current problems, problem solving, and depressive symptoms: An integrative model. *Journal of Consulting and Clinical Psychology, 53,* 693–697. doi:10.1037/0022-006X.53.5.693

Nezu, A. M., & Ronan, G. F. (1988). Stressful life events, problem solving, and depressive symptoms among university students: A prospective analysis. *Journal of Counseling Psychology, 35,* 134–138. doi:10.1037/0022-0167.35.2.134

Stern, J., Lee, M., Nezu, C. M., & Nezu, A. M. (2013, November). *Sociotropic versus autonomous social problem solving: Interactions with sex differences.* Presentation at the Annual Convention of the Association for Behavioral and Cognitive Therapies, Nashville, TN.

UNDERSTANDING PSYCHOPATHOLOGY AND BEHAVIORAL DISORDERS: A PROBLEM-SOLVING/DIATHESIS– STRESS FRAMEWORK

This chapter describes a conceptual model that attempts to explain the role that social problem solving (SPS) plays in determining adaptive versus maladaptive reactions to stressful life events. It builds upon the relational/ problem-solving model of stress described as part of our earlier work (D'Zurilla & Nezu, 2007; Nezu, 2004), but is more expansive in nature, placing the model within a larger biopsychosocial context. Specifically, it takes into account more recent research that focuses on the interplay among certain psychosocial and neurobiological variables regarding stress, emotions, coping, and adjustment. Although multiple aspects of this model are associated with empirical support, others have yet to be well researched. Thus, we offer this framework as a heuristic that can potentially inform both theory and treatment decisions, as well as provide clients with a worldview that can help them understand how emotion-centered problem-solving therapy (EC-PST) can be of therapeutic help.

Our diathesis–stress model involves the interplay among various "systems," each of which describes how certain psychosocial and biological factors impact and interact with each other to produce negative or positive health and mental health outcomes. Each system represents a dynamic among certain variables that impact the next system. The overall model is developmental in nature in that it describes distal, proximal, and immediate levels of analysis regarding how stress impacts health outcomes, as well as how SPS serves as a potential moderator and mediator of these relationships. With specific relevance to EC-PST, this model provides a context to better understand how and why this approach can be effective across multiple clinical problems and difficulties.

© Springer Publishing Company DOI: 10/1891/9780826143167.0002

A PROBLEM-SOLVING SYSTEMS MODEL OF STRESS AND ADAPTATION

This model describes the interplay among three related systems, each of which provides for a level of analysis regarding stressful events, problem solving, and health/mental health outcomes. System I is primarily a distal system and represents an initial level of analysis that focuses on the role of early life stress (ELS) and later pathology, especially as it interacts with genetics. This gene–ELS combination can lead to certain biological vulnerabilities regarding increased stress sensitization. System II, the proximal system, focuses on later life (adolescence and adulthood) and the interactions among major negative life events (e.g., divorce, combat trauma, loss of a loved one), daily stressors (e.g., chronic lack of resources, difficult problems with coworkers, marital or relationship problems), and various neurobiological systems that are etiologically related to extant distress. The third system, System IIa, is the more micro- and immediate level of analysis and represents a more microanalytic perspective that addresses the interactions among stressful stimuli, various brain components, and emotions. The role of problem solving is also described within each level of analysis. Note that System I is believed to set the stage for System II outcomes, whereas both these systems impact the outcome of System IIa, which, in turn, reciprocally impacts the more molar level System II. The effects of each of these systems then predict health and mental health outcomes for a given individual at a given time.

System I: Genetic Influences, ELS, and Early Biological Vulnerabilities

Figure 2.1 is a graphic representation of System I. It depicts how one's genotype, in combination with ELS, can produce certain biological vulnerabilities that influence one's reactivity to stress, which can lead to psychological difficulties later in life. Much of the research in this area focuses on the interaction between one's genetic makeup and ELS in predicting depression. Note that in general, the main genetic effect that may engender depression tends to be weak; rather, it is the gene X environment's *interaction* that is a much stronger predictor (Heim & Binder, 2012). For example, Gatt et al. (2010) found the interaction between ELS and the presence of two genetic factors, brain-derived neurotrophic factor (BDNF) valine 66 to methionine (Val66Met) and serotonin receptor gene 3a (*HTR3A*), to significantly predict a variety of depression risk factors. These include electroencephalogram asymmetry, emotion-elicited heart rate, and self-reported negativity bias (i.e., the tendency to see oneself and the world as negative) later in life. Animal models also provide evidence that ELS enhances

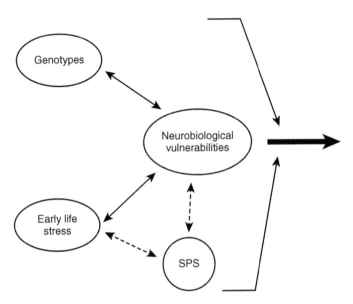

FIGURE 2.1 ■ System I (distal system): Relationships among ELS, genotypes, SPS, and neurobiological vulnerabilities.

ELS, early life stress; SPS, social problem solving.

an organism's vulnerability to stress later in life via the activation of a gene-mediated transcription within the prefrontal cortex (Uchida et al., 2010).

Note that although certain genes, in combination with ELS, do increase the risk of depression, the same genes can also enhance the beneficial effects of a positive early life environment. For example, Caspi et al. (2003) reported that adults with the short-form allele (*SS*) of a polymorphism of the serotonin transporter gene, *5-HTT*, were more likely to develop major depression after experiencing a stressful event than those adults possessing the long-form allele (*LL*). In essence, the short form of the allele is represented by reduced *5-HTT* expression and serotonin uptake and has been shown to be associated with heightened activity in the amygdala, which is involved in emotion regulation. Additional research with twins suggest that further *5-HTT* genetic variability moderates the negative impact of daily life stress and the risk of experiencing full-blown depression (Wichers et al., 2009). More specifically, these researchers found that the short/long variant of the allele appears to buffer the effects of daily stress, whereas the short/short and long/long variants were shown to increase the risk of depression.

Of particular interest to this model is a study by Wilhelm et al. (2007). The major goal of their study was to assess the problem-solving strategies people apply when coping with stress as a function of differing serotonin transporter genotypes. Ten years after a cohort of students participating in a longitudinal study completed a measure of coping with stress, they underwent genetic testing to determine their *5-HTT* genotype. Results indicated that the short variant of the *5-HTT* promoter polymorphism was associated with the use of fewer problem-solving strategies. This suggests that a possible genetic influence on later emotional difficulties involves a limited ability for individuals with the short variant to draw upon multiple problem-solving strategies when dealing with stressful events.

Although genetic factors can create a susceptibility to negative emotional states under stress, ELS itself can impact negatively on certain biological systems, including the immune system (McDade et al., 2017). For example, Pace et al. (2006) reported that depressed patients with increased ELS were found to exhibit enhanced inflammatory reactions to psychosocial stress. In addition, in a review of the literature regarding the role of childhood trauma on the neurobiology of later mood and anxiety disorders, Heim and Nemeroff (2001) concluded that the extant research strongly indicates that ELS creates a chronic and persistent hyperactivity and sensitization of various neurotransmitter systems (e.g., corticotropin-releasing factor [CRF]), which leads to increased endocrine, autonomic, and behavioral stress reactivity. Under conditions of continuous life stress, this vulnerability can result in adult depression and anxiety disorders (Silberman, Acosta, & Zorrilla Zubilete, 2016).

Additional research suggests that ELS leads to changes in the architecture of the brain itself, such as in the amygdala, which can mediate later behavioral changes related in internalizing illness (Fareri & Tottenham, 2016). A study by Hanson et al. (2015) focused on three sample groups of children exposed to the following different types of ELS—physical abuse, early neglect, and low socioeconomic status(SES). They found: (a) smaller amygdala volumes for all three groups, (b) smaller hippocampus volumes for children who were physically abused or in low SES homes, and (c) an association between smaller amygdala and hippocampus volumes and greater cumulative stress exposure. They concluded that ELS leads to differences in certain brain regions, which then serves as a diathesis for later negative outcomes.

A review of the relevant literature of both humans and rodents by Krugers et al. (2016) indicated that early life adversity impedes both hippocampal and prefrontal cortex functioning, while increasing amygdala activity and stress sensitization. This impact of ELS on both brain activity and structure then can lead to later cognitive and emotional difficulties. Moreover, Provençal and Binder (2015) noted that the role of ELS as a major risk factor for developing psychiatric and behavioral disorders later in life can actually start during intrauterine development.

The role of SPS within System I is also depicted in Figure 2.1. During this period of development, it is likely that children begin to learn how to cope with stress as a function of a combination of multiple sources, including observing how one's parents cope with stress, the rewards and punishments observed by the child regarding how others cope with stress, and the amount of stress the child actually experiences. Developmentally, children are not capable of abstract reasoning (i.e., their frontal lobes are not fully matured until later in life), so opportunities to learn concrete coping skills are likely to be limited and very dependent on the specificity of role models imparting such lessons. In other words, unless parents, guardians, or a school system provide formal instruction in coping with life skills, it is likely that a child has minimal opportunities to gain expertise in such skills, especially in terms of which skills are ultimately the correct ones to learn (e.g., planful problem solving vs. avoidant problem solving).

ELS can be minor, such as minor illnesses or continuous moves because of parental job changes, as well as very traumatic, such as emotional and/or sexual abuse. Low SES, racial discrimination, lack of physical resources, natural disasters, and being bullied constitute additional examples of ELS. How one, as a child, deals with these stressors impacts the quality of one's coping skills, including SPS, that will persist later in life, and can also serve to moderate the negative effects of such stress at that time. For example, it is possible that even if one has a particular genotype for heightened stress reactivity, if certain stressors are effectively handled, the negative biological impact on the immune system, for example, may be attenuated or at least minimize consequent behavioral problems. However, because such coping reactions are still developing, especially given that the child's brain is also developing, the role of SPS in this capacity is also likely to be minimal (hence dotted lines are used to denote a somewhat weaker relationship when connecting SPS to other factors in Figure 2.1). Moreover, if the stressors are particularly intense (e.g., loss of a parent, sexual abuse), they are likely to overtax one's coping ability, leading to an increased risk for negative biological consequences as well as having a negative impact on one's coping ability (i.e., ineffective problem solving).

It is also worthwhile to note that some ELS may be necessary to provide the opportunity for children to learn how to cope with adversity (Liu, 2015). For example, Gunnar, Frenn, Wewerka, and Van Ryzin (2009) found that children with moderate levels of ELS were characterized by lesser physiological stress reactions than children with either lower or higher levels. Seery (2011) also found that some stress during childhood is related to better health outcomes than a history of significant life stress or a history of *no early adversity*. A further study by Seery, Leo, Lupien, Kondrak, and Almonte (2013) indicated that in comparison to individuals with a history of either no adversity or "nonextreme high" adversity, persons characterized by having a moderate number of adverse life events were associated with less negative responses to a laboratory pain test, as well as more positive psychophysiological responses while taking a test.

Somewhat related to the just-mentioned discussion, a last point worth noting addresses the influence that the caregiving style of one's parents or guardians can have on the development of a child's problem-solving and other coping skills. For example, if a given set of parents' style of handling difficult family issues is to minimize the amount of stress the child experiences (e.g., encouraging the child not to cry, being overprotective, being intolerant of the child's emotional life), it is likely that the child will not be able to learn effective problem-solving skills because of the lack of opportunities to do so.

In summary, System I suggests that certain genotypes, in combination with ELS, can predispose one to certain negative neurobiological vulnerabilities that, when experiencing future stressful circumstances in adolescence or adulthood, increase the likelihood of negative physical and psychological symptomatology. In fact, another review of the overall literature regarding gene–ELS relationships concludes that there is definite and significant support for the effects of such interactions regarding the risk for depressive and anxiety disorders later in life (Nugent, Tyrka, Carpenter, & Price, 2011). In addition, ELS can have decidedly negative impacts on both brain activity and brain structure, such that both serve as potential diatheses for later psychiatric disturbance and behavioral problems. In fact, a report by the American Academy of Pediatrics suggested that "many adult diseases should be viewed as developmental disorders that begin early in life" (Shonkoff & Garner, 2012). Thus, we suggest that the major impact of System I on System II lies in the creation of both biological (i.e., heightened sensitivity to stress) and psychological (e.g., poor problem-solving ability) vulnerabilities. The importance of this research base for EC-PST is to ensure that the clinician assesses these more distal variables when working with clients to obtain a fuller clinical picture (e.g., history of stress and coping).

System II: Major Negative Life Events, Daily Problems, and Neurobiological Reactions

Figure 2.2 depicts the reciprocal relationships among major negative life events, minor or daily problems, and the body's neurobiological reactions to such stressors. It also identifies the role that SPS plays regarding these factors. This system then has a major impact on one's immediate reactions to stressful triggers (System II), which ultimately predicts one's health outcomes (see Figure 2.3).

Overall, the first path identified by System II suggests that the experience of a major negative life event (e.g., divorce, loss of a loved one, spouse/partner diagnosed with a chronic illness) increases the likelihood of experiencing

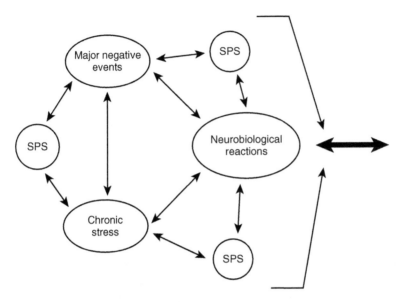

FIGURE 2.2 ■ System II (proximal system): Relationships among major negative life events, chronic daily stress, SPS, and neurobiological reactions. System II is influenced by System I.

SPS, social problem solving.

stressful daily problems or minor stressors (e.g., legal battles over custody issues, difficulties overcoming grief reactions, serving as a familial caregiver). In turn, experiencing continuous daily problems (e.g., problems with coworkers and/or a supervisor) can engender the occurrence of a major negative life event (e.g., getting fired). Moreover, *both* sources of stress independently and collectively serve to increase the likelihood of one being at a higher risk for experiencing clinical levels of distress, such as major depression and anxiety (Monroe, Slavich, & Georgiades, 2009; Nezu & Ronan, 1985). The relationship between these sources of stress (System II variables) and negative health outcomes (the end point depicted in System IIa, as seen in Figure 2.3) are believed to be mediated, in part, by neurobiological kindling and behavioral sensitization, often referred to as *stress sensitization* (Post, 2007). This is depicted in Figure 2.2 by the arrows impacting neurobiological reactions, which then have a direct impact on System IIa in terms of ultimate negative health outcomes.

Decades of research have identified both direct and indirect effects of stress on health and psychological parameters. One area of investigation involves the link between stress and cardiovascular disease (CVD). Studies continue to accumulate indicating that chronic daily stressors can increase the risk of developing and dying from CVD (Cohen, Edmondson, & Kronish, 2015). Social isolation and loneliness have been associated with a 50% increase in the incidence of CVD, whereas the increased risk associated with work-related stress was 40% (Steptoe & Kivimäki, 2013). Chronic stressors have also been significantly linked to worse prognoses in patients with existing CVD.

Another major pubic health problem, obesity, has also been linked to stress. The pathway connections between stress and obesity involve cognitive and behavioral processes (e.g., problems with self-regulation), as well as physiological and biochemical factors (e.g., changes in the hypothalamic–pituitary–adrenal [HPA] axis, increased production of certain obesity-related hormones and peptides; Tomiyama, 2019). Chronic stress has also been linked to cancer in terms of an increased susceptibility via suppression of immune functioning (i.e., type I cytokines and protective T cells; Dhabhar, 2014). In fact, collectively, life stress has been found to be "involved in the development, maintenance, or exacerbation of several mental and physical health conditions, including asthma, rheumatoid arthritis, anxiety disorders, depression, CVD, chronic pain, human immunodeficiency virus/AIDS, stroke, and certain types of cancer" (Slavich, 2016, p. 346).

As noted earlier, there is a significant link between ELS and depression. Additional biological pathways between stress and depression beyond genetic vulnerability are caused by hyperactivity of the amygdala, hypoactivity of the hippocampus, and decreased serotonergic neurotransmission, which collectively leads to increased vulnerability to stress (Tafet & Nemeroff, 2016).

Although earlier research defined life stress in terms of major negative events (e.g., loss of a loved one, loss of a job), studies beginning in the 1980s (and continuing to date) focus more on the effects of daily life stress (often referred to as minor life events, chronic stress, hassles, or daily problems). Such research suggests that over time, the accumulation of daily stressful problems can have a significant and independent impact on psychological, social, and health functioning beyond the experience of major negative events (Hammen, Kim, Eberhart, & Brennan, 2009; Monroe, Slavich, Torres, & Gotlib, 2007; Nezu & Ronan, 1985; Weinberger, Hiner, & Tierney, 1987). Moreover, recent results from the National Study of Daily Experiences, involving more than 1,300 middle-aged adults, noted a significant positive association between total number of stressors experienced across 8 consecutive days and mortality risk as prospectively assessed over the next 20 years (Chiang, Turiano, Mroczek, & Miller, 2018). It was concluded that "greater increases in negative affect in response to stress in everyday life may have long-term consequences for longevity" (p. 170).

Note that in Figure 2.2, System II is depicted as having a reciprocal relationship with the ultimate mental and physical health outcomes that are depicted in System IIa. In other words, the more negative health outcomes that are engendered by stress, the more likely that such diminished functioning will serve to increase stress (e.g., poor physical or emotional health leads to poorer work performance, which leads to increased problems at work, which leads to getting fired). This process is often referred to as the *stress generation* hypothesis (i.e., poorer health leads to increased stress), which we suggest works in conjunction with the stress sensitization process. In other words, continuous daily stress can eventually lead to a lowered threshold that triggers negative health outcomes (i.e., less stress is required to produce poor health over time—the stress sensitization hypothesis), whereas poor health can lead to or create additional sources of stress (e.g., increased daily problems and/or more severe chronic illness—the stress generation hypothesis).

Continuing within Figure 2.2, the arrows from both sources of stress impacting neurobiological reactions refer to the basic biology of the stress response. This is the beneficial evolutionary response of one's physiological and biological systems to maximize a safe outcome in reaction to encountering a stressful or threatening stimulus. In essence, the body activates two separate, but interconnected, systems—the sympathoadrenal medullary (SAM) system and the HPA axis. The SAM system activates the "fight or flight" set of responses, which involves the release of epinephrine and norepinephrine. The HPA axis is one part of the central stress response system that is primarily defined by a neuropeptide, CRF, which serves as the critical mediator of the stress response.

Activation of both systems helps the body to prepare itself to ward off harm. However, too much activation can lead to harmful effects (Dallman, Bhatnagar, & Viau, 2000). Chronic stress can alter the regulation of the HPA axis by increasing production of glucocorticoid secretion (cortisol in humans), which can be generally deleterious. For example, decades of research support the notion that dysfunction of the HPA axis can lead to psychiatric disorders, particularly depression (Gutman & Nemeroff, 2011). The effects of severe ELS, as suggested by System I, can potentially lead to abnormalities of this stress-response pattern by lowering the threshold or set point of the HPA axis to stressful events later in life (Heim, Mletzko, Purselle, Musselman, & Nemeroff, 2008). In addition, research suggests that hyperactivity of the HPA axis is a likely link between depression and one's increased risk for various medical conditions, such as diabetes, dementia, coronary heart disease, and osteoporosis (Stetler & Miller, 2011).

Another important biological system involved in the stress response is the immune system. For example, stress is known to increase one's vulnerability to both physical and psychological difficulties by its ability to suppress one's immune functioning, which generally organizes the body's responses to infections and other challenges (Dhabhar, 2011). Chronic stress can dysregulate the immune system and negatively affect health. For example, elevations in proinflammatory cytokines, such as interleukin-6 (IL-6) and C-reactive protein, serve a key role in increasing one's susceptibility to CVD, type 2 diabetes, arthritis, Alzheimer's disease, cancer, and periodontal disease (Kiecolt-Glaser, McGuire, Robles, & Glaser, 2002). The cumulative effects of daily stressors have also been found to promote elevations in these inflammatory markers, explaining how chronic stress leads to poor health (Gouin, Glaser, Malarkey, Beversdorf, & Kiecolt-Glaser, 2012). Furthermore, chronic stress can speed the rate of normal age-related immune dysregulation (Kiecolt-Glaser & Glaser, 2001). In keeping with the importance of understanding System I variables, ELS is posited to also increase the likelihood of maladaptive immune responses to stress later in life as well as having negative effects on one's nervous system and physiology (Graham, Christian, & Kiecolt-Glaser, 2006; Pace et al., 2006).

Chronic stress has also been found to damage the hippocampus, which is a brain component that is part of the limbic system and plays an important role in the consolidation of information from short-term to long-term memory. However, the damage is not direct; rather, stress depletes hippocampal neurons of glucose (the major source of energy), thereby making them less capable of performing effectively, especially under times of stress (LeDoux, 2002). The hippocampus regulates the release of cortisol, the major chemical responsible for increasing one's risk of depression, so when impaired by chronic stress, the hippocampus allows cortisol levels to increase in the bloodstream, thus being potentially unable to prevent problems of memory and depression that are related to this rise in stress hormones.

In the absence of any formal (e.g., medical or psychological therapies) or informal (e.g., increase in social support, change in physical or social environment) interventions or changes, this continuous reciprocal relationship between Systems II and IIa is likely to lead to the continuous recurrence of emotional and psychological dysfunction. This is where we posit that SPS plays a significant role. In other words, one psychosocial factor that can account for human individual variability may be largely determined by a person's way of initially reacting to and then handling stress (Nezu, 2004; Olff, 1999). This leads to the hypothesis that SPS can serve as an important moderator and/or mediator of the relationship between stress and emotional distress. Research to date supports this contention and takes the form of two differing types of studies. First, one body of literature has addressed whether ineffective problem solving is related to psychological distress. The second group of studies directly asks whether problem solving can serve as a buffer for the deleterious effects of stress.

If SPS is posited to be an important general coping strategy that can reduce or prevent the negative effects of stress, it should be significantly related to a wide range of adaptive and maladaptive reactions and consequences. A detailed description of this literature is beyond the scope of this chapter, so the reader is referred to several sources for an overview (Chang, D'Zurilla, & Sanna, 2004; D'Zurilla & Nezu, 2007; Nezu, 2004; Nezu, Wilkins, & Nezu, 2004). In general, this research, using different measures of problem solving and focusing on a wide range of subject populations, strongly underscores the relationship between ineffective problem solving and the following: depression, anxiety, suicidal ideation and behaviors, severe mental illness, hopelessness, pessimism, anger proneness, alcoholism, substance abuse, criminal offending, low global self-esteem, attachment insecurity, work stress, nonsuicidal self-injury, and sexual offending.

Deficient problem solving has further been found to be present among a variety of depressed medical patient populations, including individuals suffering from heart failure, cancer, diabetes, stroke, chronic fatigue syndrome, and low vision. It is also predictive of depression, burnout, and emotional distress among various family caregiver populations, including those caring for individuals with cancer, spinal cord injuries, stroke, diabetes, traumatic brain injury, amyotrophic lateral sclerosis (ALS), and vision loss. It has also been found to be related to noncardiac chest pain, chronic low back pain, obsessive-compulsive disorder, posttraumatic stress disorder, and borderline personality disorder (for a review of this literature, see D'Zurilla & Nezu, 2007).

Alternatively, effective SPS has been found to be significantly related to more effective overall coping, higher levels of optimism, peer-judged interpersonal competence, social adjustment, better study habits among college students, effective parenting and caregiving behaviors, higher perceived control, positive mood, positive trait affectivity, better life satisfaction, greater sense of self-mastery and hope, higher levels of empathy, higher levels of motivation, and positive subjective well-being (for a review of this literature, see D'Zurilla & Nezu, 2007).

In addition, problem solving has been found to be a better predictor of physical health than physical activity, alcohol consumption, and social support (Largo-Wight, Peterson, & Chen, 2005). It has also been found to mediate the relationship between executive functioning (i.e., reasoning, concept formation, cognitive flexibility) and social outcome among children experiencing a traumatic brain injury (Muscara, Catroppa, & Anderson, 2008). The perception of life problems being threatening and unsolvable (high negative problem orientation) and an impulsive problem-solving style were further found to predispose elderly adults to commit suicide (Gibbs et al., 2009).

As an example of the increase in empirical interest regarding the relationship between SPS and negative health and mental health variables, Box 2.1 contains a sampling of such studies published since the work of Nezu, Nezu, and D'Zurilla (2013). Note that several of these studies were conducted outside the United States, underscoring the possible universality of these relationships.

BOX 2.1 ■ RECENT STUDIES INVESTIGATING SOCIAL PROBLEM-SOLVING DEFICITS

- Aggression and depression in Turkish youth (Özdemir, Kuzucu, & Koruklu, 2013)
- Alcohol- and drug-related problems among South Africans (Sorsdahl, Stein, Carrara, & Myers, 2014)
- Asthma control and quality of life (McCormick et al., 2014)
- Depression and quality of life among Dutch and Belgian stroke outpatients (Visser et al., 2015)
- Depression among Japanese undergraduate and graduate students (Hasegawa, Kunisato, Morimoto, Nishimura, & Matsuda, 2018)
- Depression vulnerability among individuals on the autism spectrum (Jackson & Dritschel, 2016)
- Disordered eating among a nonclinical sample of women (Ridout, Matharu, Sanders, & Wallis, 2015)
- Health and mental health symptoms among Iranian college students (Ranjbar, Bayani, & Bayani, 2013)
- Mental health symptomatology among Spanish chronic pain patients (Suso-Ribera, Camacho-Guerrero, McCracken, Maydeu-Olivares, & Gallardo-Pujol, 2016)
- Moral disengagement among inner-city African American high school students (Coker, Ikpe, Brooks, Page, & Sobell, 2014)
- Motor, cognitive, and psychiatric states in Huntington's disease (Van Liew, Gluhm, Goldstein, Cronan, & Corey-Bloom, 2013)
- Posttraumatic stress disorder among victims of intimate partner violence (Reich, Blackwell, Simmons, & Beck, 2015)
- Suicidal ideation and behavior among U.S. veterans (Nezu et al., 2017)
- Suicidal ideation and sexual assault victims (Chang & Hirsch, 2015)
- Turkish psoriasis patients (vs. healthy controls; Eskin, Şavk, Uslu, & Küçükaydoğan, 2014)
- Turkish patients with tension and migraine headaches (Eskin, Akyol, Çelik, & Gültekin, 2013)
- Vision-impaired, Italian, older adult quality of life (Sgaramella, Nota, Carrieri, Soresi, & Sato, 2017)

A second group of studies directly evaluated the hypothesis that SPS is a moderator and/or mediator of the relationship between stressful events and psychological and physical distress. An early example is represented by a study conducted by Nezu and Ronan (1985) with college students (and subsequently replicated with individuals diagnosed with major depressive disorder) that found support for the following associations: (a) major negative life events increased the number of daily problems, (b) higher levels of daily problems were associated with higher levels of depressive symptomatology, and

(c) problem solving served to mediate the relationship between daily stress and depression. Another type of study found that under similar levels of high stress, college students characterized as effective problem solvers reported lower levels of depressive symptoms than their ineffective problem-solving counterparts, suggesting that problem solving, by virtue of its moderating effect on stress, served to attenuate the negative effects of experiencing high levels of such stress (Nezu, Nezu, Saraydarian, Kalmar, & Ronan, 1986). These results were later replicated with regard to anxiety (Nezu, 1986), within a longitudinal design (Nezu & Ronan, 1988), with regard to adults with major depressive disorder (Nezu, Perri, & Nezu, 1987), and adult cancer patients (Nezu, Nezu, Faddis, DelliCarpini, & Houts, 1995).

Additional investigators have found SPS to serve a similar stress-buffering function regarding, for example, interpersonal conflicts and anxiety (Londahl, Tverskoy, & D'Zurilla, 2005); suicidal behaviors and ideation among adolescents (Grover et al., 2009); depression and anxiety among middle-aged and elderly community residents (Kant, D'Zurilla, & Maydeu-Olivares, 1997); psychological well-being among middle-aged adults (Chang, D'Zurilla, & Sanna, 2009); adjustment in elementary school children (Dubow & Tisak, 1989); childhood abuse and suicidality among a juvenile delinquent sample (Esposito & Clum, 2002); daily stress and adjustment in college students (Bell & D'Zurilla, 2009); perceived stress and noncardiac chest pain (Nezu, Nezu, & Jain, 2008); depression among female college students (Brack, LaClave, & Wyatt, 1992); perfectionism and depressive symptoms among Chinese adults (Cheng, 2001); depression in adolescent girls (Frye & Goodman, 2000); childhood depression (Goodman, Gravitt, & Kaslow, 1995); anxiety and anger (Miner & Dowd, 1996); hopelessness, depression, and suicidal ideation among college students (Priester & Clum, 1993; Yang & Clum, 1994); adjustment, health, and academic performance of British university students (Baker, 2003); suicide ideators and attempters (Rudd, Rajab, & Dahm, 1994); suicidality among college students (Clum & Febbraro, 1994; Stern et al., 2015); adolescent depression (Spence, Sheffield, & Donovan, 2003); and suicide ideation among U.S. military veterans (Nezu et al., 2017).

Collectively, the previously mentioned findings are consistent with the assumptions posited by our model, which characterize SPS as an important coping mechanism that can attenuate the negative effects of various sources of stress. Thus, these results suggest that teaching individuals to better cope with stressful circumstances via EC-PST can serve as an effective means of attenuating extant pathology, increasing one's resilience to stress, and possibly preventing future health and mental health difficulties. In other words, learning to more effectively cope with stress can serve to decrease the experience of major negative life events and chronic daily problems as well as potentially attenuate the impact that such stress can have on one's immune functioning, physiology, and neurobiology.

It is interesting to note that sometimes the inability to tolerate the negative neurobiological effects of stress is associated with poorer problem solving. For example, as described in Chapter 1, we characterized a negative problem orientation, in part, as involving difficulties with simply experiencing negative emotions. Furthermore, an avoidant problem-solving style can be negatively reinforced if one successfully avoids feeling negative affect by either engaging in avoidant behavior (e.g., drinking) or impulsive behavior (e.g., quickly trying to deal with the problem to not have to experience the negative emotion). A particularly serious example of this scenario is presented by Nock and Mendes (2008), who found that adolescents who frequently engage in nonsuicidal self-injury (NSSI; e.g., self-cutting) do so because they (a) experience heightened physiological arousal following a stressful event; (b) use NSSI to regulate this emotional distress; and (c) have deficits in their problem-solving skills, particularly with regard to decision making and having a negative problem orientation, that limit their ability to identify and engage in more adaptive social responses.

In summary, System II focuses on a global picture of how two sources of stress, major negative life events and chronic daily problems, serve to increase the likelihood of ultimately experiencing symptoms and problems on a clinical level, such as major depression. The means by which this occurs involves the impact of stress on various biological systems, including the SAM system, the HPA axis, and the immune system. Although the evolutionary benefit of having such alarm systems is to increase survival, that is, to have the body become better prepared to either "fight" a given threat or to "flee" it, overtaxing these systems can lead to harmful effects. The outcome of System I processes leads to increased stress sensitivity, so even normal levels of daily stress can trigger significant pathology. In addition, the experience of either major negative life events or chronic daily problems was shown to potentially serve as sources of stress generation. In other words, major negative life events can lead to multiple daily problems and, reciprocally, chronic daily problems can create a major negative life event. Having both processes (stress sensitization and stress generation) continue to occur in the absence of any formal or informal intervention or change is hypothesized to increase the probability of an individual experiencing a variety of both health and mental health difficulties.

System IIa: Stress, Emotions, the Brain, and SPS

System IIa, as depicted in Figure 2.3, is not a system independent of System II. Rather, it is a more microanalytic and immediate representation of how components of the brain react to stress, both consciously and nonconsciously, to produce emotional reactions, which, depending on their intensity and chronicity, may lead to poor health and psychological outcomes. Thus, this analysis represents another major departure from our prior relational problem-solving model of stress in which we previously gave primacy to Lazarus's (1999) depiction of emotion as being primarily cognitive and conscious in nature. In the current model, we contend that physiologic arousal occurs within milliseconds, which often can engender negative emotional reactions in the absence of cognitive appraisals (Damasio, 1999; LeDoux, 1996). In fact, difficulties in solving real-life stressful problems can result from a person *not* knowing or being able to cognitively label an emotional response (e.g., as sadness, anger, anxiety), even though such a response directs both further emotional and behavioral reactions. For example, consider a previously deployed combat veteran who feels panicky in a crowd; this leads him to run away, pushing people while doing so, and experiencing significant physical anxiety symptoms in the absence of being able to label such a response as a panic attack because of the similarity between certain stimulus cues felt in the crowd compared with previous combat events. In other words, we often experience a feeling without even knowing that a feeling is taking place (Damasio, 1999).

This disconnect between one's immediate emotional response and subsequent behavior (especially attempts to solve or cope with stressful life problems), which can often be ineffective under stress, has substantial implications for treatment. For example, our therapy protocol for more effectively handling immediate negative-emotion responses has greatly expanded (see *The Stop, Slow Down, Think, and Act* method of problem solving described in Chapter 10) to help individuals make better decisions regarding what strategies to use to solve problems while under stress, in part, by better understanding their emotional reactions.

Figure 2.3, in part, can be viewed as the microanalytic system that occurs with the neurobiological reactions box in System II with specific regard to brain functioning. In addition, the box labeled "stress triggers" represents the immediate stimuli, both external (e.g., loud noise, angry boss) and internal (e.g., physical sensations of pain, thoughts about an upcoming stressful business meeting), which can trigger an emotional reaction in a given individual. As depicted in Figure 2.3, information about such stressful or threatening stimuli directly reaches the amygdala by way of the sensory thalamus, as well as via an indirect path through the cortex. Before we continue, we need to remind the reader about these brain functions (note that because a detailed description of brain functions and their relation to emotions is far beyond the scope of this book, we refer the reader to several sources—Damasio, 1999; Korb, 2015; LeDoux, 1996, 2002).

The thalamus is a part of the brain, situated between the cerebral cortex and midbrain, that is responsible for relaying sensory and motor signals to other parts of the brain, particularly the cerebral cortex. It can be thought of as the

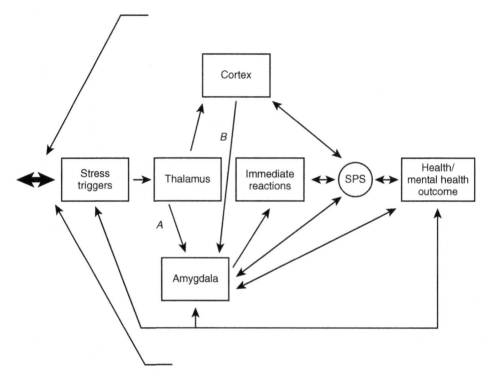

FIGURE 2.3 ■ System IIa (micro-level system): Relationships among stress, brain components, immediate emotional reactions, SPS, and health outcomes. System IIa is influenced by Systems I and II and it reciprocally influences System II.

SPS, social problem solving.

brain's switchboard. The amygdala, part of the limbic system, is an almond-shaped cluster of nuclei located deep within the brain's medial temporal lobe and is considered the neural structure most closely tied to the processing and memory of emotions. The cerebral cortex is the outermost tissue of the cerebrum (one's grey matter) and plays a key role in the brain's higher level cognitive functioning processes, such as memory, attention, awareness, thought, language, and consciousness.

Relevant to this discussion, it is important to note that research has shown that damage to the amygdala is associated with impairment in decision making in both experimental tasks (Bechara, Damasio, Damasio, & Lee, 1999) and in real-life situations (Tranel & Hyman, 1990). To some degree, this also points to the importance of emotions in facilitating effective judgments (Damasio, 1999), which is an important aspect of EC-PST, in that we believe both (i.e., reason and emotion) are important for effective coping and problem solving.

In part, Figure 2.3 depicts not only how emotion stimuli (i.e., stress triggers) are processed via these parts of the brain but also, more important, how such processing can lead to one's immediate emotional responses. LeDoux (1996, 2002) referred to the path in Figure 2.3 (stimulus to the thalamus to the amygdala, labeled *A*) as the *low road*, which is shorter and faster. Having this sensory input occur so quickly allows us to react to threats in a timely manner for survival value. However, this low road, because it is so fast (milliseconds), unfortunately provides the amygdala with less complete and accurate information about the threat. The second path (thalamus to cortex to amygdala, labeled *B* in Figure 2.3) is slower, but because it travels through the cortex, allows for a more accurate representation of the emotion stimulus. LeDoux referred to this as the *high road*.

To better understand the implications of these two pathways to emotions, LeDoux (1996) provided an illustration: Imagine yourself walking in the woods and you hear a crackling noise. The noise represents the incoming stimulus, which is received by the thalamus and goes straight to the amygdala (the low road). On the basis of previous experiences, the amygdala may interpret this sound as that of a rattlesnake shaking its tail. However, the noise stimulus also travels from the thalamus to the cortex (the high road), which may ultimately recognize the noise to be that of a dry twig being snapped as you walk through the woods. But as LeDoux continued to explain—"by the time the cortex has figured this out, the amygdala is already starting to defend against the snake. The information received from the thalamus is unfiltered and biased toward evoking responses. The cortex's job is to prevent the inappropriate response rather than to produce the appropriate one" (p. 165). Note that this analysis is not implying that the high road is actually the conscious path to the amygdala. The amygdala only engages in implicit processing, regardless of which route the sensory information travels (LeDoux, 2002). The emotion stimulus only reaches our consciousness when we process the information through brain networks involved in working memory.

Thus, it is this nonconscious emotional reactivity that can direct behavior, for better or for worse. As noted in LeDoux's (1996) example, one's nonconscious reaction to a noise can result at times in fear (if processed as a snake via the "low road") or nonchalant neutrality (if processed as a twig snap via the "high road"). For the person to correctly appraise the true nature of the threat (e.g., is it a snake, a dry twig, or a wolf stepping on a dry twig?), the emotion stimulus needs to be processed more consciously. In essence, as Pessoa (2010) contended, the amygdala can be viewed as the brain structure that attempts to answer two questions: (a) "What is it?" (i.e., what is this emotion stimulus, e.g., a snake or a twig?) and (b) "What's to be done?" (i.e., should I fight the snake, run away because it is too scary and ferocious, or do nothing because it's just a twig?). In trying to answer these questions, the amygdala serves to mobilize the organism to obtain additional information from the environment. From an EC-PST perspective, this implies that it may be important to help individuals to (a) better understand how their emotional reactions may or may not be appropriate or effective given the emotion stimulus that initially triggered the response; and (b) help them to discover, invent, or identify more effective ways of coping with stressful difficulties (i.e., to become better problem solvers), if, in general, such reactions are *not* effective (i.e., the problem does not get solved). In other words, it is important to help direct the amygdala to choose a more effective response, especially because emotion stimuli can frequently impair cognitive performance, such as disrupting goal-attainment behavior (Dolcos & McCarthy, 2006).

It should also be emphasized that chronic daily stress represents a much larger impact on the brain and the body than a singular encounter with a "snake/twig sound." Continuous daily stress (e.g., marital distress, poor work environment, lack of financial resources) leads to continuous activation of the amygdala, which can negatively impact one's ability to engage in more high-road processing unless provided with the opportunity to "stop and think." In the event that environmental (e.g., demanding boss at work) and/or internal (e.g., negative ruminative thinking) emotion stimuli continuously activate the amygdala, immediate emotional reactions to such stimuli can be difficult to handle in the absence of effective coping strategies.

Research by Richard J. Davidson and his colleagues (a summary of this research is provided in Davidson & Begley, 2012) regarding resilience is of additional significant relevance to this aspect of the model. In essence, Davidson suggests that people who have significant difficulty bouncing back from adversity are characterized by having fewer signals traveling from the prefrontal cortex to the amygdala. This can be caused by low activity in the cortex itself or from a lack of actual neural connections between the left prefrontal cortex and the amygdala. People characterized as being particularly resilient have been found to have the opposite: strong left prefrontal cortex activation in response to adversity and strong connections between the cortex and the amygdala. The implications of this process are significant: "By damping down the amygdala, the prefrontal cortex is able to quiet signals associated with negative emotions, enabling the brain to plan and act effectively without being distracted by negative emotion" (Davidson & Begley, 2012, p. 72).

Although they do not map onto each other 100% (remember that LeDoux [2002] emphasized that the high road is not a conscious pathway), it is interesting to note that various decision-making researchers have also proposed dual-system models, albeit not necessarily biological in nature, that differentiate between more implicit and explicit pathways to human judgment. For example, Stanovich and West (2000) proposed two systems of cognitive functioning that provide for a remarkably similar model to that of LeDoux (see also Kahneman, 2011). These decision-making researchers differentiate between two differing systems. System I refers to one's intuitive system, characterized as being fast, automatic, effortless, implicit, and emotional (similar to LeDoux's low road). System II, on the contrary, reflects the reasoning pathway that is slower, conscious, effortful, explicit, and logical (at least in function, somewhat similar to LeDoux's high road).

Also, similar to LeDoux's (2002) description of the brain pathways, Stanovich and West (2000) suggested that both these systems can be involved in making a given choice or decision. Furthermore, System II can improve upon the product of an impulsive, System I judgment and make a better decision (this function parallels that of the high road improving upon the accuracy of recognizing the exact nature of the emotion stimulus or trigger). However, if the person making the decision is under pressure or stress, or if System II functioning is overtaxed, it is likely that System I will take precedence.

In addition, similar to the notion that at times low-road information can be very important (i.e., to alert the individual that a threat or aversive stimulus may be present, such as the snake), System I thinking can also be helpful to survival. For example, not having enough time to decide whether the noise was that of a snake, the choice to flee the area is probably a good one, even if it was only a twig breaking, because the cost–benefit payoff of avoiding danger is much lower than the loss of staying in one place for a longer time, regardless if that part of the woods was perceived as beautiful or peaceful immediately before the noise was heard. However, stress can also potentially impact decision-making effectiveness negatively and stress conditions can lead to choices that are disadvantageous and more risk taking than nonstress conditions (Starcke & Brand, 2016).

Collectively, the research described earlier from both neuroscience and decision theory appears to underscore the importance of including information from two differing systems to maximize the success of one's attempts at problem solving real-life stressful difficulties.

Referring to Figure 2.3, in the absence of any formal or informal changes or interventions, we suggest that the cumulative processes of Systems I, II, and IIa that we posit can ultimately lead to negative health and mental health outcomes. The experience of such negative symptomatology, because of its reciprocal relationships with elements of System II, can further impact negatively, via stress generation and stress sensitivity, on other components of this model, including one's coping or problem-solving ability. For example, Leykin, Roberts, and DeRubeis (2011) found that individuals characterized by high levels of depressive symptomatology sought less information that could be helpful in their attempts at problem solving, made use of fewer resources, were less likely to make decisions that would resolve ambiguous situations, and made poorer decisions overall. In addition, Keinan (1987) found that individuals under stress, regardless of how controllable that stress was perceived to be, were more likely to make impulsive decisions and to not consider a wide range of alternatives that could have resulted in better decision making.

More important, according to our model, if one is an effective problem solver, it is possible that he or she can respond to stressful situations in ways that can attenuate these negative effects of stress (i.e., effectively solve stressful problems), as supported by the many outcome studies described in Chapter 3.

A NOTE ABOUT NEUROPLASTICITY

Central to the notion that stressful life events can influence brain architecture and activity is the process of plasticity. Also known as *neuroplasticity*, this term refers to the brain's ability to change and adapt as a result of experience. In essence, individual synaptic connections between and among brain cells are constantly being removed or created, dependent on the neurons that are involved. Activity-dependent plasticity is a form of neuroplasticity that arises from intrinsic or endogenous activity, for example, cognitive functions, such as new memories, as well as personal experience. It is as a function of this plasticity that stress can impact the structure and function of the brain, particularly the prefrontal cortex (McEwen & Morrison, 2013). However, it is also because of this plasticity that the brain is able to adapt and change as a function of various environmental factors. According to Davidson and McEwen (2012)—"these factors include both incidental influences, such as early adversity, and intentional influences that can be produced in humans through specific interventions designed to promote prosocial behavior and well-being" (p. 689). In other words, there is neuroscience evidence to support the EC-PST premise of using the various tools to help "train one's brain."

SUMMARY

This chapter presented a problem-solving/diathesis–stress model of pathology in which three systems were identified: one being distal in nature (early childhood), the second system being more proximal (current stress), and the third more immediate and microanalytic. This model is offered as a heuristic framework that explains (a) how ELS, in combination with certain genotypes, can negatively impact later reactivity to negative life events and daily problems during adolescence and adulthood by increasing one's stress sensitivity; (b) how two sources of stress (major events and daily problems) reciprocally interact with each other via a stress-generation process (i.e., major events can create or generate daily problems and daily problems can engender major life events); (c) how such stress impacts various neurobiological systems that serve to increase one's survival potential under normal conditions (i.e., prepare the body to fight or flee from a negative-emotion stimulus), but if overtaxed (i.e., either via the experience of significant stress in the form of major trauma or chronic daily stress or both, or if one's coping ability is insufficient to effectively handle such stress) can lead to harmful negative health outcomes (e.g., depression, anxiety, chronic medical illness); (d) how emotion stimuli are processed in dual systems (the "low road" and the "high road"), both of which involve implicit processing by the amygdala, and can lead to variable behavioral and emotional reactions; and (e) how SPS can serve to moderate these relationships such that effective problem solving can potentially attenuate the negative effects of stress on well-being at multiple levels throughout the three systems. Although aspects of this model are yet to be empirically supported (e.g., does problem solving have any direct impact on neurobiological parameters?), on the molar level of focusing on the moderating role of problem solving regarding major and minor stressful events, substantial research does point to the buffering aptitude of effective problem solving, hence supporting the rationale for viewing EC-PST as an efficacious intervention.

REFERENCES

Baker, S. R. (2003). A prospective longitudinal investigation of social problem-solving appraisals on adjustment to university, stress, health, and academic motivation and performance. *Personality and Individual Differences, 35*, 569–591. doi:10.1016/S0191-8869(02)00220-9

Bechara, A., Damasio, H., Damasio, A. R., & Lee, G. P. (1999). Different contributions of the human amygdala and ventromedial prefrontal cortex to decision-making. *Journal of Neuroscience, 19*, 5473–5481. doi:10.1523/JNEUROSCI.19-13-05473.1999

Bell, A. C., & D'Zurilla, T. J. (2009). The influence of social problem-solving ability on the relationship between daily stress and adjustment. *Cognitive Therapy and Research, 33*, 439–448. doi:10.1007/s10608-009-9256-8

Brack, G., LaClave, L., & Wyatt, A. S. (1992). The relationship of problem solving and reframing to stress and depression in female college students. *Journal of College Student Development, 33*, 124–131.

Caspi, A., Sugden, K., Moffitt, T. E., Taylor, A., Craig, I. W., Harrington, H., ... Poulton, R. (2003). Influence of life stress on depression: Moderation by a polymorphism in the 5-HTT gene. *Science, 301*, 386–389. doi:10.1126/science.1083968

Chang, E. C., D'Zurilla, T. J., & Sanna, L. J. (2009). Social problem solving as a mediator of the link between stress and psychological well-being in middle-adulthood. *Cognitive Therapy and Research, 33,* 33–49. doi:10.1007/s10608-007-9155-9

Chang, E. C, D'Zurilla, T. J., & Sanna, L. J. (Eds.). (2004). *Social problem solving: Theory, research, and training.* Washington, DC: American Psychological Association.

Chang, E. C., & Hirsch, J. K. (2015). Social problem solving under assault: Understanding the impact of sexual assault on the relation between social problem solving and suicidal risk in female college students. *Cognitive Therapy and Research, 39,* 403–413. doi:10.1007/s10608-014-9664-2

Cheng, S. K. (2001). Life stress, problem solving, perfectionism, and depressive symptoms in Chinese. *Cognitive Therapy and Research, 25,* 303–310. doi:10.1023/A:1010788513083

Chiang, J. J., Turiano, N. A., Mroczek, D. K., & Miller, G. E. (2018). Affective reactivity to daily stress and 20-year mortality risk in adults with chronic illness: Findings from the National Study of Daily Experiences. *Health Psychology, 37,* 170. doi:10.1037/hea0000567

Clum, G. A., & Febbraro, G. A. R. (1994). Stress, social support, and problem-solving appraisal/skills: Prediction of suicide severity within a college sample. *Journal of Psychopathology and Behavioral Assessment, 16,* 69–83. doi:10.1007/BF02229066

Cohen, B. E., Edmondson, D., & Kronish, I. M. (2015). State of the art review: Depression, stress, anxiety, and cardiovascular disease. *American Journal of Hypertension, 28,* 1295–1302. doi:10.1093/ajh/hpv047

Coker, K. L., Ikpe, U. N., Brooks, J. S., Page, B., & Sobell, M. B. (2014). The effect of social problem solving skills in the relationship between traumatic stress and moral disengagement among inner-city African American high school students. *Journal of Child & Adolescent Trauma, 7,* 87–95. doi:10.1007/s40653-014-0012-1

D'Zurilla, T. J., & Nezu, A. M. (2007). *Problem-solving therapy: A positive approach to clinical intervention* (3rd ed.). New York, NY: Springer Publishing.

Dallman, M. F., Bhatnagar, S., & Viau, V. (2000). Hypothalamo–pituitary–adrenal axis. In G. Fink (Ed.), *Encyclopedia of stress* (pp. 468–477). New York, NY: Academic Press.

Damasio, A. R. (1999). *The feeling of what happens.* New York, NY: Harcourt & Brace.

Davidson, R. J., & Begley, S. (2012). *The emotional life of your brain: How its unique patterns affect the way you think, feel and live—And how you can change them.* New York, NY: Hudson Street Press.

Davidson, R. J., & McEwen, B. S. (2012). Social influences on neuroplasticity: Stress and interventions to promote well-being. *Nature Neuroscience, 15,* 689. doi:10.1038/nn.3093

Dhabhar, F. S. (2011). Effects of stress on immune function: Implications for immune-protection and immunopathology. In R. J. Contrada & A. Baum (Eds.), *The handbook of stress science: Biology, psychology, and health* (pp. 47–63). New York, NY: Springer Publishing.

Dhabhar, F. S. (2014). Effects of stress on immune function: The good, the bad, and the beautiful. *Immunologic Research, 58,* 193–210. doi:10.1007/s12026-014-8517-0

Dolcos, F., & McCarthy, G. (2006). Brain systems mediating cognitive interference by emotional distraction. *Journal of Neuroscience, 26,* 2071–2079. doi:10.1523/JNEUROSCI.5042-05.2006

Dubow, E. F., & Tisak, J. (1989). The relation between stressful life events and adjustment in elementary school children: The role of social support and social problem-solving skills. *Child Development, 60,* 1412–1423. doi:10.2307/1130931

Eskin, M., Akyol, A., Çelik, E. Y., & Gültekin, B. K. (2013). Social problem-solving, perceived stress, depression and life-satisfaction in patients suffering from tension type and migraine headaches. *Scandinavian Journal of Psychology, 54,* 337–343. doi:10.1111/sjop.12056

Eskin, M., Şavk, E., Uslu, M., & Küçükaydoğan, N. (2014). Social problem-solving, perceived stress, negative life events, depression and life satisfaction in psoriasis. *Journal of the European Academy of Dermatology and Venereology, 28,* 1553–1559. doi:10.1111/jdv.12355

Esposito, C. L., & Clum, G. A. (2002). Psychiatric symptoms and their relationship to suicidal ideation in a high-risk adolescent community sample. *Journal of the American Academy of Child and Adolescent Psychiatry, 41,* 44–51. doi:10.1097/00004583-200201000-00010

Fareri, D. S., & Tottenham, N. (2016). Effects of early life stress on amygdala and striatal development. *Developmental Cognitive Neuroscience, 19,* 233–247. doi:10.1016/j.dcn.2016.04.005

Frye, A. A., & Goodman, S. H. (2000). Which social problem-solving components buffer depression in adolescent girls? *Cognitive Therapy and Research, 24,* 637–650. doi:10.1023/A:1005583210589

Gatt, J. M., Nemeroff, C. B., Schofield, P. R., Paul, R. H., Clark, C. R., Gordon, E., & Williams, L. M. (2010). Early life stress combined with serotonin 3A receptor and brain-derived neurotrophic factor valine 66 to methionine genotypes impacts emotional brain and arousal correlates of risk for depression. *Biological Psychiatry, 68,* 818–824. doi:10.1016/j.biopsych.2010.06.025

Gibbs, L. M., Dombrovski, A. Y., Morse, J., Siegle, G. J., Houck, P. R., & Szanto, K. (2009). When the solution is part of the problem: Problem solving in elderly suicide attempters. *International Journal of Geriatric Psychiatry, 24,* 1396–1404. doi:10.1002/gps.2276

Goodman, S. H., Gravitt, G. W., Jr., & Kaslow, N. J. (1995). Social problem solving: A moderator of the relation between negative life stress and depression symptoms in children. *Journal of Abnormal Child Psychology, 23,* 473–485. doi:10.1007/BF01447209

Gouin, J. P., Glaser, R., Malarkey, W. B., Beversdorf, D., & Kiecolt-Glaser, J. (2012). Chronic stress, daily stressors, and circulating inflammatory markers. *Health Psychology, 31,* 264–268. doi:10.1037/a0025536

Graham, J. E., Christian, L. M., & Kiecolt-Glaser, J. K. (2006). Stress, age, and immune function: Toward a lifespan approach. *Journal of Behavioral Medicine, 29,* 389–400. doi:10.1007/s10865-006-9057-4

Grover, K. E., Green, K. L., Pettit, J. W., Monteith, L. L., Garza, M. J., & Venta, A. (2009). Problem solving moderates the effects of life event stress and chronic stress on suicidal behaviors in adolescence. *Journal of Clinical Psychology, 65,* 1281–1290. doi:10.1002/jclp.20632

Gunnar, M. R., Frenn, K., Wewerka, S. S., & Van Ryzin, M. J. (2009). Moderate versus severe early life stress: Associations with stress reactivity and regulation in 10-12-year-old children. *Psychoneuroendocrinology, 34,* 62–75. doi:10.1016/j.psyneuen.2008.08.013

Gutman, D. A., & Nemeroff, C. B. (2011). Stress and depression. In R. J. Contrada & A. Baum (Eds.), *The handbook of stress science: Biology, psychology, and health* (pp. 345–357). New York, NY: Springer Publishing.

Hammen, C., Kim, E. Y., Eberhart, N. K., & Brennan, P. A. (2009). Chronic and acute stress and the prediction of major depression in women. *Depression and Anxiety, 26,* 718–723. doi:10.1002/da.20571

Hanson, J. L., Nacewicz, B. M., Sutterer, M. J., Cayo, A. A., Schaefer, S. M., Rudolph, K. D., … Davidson, R. J. (2015). Behavioral problems after early life stress: Contributions of the hippocampus and amygdala. *Biological Psychiatry, 77,* 314–323. doi:10.1016/j.biopsych.2014.04.020

Hasegawa, A., Kunisato, Y., Morimoto, H., Nishimura, H., & Matsuda, Y. (2018). How do rumination and social problem solving intensify depression? A longitudinal study. *Journal of Rational-Emotive & Cognitive-Behavior Therapy, 36,* 28–46. doi:10.1007/s10942-017-0272-4

Heim, C., & Binder, E. B. (2012). Current research trends in early life stress and depression: Review of human studies on sensitive periods, gene-environment Interactions, and epigenetics. *Experimental Neurology, 233,* 102–111. doi:10.1016/j.expneurol.2011.10.032

Heim, C., Mletzko, T., Purselle, D., Musselman, D. L., & Nemeroff, C. B. (2008). The dexamethasone/corticotropin-releasing factor test in men with major depression: Role of childhood trauma. *Biological Psychiatry, 63,* 398–405. doi:10.1016/j.biopsych.2007.07.002

Heim, C., & Nemeroff, C. B. (2001). The role of childhood trauma in the neurobiology of mood and anxiety disorders: Preclinical and clinical studies. *Biological Psychiatry, 49,* 1023–1039. doi:10.1016/S0006-3223(01)01157-X

Jackson, S. L. J., & Dritschel, B. (2016). Modeling the impact of social problem-solving deficits on depressive vulnerability in the broader autism phenotype. *Research in Autism Spectrum Disorders, 21,* 128–138. doi:10.1016/j.rasd.2015.10.002

Kahneman, D. (2011). *Thinking, fast and slow.* New York, NY: Farrar, Straus & Giroux.

Kant, G. L., D'Zurilla, T. J., & Maydeu-Olivares, A. (1997). Social problem solving as a mediator of stress-related depression and anxiety in middle-aged and elderly community residents. *Cognitive Therapy and Research, 21,* 73–96. doi:10.1023/A:1021820326754

Keinan, G. (1987). Decision making under stress: Scanning of alternatives under controllable and uncontrollable threats. *Journal of Personality and Social Psychology, 52,* 639–644. doi:10.1037/0022-3514.52.3.639

Kiecolt-Glaser, J. K., & Glaser, R. (2001). Stress and immunity: Age enhances the risks. *Current Directions in Psychological Science, 10,* 18–21. doi:10.1111/1467-8721.00105

Kiecolt-Glaser, J. K., McGuire, L., Robles, T. F., & Glaser, R. (2002). Emotions, morbidity, and mortality: New perspectives from psychoneuroimmunology. *Annual Review of Psychology, 53,* 83–107. doi:10.1146/annurev.psych.53.100901.135217

Korb, A. (2015). *The upward spiral: Using neuroscience to reverse the course of depression, one small change at a time.* Oakland, CA: New Harbinger Publications.

Krugers, H. J., Arp, J. M., Xiong, H., Kanatsou, S., Lesuis, S. L., Korosi, A., … Lucassen, P. J. (2016). Early life adversity: Lasting consequences for emotional learning. *Neurobiology of Stress, 6,* 14–21. doi:10.1016/j.ynstr.2016.11.005

Largo-Wight, E., Peterson, P. M., & Chen, W. W. (2005). Perceived problem solving, stress, and health among college students. *American Journal of Health Behavior, 29,* 360–370. doi:10.5993/AJHB.29.4.8

Lazarus, R. S. (1999). The cognition–emotion debate: A bit of history. *Handbook of Cognition and Emotion, 5,* 3–19. doi:10.1002/0470013494.ch1

LeDoux, J. (1996). *The emotional brain.* New York, NY: Simon & Schuster.

LeDoux, J. (2002). *Synaptic self: How our brains become who we are.* New York, NY: Penguin Books.

Leykin, Y., Roberts, C. S., & DeRubeis, R. J. (2011). Decision-making and depressive symptomatology. *Cognitive Therapy and Research, 35,* 333–341. doi:10.1007/s10608-010-9308-0

Liu, R. T. (2015). A developmentally informed perspective on the relation between stress and psychopathology: When the problem with stress is that there is not enough. *Journal of Abnormal Psychology, 124*, 80–92. doi:10.1037/abn0000043

Londahl, E. A., Tverskoy, A., & D'Zurilla, T. J. (2005). The relations of internalizing symptoms to conflict and interpersonal problem solving in close relationships. *Cognitive Therapy and Research, 29*, 445–462. doi:10.1007/s10608-005-4442-9

McCormick, S. P., Nezu, C. M., Nezu, A. M., Sherman, M., Davey, A., & Collins, B. N. (2014). Coping and social problem solving correlates of asthma control and quality of life. *Chronic Respiratory Disease, 11*, 15–21. doi:10.1177/1479972313516878

McDade, T. W., Ryan, C., Jones, M. J., MacIsaac, J. L., Morin, A. M., Meyer, J. M., ... Kuzawa, C. W. (2017). Social and physical environments early in development predict DNA methylation of inflammatory genes in young adulthood. *Proceedings of the National Academy of Sciences of the United States of America, 114*, 7611–7616. doi:10.1073/pnas.1620661114

McEwen, B. S., & Morrison, J. H. (2013). The brain on stress: Vulnerability and plasticity of the prefrontal cortex over the life course. *Neuron, 79*, 16–29. doi:10.1016/j.neuron.2013.06.028

Miner, R. C., & Dowd, E. T. (1996). An empirical test of the problem solving model of depression and its application to the prediction of anxiety and anger. *Counselling Psychology Quarterly, 9*, 163–176. doi:10.1080/09515079608256361

Monroe, S. M., Slavich, G. M., & Georgiades, K. (2009). The social environment and life stress in depression. In I. H. Gotlib & C. L. Hammen (Eds.), *Handbook of depression* (pp. 340–360). New York, NY: Guilford Press.

Monroe, S. M., Slavich, G. M., Torres, L. D., & Gotlib, I. H. (2007). Major life events and major chronic difficulties are differentially associated with history of major depression. *Journal of Abnormal Psychology, 116*, 116–124. doi:10.1037/0021-843X.116.1.116

Muscara, F., Catroppa, C., & Anderson, V. (2008). Social problem-solving skills as a mediator between executive function and long-term social outcome following paediatric traumatic brain injury. *Journal of Neuropsychology, 2*, 445–461. doi:10.1348/174866407X250820

Nezu, A. M. (1986). Negative life stress and anxiety: Problem solving as a moderator variable. *Psychological Reports, 58*, 279–283. doi:10.2466/pr0.1986.58.1.279

Nezu, A. M. (2004). Problem solving and behavior therapy revisited. *Behavior Therapy, 35*, 1–33. doi:10.1016/S0005-7894(04)80002-9

Nezu, A. M., Nezu, C. M., & D'Zurilla, T. J. (2013). *Problem-solving therapy: A treatment manual.* New York, NY: Springer Publishing.

Nezu, A. M., Nezu, C. M., Faddis, S., DelliCarpini, L. A., & Houts, P. S. (1995, November). *Social problem solving as a moderator of cancer-related stress.* Paper presented at the Annual Convention of the Association for Advancement of Behavior Therapy, Washington, DC.

Nezu, A. M., Nezu, C. M., & Jain, D. (2008). Social problem solving as a mediator of the stress-pain relationship among individuals with noncardiac chest pain. *Health Psychology, 27*, 829–832. doi:10.1037/0278-6133.27.6.829

Nezu, A. M., Nezu, C. M., Saraydarian, L., Kalmar, K., & Ronan, G. F. (1986). Social problem solving as a moderating variable between negative life stress and depressive symptoms. *Cognitive Therapy and Research, 10*, 489–498. doi:10.1007/BF01177813

Nezu, A. M., Nezu, C. M., Stern, J. B., Greenfield, A. P., Diaz, C., & Hays, A. M. (2017). Social problem solving moderates emotion reactivity in predicting suicide ideation among U.S. Veterans. *Military Behavioral Health, 5*, 417–426. doi:10.1080/21635781.2017.1337595

Nezu, A. M., Perri, M. G., & Nezu, C. M. (1987, August). *Validation of a problem-solving/stress model of depression.* Paper presented at the Annual Convention of the American Psychological Association, New York, NY.

Nezu, A. M., & Ronan, G. F. (1985). Life stress, current problems, problem solving, and depressive symptoms: An integrative model. *Journal of Consulting and Clinical Psychology, 53*, 693–697. doi:10.1037/0022-006X.53.5.693

Nezu, A. M., & Ronan, G. F. (1988). Stressful life events, problem solving, and depressive symptoms among university students: A prospective analysis. *Journal of Counseling Psychology, 35*, 134–138. doi:10.1037/0022-0167.35.2.134

Nezu, A. M., Wilkins, V. M., & Nezu, C. M. (2004). Social problem solving, stress, and negative affect. In E. C. Chang, T. J. D'Zurilla, & L. J. Sanna (Eds.), *Social problem solving: Theory, research, and training* (pp. 49–65). Washington, DC: American Psychological Association.

Nock, M. K., & Mendes, W. B. (2008). Physiological arousal, distress tolerance, and social problem-solving deficits among adolescent self-injurers. *Journal of Consulting and Clinical Psychology, 76*, 28–38. doi:10.1037/0022-006X.76.1.28

Nugent, N. R., Tyrka, A. R., Carpenter, L. L., & Price, L. H. (2011). Gene–environment interactions: Early life stress and risk for depressive and anxiety disorders. *Psychopharmacology, 214*, 175–196. doi:10.1007/s00213-010-2151-x

Olff, M. (1999). Stress, depression and immunity: The role of defense and coping styles. *Psychiatry Research, 85*, 7–15. doi:10.1016/S0165-1781(98)00139-5

Özdemir, Y., Kuzucu, Y., & Koruklu, N. (2013). Social problem solving and aggression: The role of depression. *Journal of Psychologists and Counsellors in Schools, 23*, 72–81.

Pace, T. W., Mletzko, T. C., Alagbe, O., Musselman, D. L., Nemeroff, C. B., … Heim, C. M. (2006). Increased stress-induced inflammatory responses in male patients with major depression and increased early life stress. *American Journal of Psychiatry, 163*, 1630–1633. doi:10.1176/ajp.2006.163.9.1630

Pessoa, L. (2010). Emotion and cognition and the amygdala: From "what is it?" to "what's to be done?" *Neuropsychologia, 48*, 3416–3429. doi:10.1016/j.neuropsychologia.2010.06.038

Post, R. M. (2007). Kindling and sensitization as models for affective episode recurrence, cyclicity, and tolerance phenomena. *Neuroscience and Biobehavioral Reviews, 31*, 858–873. doi:10.1016/j.neubiorev.2007.04.003

Priester, M. J., & Clum, G. A. (1993). Perceived problem-solving ability as a predictor of depression, hopelessness, and suicide ideation in a college population. *Journal of Counseling Psychology, 40*, 79–85. doi:10.1037/0022-0167.40.1.79

Provençal, N., & Binder, E. B. (2015). The effects of early life stress on the epigenome: From the womb to adulthood and even before. *Experimental Neurology, 268*, 10–20. doi:10.1016/j.expneurol.2014.09.001

Ranjbar, M., Bayani, A. A., & Bayani, A. (2013). Social problem solving ability predicts mental health among undergraduate students. *International Journal of Preventive Medicine, 4*, 1337–1341.

Reich, C. M., Blackwell, N., Simmons, C. A., & Beck, J. G. (2015). Social problem solving strategies and posttraumatic stress disorder in the aftermath of intimate partner violence. *Journal of Anxiety Disorders, 32,* 31–37. doi:10.1016/j.janxdis.2015.02.007

Ridout, N., Matharu, M., Sanders, E., & Wallis, D. J. (2015). The influence of eating psychopathology on autobiographical memory specificity and social problem-solving. *Psychiatry Research, 228,* 295–303. doi:10.1016/j.psychres.2015.06.030

Rudd, M. D., Rajab, M. H., & Dahm, P. F. (1994). Problem-solving appraisal in suicide ideators and attempters. *American Journal of Orthopsychiatry, 64,* 136–149. doi:10.1037/h0079492

Seery, M. D. (2011). Resilience: A silver lining to experiencing adverse life events. *Current Directions in Psychological Science, 20,* 390–394. doi:10.1177/0963721411424740

Seery, M. D., Leo, R. J., Lupien, S. P., Kondrak, C. L., & Almonte, J. L. (2013). An upside to adversity? Moderate cumulative lifetime adversity is associated with resilient responses in the face of controlled stressors. *Psychological Science, 24,* 1181–1189. doi:10.1177/0956797612469210

Sgaramella, T. M., Nota, L., Carrieri, L., Soresi, S., & Sato, G. (2017). Daily functioning, problem solving and satisfaction for quality of life in visually impaired old persons. *International Journal on Disability and Human Development, 16,* 225–232. doi:10.1515/ijdhd-2016-0010

Shonkoff, J. P., Garner, A. S., Committee on Psychosocial Aspects of Child and Family Health, Committee on Early Childhood, Adoption, and Dependent Care., & Section on Developmental and Behavioral Pediatrics. (2012). The lifelong effects of early childhood adversity and toxic stress. *Pediatrics, 129,* e232–e246. doi:10.1542/peds.2011-2663

Silberman, D. M., Acosta, G. B., & Zorrilla Zubilete, M. A. (2016). Long-term effects of early life stress exposure: Role of epigenetic mechanisms. *Pharmacological Research, 109,* 64–73. doi:10.1016/j.phrs.2015.12.033

Slavich, G. M. (2016). Life stress and health: A review of conceptual issues and recent findings. *Teaching of Psychology, 43,* 346–355. doi:10.1177/0098628316662768

Sorsdahl, K., Stein, D. J., Carrara, H., & Myers, B. (2014). Problem solving styles among people who use alcohol and other drugs in South Africa. *Addictive Behaviors, 39,* 122–126. doi:10.1016/j.addbeh.2013.09.011

Spence, S. H., Sheffield, J. K., & Donovan, C. L. (2003). Preventing adolescent depression: An evaluation of the problem solving for life program. *Journal of Consulting and Clinical Psychology, 71,* 3–13. doi:10.1037/0022-006X.71.1.3

Stanovich, K. E., & West, R. F. (2000). Individual differences in reasoning: Implications for the rationality debate? *Behavioral and Brain Sciences, 23,* 645–665. doi:10.1017/S0140525X00003435

Starcke, K., & Brand, M. (2016). Effects of stress on decisions under uncertainty: A meta-analysis. *Psychological Bulletin, 142,* 909–933. doi:10.1037/bul0000060

Steptoe, A., & Kivimäki, M. (2013). Stress and cardiovascular disease: An update on current knowledge. *Annual Review of Public Health, 34,* 337–354. doi:10.1146/annurev-publhealth-031912-114452

Stern, J. B., Nezu, A. M., Nezu, C. M., Greenfield, A. P., Diaz, C. E., & Hays, A. M. (2015, November). *Social problem solving, emotional reactivity, suicidal ideation, and self-harm among college students.* Paper presented at the Annual Convention of the Association of Behavioral and Cognitive Therapies, Chicago, IL.

Stetler, C., & Miller, G. E. (2011). Depression and hypothalamic–pituitary–adrenal activation: A quantitative summary of four decades of research. *Psychosomatic Medicine, 73*, 114–126. doi:10.1097/PSY.0b013e31820ad12b

Suso-Ribera, C., Camacho-Guerrero, L., McCracken, L. M., Maydeu-Olivares, A., & Gallardo-Pujol, D. (2016). Social problem solving in chronic pain: An integrative model of coping predicts mental health in chronic pain patients. *Journal of Health Psychology, 21*, 1015–1025. doi:10.1177/1359105314544133

Tafet, G. E., & Nemeroff, C. B. (2016). The links between stress and depression: Psychoneuroendocrinological, genetic, and environmental interactions. *Journal of Neuropsychiatry and Clinical Neurosciences, 28*, 77–88. doi:10.1176/appi.neuropsych.15030053

Tomiyama, A. J. (2019). Stress and obesity. *Annual Review of Psychology, 70*. doi:10.1146/annurev-psych-010418-102936

Tranel, D., & Hyman, B. T. (1990). Neuropsychological correlates of bilateral amygdala damage. *Archives of Neurology, 47*, 349–355. doi:10.1001/archneur.1990.00530030131029

Uchida, S., Hara, K., Kobayashi, A., Funato, H., Hobara, T., Otsuki, K., ... Watanabe, Y. (2010). Early life stress enhances behavioral vulnerability to stress through the activation of REST4-mediated gene transcription in the medial prefrontal cortex of rodents. *Journal of Neuroscience, 30*, 15007–15018. doi:10.1523/JNEUROSCI.1436-10.2010

Van Liew, C., Gluhm, S., Goldstein, J., Cronan, T. A., & Corey-Bloom, J. (2013). The functional implications of motor, cognitive, psychiatric, and social problem-solving states in Huntington's disease. *Psychiatry, 76*, 323–335. doi:10.1521/psyc.2013.76.4.323

Visser, M. M., Heijenbrok-Kal, M. H., Spijker, A. V., Oostra, K. M., Busschbach, J. J., & Ribbers, G. M. (2015). Coping, problem solving, depression, and health-related quality of life in patients receiving outpatient stroke rehabilitation. *Archives of Physical Medicine and Rehabilitation, 96*, 1492–1498. doi:10.1016/j.apmr.2015.04.007

Weinberger, M., Hiner, S. L., & Tierney, W. M. (1987). In support of hassles as a measure of stress in predicting health outcomes. *Journal of Behavioral Medicine, 10*, 19–31. doi:10.1007/BF00845125

Wichers, M., Geschwind, N., Jacobs, N., Kenis, G., Peeters, F., Derom, C., ... van Os, J. (2009). Transition from stress sensitivity to a depressive state: Longitudinal twin study. *British Journal of Psychiatry, 195*, 498–503. doi:10.1192/bjp.bp.108.056853

Wilhelm, K., Siegel, J. E., Finch, A. W., Hadzi-Pavlovic, D., Mitchell, P. B., ... Schofield, P. R. (2007). The long and the short of it: Associations between 5-HTT genotypes and coping with stress. *Psychosomatic Medicine, 69*, 614–620. doi:10.1097/PSY.0b013e31814cec64

Yang, B., & Clum, G. A. (1994). Life stress, social support, and problem-solving skills predictive of depressive symptoms, hopelessness, and suicide ideation in an Asian student population: A test of a model. *Suicide and Life-Threatening Behavior, 24*, 127–139.

PROBLEM-SOLVING–BASED THERAPIES: EMPIRICAL SUPPORT AND TRANSDIAGNOSTIC CAPABILITIES

3

Since the initial publication of the D'Zurilla and Goldfried (1971) training model, clinical researchers have applied and evaluated problem-solving therapy (PST), both as a singular intervention strategy and as part of a larger treatment package, with regard to a wide variety of patient populations and problems. Box 3.1, which appears later in the chapter, provides a listing of such studies by participant group that have been published since our last book (Nezu, Nezu, & D'Zurilla, 2013). Perusal of this box suggests that there is an increased interest in studying the efficacy of PST-based interventions and that there is a wider range of both health and behavioral health problems being addressed, as well as different participant groups being treated. Thus, it can be stated that this approach is transdiagnostic in nature. Before we comment of this characterization, we briefly describe several meta-analyses and systematic reviews of PST. In keeping with the growing number of empirically supported trials, such reviews have also increased during the past several years. We present this review as strong evidence in support of the overall efficacy of PST.

RESULTS OF META-ANALYSES

Several systematic reviews and meta-analyses have been conducted regarding the efficacy of PST during the past decade. These are categorized in the following text according to the targeted problem and/or population served.

PST for Various Mental and Physical Health Problems

The first published meta-analysis regarding PST was conducted by Malouff, Thorsteinsson, and Schutte (2007); it contained 32 studies encompassing 2,895 participants. It included randomized controlled trials (RCTs) that evaluated the efficacy of PST across a variety of mental and physical health problems. Results of their meta-analysis found that although there was a trend in favor of PST when compared with other "bona fide" interventions (e.g., antidepressants, rational emotive therapy, cognitive behavioral therapy), that difference was not significant ($d = 0.022$). In other words, PST was found to be equally effective as other legitimate forms of psychotherapy. Furthermore, PST was found to be more effective than no treatment ($d = 1.37$), attention placebo control conditions ($d = 0.54$), and treatment as usual ($d = 0.54$). These results strongly suggest that PST is an efficacious clinical intervention. In addition to these main effects, the authors also tested the relevance of various moderators of outcome. Significant moderators included whether the PST protocol being evaluated included training in the problem-orientation component, whether homework was assigned, or whether a developer of PST (i.e., A. M. Nezu) was a coauthor of a particular study.

Although a trend in favor of a higher number of hours of treatment was associated with greater effect sizes, this was not found to be significant. Additional analyses indicated that the following variables were also not significantly associated with outcome: whether treatment was provided in a group setting or individually; whether the participants had been identified before the study as having a clinical problem; whether that problem involved depression; whether the investigation used self-report, objective, or both types of measures; and the length of the follow-up assessment.

PST for Depression

The first meta-analysis that focused exclusively on studies evaluating PST for depression was conducted by Cuijpers, van Straten, and Warmerdam (2007). Their analysis included 13 RCTs representing a total of 1,133 participants. Overall, their review indicated that the majority of these studies identified favorable results for PST. More specific, the mean standardized effect size within a fixed-effects model was 0.34 and 0.83 in a random-effects model. Although these authors identified significant heterogeneity among the RCTs, their subgroup analyses were not able to provide a clear understanding of what caused such heterogeneity. In addition, in contrast to the Malouff et al. (2007) meta-analysis, Cuijpers et al. (2007) identified a stronger outcome for group interventions than individual interventions. They further concluded that although additional research was necessary, especially in light of the variability in outcomes across the included studies, PST appears to be an effective approach for the treatment of depression.

A second meta-analysis that focused on PST investigations for depression was conducted by A. C. Bell and D'Zurilla (2009) and included seven additional studies beyond that encompassing the pool in the Cuijpers et al. (2007) meta-analysis. In essence, these authors came to the same conclusion, that is, PST is an effective treatment for depression (standardized mean effect size was $d = 0.40$). In addition, PST was found to be equally as effective as both alternative psychosocial therapies and pharmacological treatments, but more effective than supportive therapy (ST) and attention control groups. Moreover, significant moderators of treatment outcome included whether the PST program included problem-orientation training, whether all four problem-solving skills (i.e., problem definition, generating alternatives, decision making, and solution implementation and verification) were included, and whether all five components were included (i.e., problem orientation and the four problem-solving skills). This strongly suggests that a more comprehensive therapy approach is important. In other words, not addressing various problem-orientation variables, including training one to better understand the role that emotions play within problem solving, appears to lead to less favorable outcomes.

Nieuwsma et al. (2012) conducted a systematic review of studies that evaluated brief psychotherapy protocols for depression in general that were not specific to PST. Their criteria for inclusion involved RCTs of evidence-based approaches of eight or fewer sessions, a focus on treating depression among adults, containing an acceptable control condition, published in English, and incorporated validated measures of depressive symptoms. This led to the identification of two previously conducted systematic reviews and 15 RCTs evaluating cognitive behavioral therapy, PST, and mindfulness-based cognitive therapy. On the basis of their review, these authors concluded that "depression can be efficaciously treated with six to eight sessions of psychotherapy, particularly cognitive behavioral therapy and problem-solving therapy" (p. 130).

Cuijpers, de Wit, Kleiboer, Karyotaki, and Ebert (2018) recently published an update of their meta-analysis of PST for the treatment of depression. In this review, 30 studies were included that represented 3,530 patients. They also conducted a comparison of these RCTs with 259 trials of other psychotherapies for adult depression. The significant effect size of PST versus control conditions was found to be $g = 0.79$; similar to their earlier meta-analysis, they also identified high heterogeneity among studies. When specifically focused on a subgroup of nine studies with low risk of bias and low heterogeneity, the effect size was found to be $g = 0.34$. However, in direct comparisons, PST was found to be "a little more effective than other therapies in direct comparisons" (p. 27), although these authors posit that this difference could have occurred because a considerable number of the PST studies were conducted by individuals with possible research allegiance to PST. Nevertheless, Cuijpers et al. (2018) conclude that the effects of PST are comparable to those found for other psychological treatments of depression.

PST in Primary Care

A recently published meta-analysis of PST clinical trials focused on the treatment of depressive and/or anxiety disorders specifically among primary care patients (Zhang, Park, Sullivan, & Jing, 2018). The search by Zhang et al. yielded an initial pool of 153 primary studies, eventually leading to 11 investigations that met their inclusion criteria. These RCTs represented 2,072 participants. The effect size for primary care depression and/or anxiety was found to be $d = 0.67$, indicating a significant treatment effect. No differences in efficacy were identified as a function of the targeted clinical problem, that is, depression versus anxiety. Although participants' ethnic/racial background or marital status did not moderate the overall treatment outcome, age was found to be a significant moderator. More specifically, the older the participant, the higher is the treatment effect. Additional moderator analyses yielded no significant differences regarding treatment modality (individual vs. group treatment), methods of protocol delivery (in-person vs. telehealth), number of sessions, or length of a given PST session. It is interesting to note that the background of the PST provider and the involvement of a primary care physician in the clinical trial were further treatment outcome moderators. Specifically, master's-level therapists had significantly higher treatment effects than doctoral-level providers and those studies without physician involvement reported significantly greater treatment effects than physician-involved primary care-based PST. The authors concluded, on the basis of their systematic review, that PST is efficacious for treating depression and anxiety disorders among primary care populations.

Similar to the Zhang et al. (2018) study, Cape, Whittington, Buszewicz, Wallace, and Underwood (2010) focused on the treatment of depression and anxiety in primary care populations. However, more similar to the Nieuwsma et al. (2012) review, these authors were interested in a variety of brief psychological therapies rather than a single type, such as PST. Their meta-analysis and meta-regression included 34 investigations, which represented 3,962 patients. The majority of these studies were trials of brief forms of cognitive behavioral therapy, counseling, or PST. With regard to the PST protocols, the mean effect size comparing PST with treatment as usual was found to be $d = -0.21$, adding to the growing review literature underscoring the efficacy of PST. It is important to note that a meta-regression analysis found no differences among cognitive behavioral therapy, counseling, and PST.

A third systematic review and meta-analysis that focused on primary care settings involved a comparison between various psychological interventions, PST being one of them, and usual care or placebo regarding the treatment of depression among adults (Linde et al., 2015). Collectively, 30 studies were included representing 5,159 patients. Relevant to this discussion, the standardized mean difference at completion of treatment for face-to-face PST was −0.24 and −0.56 for remote therapist-led PST (e.g., telehealth protocols), providing further evidence for the efficacy of PST for treating depressed primary care patients. Similar to the reviews described earlier, no significant differences were identified between PST and the other various therapies (including cognitive behavioral therapy and interpersonal psychotherapy) regarding overall treatment outcome.

PST Among Older Adults

Areán et al. (1993) published the first clinical trial evaluating the efficacy of PST in treating depression among an older adult population. Since then, multiple researchers have applied PST to address a wide range of clinical problems experienced by older adults. This has engendered three systematic reviews. Kirkham, Choi, and Seitz (2016) conducted a meta-analysis that focused on PST for the treatment of major depressive disorder (MDD) among this age group. Their major inclusion criteria involved RCTs that compared PST to a control condition or other treatment approach for MDD in persons aged 60 years or older. Nine studies were identified that represented 569 participants. The majority of these studies involved in-person PST and varied between 6 and 12 weeks in duration. These authors conducted subgroup analyses depending on the measure of depression used in a given study. Regardless of the assessment procedure, they found PST to be associated with significant reductions in depressive symptoms in contrast to a comparator condition. For example, the pooled mean difference for the six studies incorporating the Hamilton Rating Scale for Depression was found to be −6.94 (p = .0006). In addition, Kirkham et al. (2016) found that PST was also effective in significantly reducing disability in studies that included such measures.

Simon, Cordás, and Bottino (2015) conducted a systematic review to investigate the effectiveness of cognitive behavioral therapies in fostering improvements in depressive symptoms, disability, and cognition among older adults experiencing depression and cognitive deficits. Six studies eventually met all inclusion criteria; however, it should be noted that three of these publications referred to the same study sample. In essence, these authors concluded that cognitive behavioral approaches that focus on problem solving consistently led to better outcomes in depression and disability than supportive therapies. Although they noted improvements in cognitive dimensions (e.g., executive functioning, processing speed, problem solving), Simon et al. (2015) also indicated that more studies are necessary before definitive conclusions can be articulated.

As mentioned earlier, during the past decade, PST has been evaluated across a wide range of targeted problems experienced by older adults. Kiosses and Alexopoulos (2014) conducted a systematic review of RCTs of PST across such areas. Major findings included the following: (a) PST >ST (supportive therapy) and reminiscence therapy regarding late-life MDD; (b) PST = paroxetine in patients with minor depression and dysthymia; (c) PST >home healthcare in depressed patients; (d) PST >ST in patients with major depression and executive dysfunction; (e) PST = ST concerning vision-related disability in patients with macular degeneration, but PST >ST regarding vision-related quality of life; (f) among patients with macular degeneration, PST >usual care regarding 2-month incidence rates of major depression and were less likely to experience persistent depression at 6 months; and (g) PST delivered via telehealth protocols were comparable to in-person PST. Collectively, these results provide support for the overall efficacy of PST for a wide range of difficulties that older adults suffer.

PST for Diabetes Self-Management and Control

Many clinicians and researchers who treat patients with diabetes suggest that problem solving is an important core skill for patient self-management and education. Fitzpatrick, Schumann, and Hill-Briggs (2013) conducted a systematic review of this literature, which included 24 studies (16 RCTs and eight intervention studies that involved quasi-experimental designs). These authors noted that the actual approach to PST varied across the investigations. For example, some researchers conceptualized problem solving as an educational topic, whereas others described it as a process that is support group based or as an actual structured therapeutic approach. With regard to treatment outcome, these authors noted that 36% of adult problem-solving interventions and 42% of children/adolescent problem-solving interventions demonstrated significant improvement in hemoglobin A1C (blood sugar) levels, whereas psychosocial outcomes appeared more promising.

PST for Vision-Impaired Adults

During the past several years, researchers have increasingly applied PST to improve psychosocial outcomes of adults with various vision problems. Holloway, Xie, Sturrock, Lamoureux, and Rees (2015) conducted a systematic review and meta-analysis of this literature that included 11 such studies (reporting on eight trials). Results of their meta-analysis found significant mean effects concerning improvements in both vision-related functioning and emotional distress, but not with regard to depressive symptoms per se and overall quality of life. Given the small number of actual trials identified, these authors called for additional research while noting that "problem-solving skills may be important for nurturing daily functioning and reducing emotional distress for adults with vision impairment" (p. 553). A related study focused on assessing the effects of training vision rehabilitation staff to deliver PST in primary care over the telephone to adults with depressive symptoms and low vision (Sturrock et al., 2016). Results of this open trial indicated both an increase in the understanding of PST and increase in provider competency. Staff also reported high levels of satisfaction.

SPST in School Settings

The large majority of the PST studies included in the reviews discussed earlier involved PST interventions for adults and older adults. PST has also been implemented in a variety of school settings. The purpose of such programs generally involves efforts to decrease students' problem behaviors and to increase their social competence. Merrill, Smith, Cumming, and Daunic (2017) recently published a review of PST interventions (note that these are referred to in the literature as *social problem solving [SPS] interventions*) in K–12 settings from 1993 to 2015. Their search strategies led to 18 articles that met their inclusion criteria, one of which involved only including studies whereby the problem-solving intervention was implemented in schools during school hours and not before or in after-school programs. The total number of participants across studies was 4,985 and included students mostly in the third grade (range of kindergarten to eighth grade). Given that this article represented more of a description of the various studies, rather than a meta-analysis, no statistical synthesis was attempted. In general, these authors suggest, on the basis of their review, that PST programs were effective with regard to improving student behaviors, social problem-solving ability, and emotion regulation. However, because of various limitations among the studies (e.g., lack of multiple outcome measures incorporated, lack of adequate intervention descriptions), additional research was suggested as being necessary.

Barnes, Wang, and O'Brien (2018) recently published a meta-analysis of SPS interventions for younger children than those included in the Merrill et al. (2017) study; that is, interventions conducted in a day-care or preschool setting. Their analysis involved 26 articles, 16 of which included preschool-based reports of child externalizing behavior and 23 included measures of social competence. The average raw mean difference scores for externalizing behaviors and social competence assessment were −0.28 and 0.49, respectively. Note that these involved reports by school personnel. Although these effect sizes are significant, those emanating from six of the 23 trials that included home-based reports of both variables were not (−0.27 and 0.09, respectively, $p > .05$).

In summary, the various systematic reviews and meta-analyses described earlier provide substantial support for the efficacy of PST-based interventions across various age groups (preschool, school-aged, adults, older adults) in reducing depression and anxiety symptomatology, improving social problem-solving ability and competence, and enhancing health-related well-being (e.g., vision-related quality of life, blood sugar levels of persons with diabetes). In the next section, we highlight the flexibility of PST across targeted problem areas.

PST AS A TRANSDIAGNOSTIC APPROACH

Box 3.1 contains a list of clinical trials of PST across various diagnostic groups and clinical problems among adolescents, adults, and older adults (see Barnes et al. [2018] and Merrill et al. [2017] for lists of PST interventions for school-aged and preschool-aged children) that were published subsequent to our 2013 book (Nezu et al.).[1] In support of our characterization of PST as a flexible and transdiagnostic approach, note that the targeted problem areas include various mental and behavioral health problems (autism spectrum disorder, depression, anxiety, postpartum depression, posttraumatic stress symptoms, substance use, suicidality, self-harm), as well as various medical and physical problems (pain, insomnia, cancer, cardiovascular disease, chronic pulmonary disease, diabetes, early-stage renal disease, geriatric frailty, HIV/AIDS, infertility, stroke, vision problems, traumatic brain injury). In addition, various specific populations have been the focus of attention, including parental and informal caregivers of individuals experiencing a wide range of difficulties (severe disabilities, cancer, first-episode psychosis, dementia, autism, stroke, chronic pain, and traumatic brain injury), pregnant women, military veterans, and active military service members. To provide an even more complete picture of the range of PST trials, although not included in Box 3.1, the following additional problem areas were listed in our 2013 book: Alzheimer's disease, arthritis, hypertension, couples therapy, obesity, criminal offenders, personality disorders, schizophrenia, social anxiety, and unexplained medical symptoms. In the following text we highlight several important features of this PST outcome literature.

---

[1]We apologize if we did not include all PST clinical trials published since 2012/2013. Note that we did not include articles that describe a study protocol yet to be conducted or single case reports.

BOX 3.1 ■ PROBLEM-SOLVING THERAPY/TRAINING OUTCOME STUDIES PUBLISHED SINCE NEZU ET AL. (2013)

Adolescents With Emotional/Behavioral Disorders
- Van Loan, Garwood, Smith, and Daunic (2018)—Middle school students

Anxiety/Depression
- Beaudreau, Gould, Mashal, Huh, and Fairchild (in press)—Older adults with generalized anxiety (case studies)
- Kleiboer et al. (2015)—Adults in community with mild to moderate symptoms of anxiety and/or depression; the Netherlands

Asperger Syndrome/Autism Spectrum Disorders
- Bonete, Calero, and Fernández-Parra (2015)—Adults with Asperger's syndrome; pilot study to assess feasibility and initial efficacy
- Pugliese and White (2014)—College students with autism spectrum disorder; pilot program

Cancer
- Hirai et al. (2012)—Postsurgery breast cancer patients; Japan
- Syrjala et al. (2018)—Cancer survivors after hematopoietic cell transplantation; online protocol
- Yoon et al. (2018)—Depressed older cancer patients; Korea

Cardiology
- Lilly et al. (2014)—Low-income/underserved adults in cardiovascular disease prevention program

Chronic Obstructive Pulmonary Disease
- Lee et al. (2014)—Telephone-based intervention; Korea

Depression Among Adults
- Berman et al. (2014)—Moderate–severe depressive symptoms; multimedia electronic program
- Buntrock et al. (2016)—Prevention of major depression in adults with subthreshold depression; web-based protocol; Germany
- Camacho et al. (2015)—Low-income Hispanic/Latinos; open trial
- Ebert et al. (2014)—Teachers with elevated depression scores; Internet-based program; Germany, the Netherlands, Sweden
- Junge et al. (2015)—Employees reporting depressive symptoms
- Sandoval et al. (2017)—Computerized interactive media-based protocol

Depression Among Older Adults
- Alexopoulos et al. (2016)—Low-income, disabled older adults
- Areán et al. (2005)—Low-income older depressed adults with a disability
- Choi et al. (2014)—Low-income, homebound older adults; PST provided via Skype video calls

(continued)

BOX 3.1 ■ PROBLEM-SOLVING THERAPY/TRAINING OUTCOME STUDIES PUBLISHED SINCE NEZU ET AL. (2013) (*continued*)

- Gellis, Kenaley, and Ten Have (2014)—Geriatric home care patients who were depressed and suffered from comorbid chronic illness; telehealth protocol
- Karp et al. (2018)—Depressed older adults with back pain; concurrently on antidepressant pharmacotherapy
- Mackin et al. (2014)—Depressed older adults with executive dysfunction
- Reinhardt, Horowitz, Cimarolli, Eimicke, and Teresi (2014)—Residents of long-term-care facilities
- Reynolds et al. (2014)—Prevention of major depression among Black and White older adults with subsyndromal depressive symptoms
- Stahl et al. (2017)—Depression prevention trial

Diabetes
- Lakerveld et al. (2013)—Type 2 diabetes; PST combined with motivational interviewing
- Rees et al. (2017)—Adults with diabetic retinopathy and diabetes-specific distress; pilot study
- Villamil-Salcedo et al. (2018)—Distressed type 2 diabetes patients with depressive and anxiety symptoms; Mexico
- Wu et al. (2018)—Depressed adults with type 2 diabetes in safety-net primary care settings; collaborative care model; automated routine screening/monitoring of depressive symptoms; majority of patients were Hispanic/Latino and female

Early-Stage Renal Disease
- Erdley-Kass et al. (2018)—Older adults undergoing hemodialysis

Geriatric Frailty
- Chan et al. (2012)—Older adults; Taiwan

Healthy Older Adults
- C. M. Nguyen, Chen, and Denburg (2018)—Cognitively healthy older adults living in the community; focus of treatment on improving executive functioning and decision making

HIV/AIDS
- Chibanda et al. (2017)—Patients in primary care setting with HIV and "common mental disorders"; description of the experience of lay health workers delivering a PST program; Zimbabwe
- Gross et al. (2013)—HIV-1 infected patients undergoing antiretroviral therapy; focus was on increasing adherence to medical treatment

Infertility
- Gojani et al. (2017)—Women waiting for intrauterine insemination treatment; Iran

(continued)

BOX 3.1 ■ PROBLEM-SOLVING THERAPY/TRAINING OUTCOME STUDIES PUBLISHED SINCE NEZU ET AL. (2013) (*continued*)

Insomnia
- Pech and O'Kearney (2013)—Adults experiencing insomnia; PST combined with behavioral sleep strategies; Australia

Intellectual Disabilities
- Ailey, Miller, and Fogg (2014)—Adults with intellectual disabilities living in staffed community homes; pilot study to assess feasibility and initial efficacy

Pain
- Linton, Boersma, Traczyk, Shaw, and Nicholas (2016)—Prevent back pain disability among high-risk workers and their supervisors

Parental/Family/Informal Caregivers
- Berry, Elliott, Grant, Edwards, and Fine (2012)—Family carers of persons with severe disabilities
- Bevans et al. (2014)—Informal carers of allogeneic hematopoietic stem cell transplantation patients
- Chien, Thompson, Lubman, and McCann (2016)—Family carers of adults with first-episode psychosis; bibliotherapy; Hong Kong
- Chien, Yip, Liu, and McMaster (2016)—Family carers of adults with recent-onset psychosis; Hong Kong
- Chiu, Pauley, Wesson, Pushpakumar, and Sadavoy (2015)—Informal carers of adults with dementia receiving in-home care; Canada
- Easom, Wang, Moore, Wang, and Bauer (2018)—Carers of military service members and veterans
- Feinberg et al. (2014)—Mothers of children recently diagnosed with autism spectrum disorder
- Ferré-Grau et al. (2014)—Family caregivers of chronically ill adults; Spain
- Garand et al. (2014)—Family carers of persons with a new diagnosis of mild cognitive impairment or early dementia
- Vázquez González et al. (2013)—Nonprofessional female carers; Spain
- Habibi, Zamani, Abedini, and Jamshidnejad (2015)—Mothers of children with special needs; Iran
- King et al. (2012)—Family carers of stroke survivors
- Law et al. (2017)—Parents of children with idiopathic chronic pain conditions receiving intensive pain rehabilitation; feasibility study
- McCann, Cotton, and Lubman (2017)—Carers of young people with first-episode psychosis; PST delivered via bibliotherapy; Australia
- C. T. Nguyen, Fairclough, and Noll (2016)—Mothers of children recently diagnosed with autism spectrum disorder
- Palermo, Law, Essner, Jessen-Fiddick, and Eccleston (2014)—Parents of children with chronic pain; pilot study

(*continued*)

BOX 3.1 ■ PROBLEM-SOLVING THERAPY/TRAINING OUTCOME STUDIES PUBLISHED SINCE NEZU ET AL. (2013) *(continued)*

- Pfeiffer et al. (2014)—Family carers of stroke survivors; telephone-based program
- Sahler et al. (2013)—Mothers of children newly diagnosed with cancer; included both English-speaking and Spanish-speaking mothers
- Wade et al. (2012)—Carers of adolescents with TBI; online program

Perinatal/Postpartum Depression
- Bhat et al. (2017)—Depressed pregnant and postpartum women; open trial to assess feasibility, acceptance, and initial efficacy; conducted in rural obstetric setting
- Chibanda et al. (2014)—Depressed postpartum mothers; group therapy; Zimbabwe
- Danasabe (2017)—Depressed postpartum women; quasi-experimental design; compared PST to Muslim-adapted PST (Islamic PST); Nigeria
- Danasabe and Elias (2016)—Depressed postpartum women; quasi-experimental design; Nigeria
- Nasiri, Kordi, Gharavi, and Lotfabadi (2018)—Women in their third postpartum week; Iran
- Sampson, Villarreal, and Rubin (2016)—Low-income pregnant women at risk for postpartum depression; pilot study combining motivational interviewing and PST

Pregnant Women
- Kaaya et al. (2013)—HIV-positive depressed pregnant women; Tanzania

Psychological Distress
- Eskin, Kurt, and Demirkiran (2012)—Nurses in academic hospital setting; Turkey

PTSD/PTSD Symptoms
- Dawson et al. (2018)—Islamic children with PTSD; Indonesia
- Kasckow et al. (2012)—Individuals presenting with subsyndromal depression and history of traumatic exposure

Stoke
- Mikami et al. (2013)—Prevention of poststroke apathy
- Robinson et al. (2017)—Prevention of poststroke mortality
- Visser et al. (2015)—Adult stroke patients; PST combined with standard outpatient rehabilitation

Substance Use
- Rosen, Engel, McCall, and Greenhouse (2017)—Opioid-addicted older adults attending a methadone clinic; PST paired with treatment as usual
- Sorsdahl et al. (2015)—Patients presenting for emergency services at high risk of substance use; PST paired with motivational interviewing; South Africa

(continued)

BOX 3.1 ▪ PROBLEM-SOLVING THERAPY/TRAINING OUTCOME STUDIES PUBLISHED SINCE NEZU ET AL. (2013) (*continued*)

Suicidality/Self-Harm
- Choi, Marti, and Conwell (2016)—Depressed low-income homebound older adults
- Gustavson et al. (2016)—Depressed older adults with executive dysfunction
- Hopko et al. (2013)—Follow-up of previous study with depressed breast cancer patients to determine impact in suicidal ideation
- Mackie et al. (2017)—Men who presented to a hospital with self-harm; combined PST with smartphone app; pilot study; Canada

Traumatic Brain Injury
- Kurowski et al. (2014)—Adolescents with TBI; counselor-assisted online program
- Kurowski et al. (2018)—Adolescents with TBI; focus on improving executive functioning; online protocol
- Raj et al. (2018)—Online PST protocol for adolescents with TBI and their parents
- Wade et al. (2014)—Children and adolescents with complicated mild to severe TBI; online, counselor-assisted protocol
- Wade et al. (2015)—Adolescents with TBI; online protocol
- Wade et al. (2017)—Children and adolescents with TBI; family, online PST

Veteran/Military Service Populations
- Ahmadizadeh et al. (2010)—Iranian war veterans after Iran–Iraq war
- Bedford, Dietch, Taylor, Boals, and Zayfert (in press)—Student veterans experiencing symptoms of depression, PTSD, and insomnia; computer-guided protocol; pilot study
- K. R. Bell et al. (2017)—Service members with mild TBI; telephone-delivered protocol
- Kasckow et al. (2014)—Veterans with subsyndromal depression; pilot study
- Vuletic et al. (2016)—Active duty service members with combat-related mild TBI; telephone-based protocol; focus of treatment on improving sleep quality
- Tenhula et al. (2014)—Improving resilience and reducing distress among veterans

Vision Problems
- Dreer et al. (2016)—Pilot study to assess feasibility, acceptance, and preliminary effectiveness of a program that combined motivational interviewing with PST to enhance glaucoma medication adherence among African Americans
- Rovner et al. (2013)—Vision functioning in age-related macular degeneration

ASD, autism spectrum disorder; PST, problem-solving therapy; PTSD, posttraumatic stress disorder; TBI, traumatic brain injury.

PST Interventions Targeting Medical Outcomes

It should be noted that several of the PST interventions for medical patient populations targeted relevant medical variables in addition to psychosocial outcomes (e.g., emotional distress, quality of life). For example, as noted in the Fitzpatrick et al. (2013) systematic review of interventions for patients with diabetes, patients received PST in part to lower their hemoglobin A1C blood-sugar levels. For example, in a recent study by Villamil-Salcedo et al. (2018), which included adult diabetic patients, it was found that PST led to significant reductions in depressive and anxiety symptoms, as well as reductions in total cholesterol, hemoglobin A1C, and low-density lipoprotein (LDL) levels. In addition, Choi et al. (2014) found PST to improve disability levels among depressed, low-income, homebound older adults; Pech and O'Kearney (2013) found PST to significantly improve sleep efficiency and hygiene among adults suffering from insomnia; and Kurowski et al. (2018) recently reported an online PST intervention that led to significant improvements in executive function behaviors among older adolescents.

Of special significance is the report by Robinson, Jorge, and Long (2017) that examined the role of PST as a means of preventing poststroke mortality. Their initial clinical trial indicated that an 18-month follow-up showed that stopping escitalopram, but not PST, led to a significant increase in depression (Robinson et al., 2008). Given this finding, these researchers conducted the 2017 study, which represented an 8- to 10-year follow-up, to assess the hypothesis that PST would be associated with the longest time to death. Results indicated that PST significantly and independently increased the time to mortality of these stroke patients.

PST as a Prevention Approach

As noted earlier, the Robinson et al. (2017) reported highlighted PST as a means of preventing poststroke mortality. Related findings indicated that their original study found PST to prevent poststroke depression (Robinson et al., 2008), whereas a subsequent investigation identified PST to be responsible for preventing poststroke apathy, a condition related to poststroke mortality (Mikami et al., 2013). In addition, Buntrock et al. (2016) found PST prevented major depression in adults currently experiencing subthreshold depression; Linton, Boersma, Traczyk, Shaw, and Nicholas (2016) administered PST to prevent back pain disability among high-risk workers; and Vázquez González et al. (2013) applied PST to prevent depression among a group of nonprofessional caregivers.

PST for Caregivers

As shown in Box 3.1, a large number of studies have been conducted administering PST to address the needs of family, parental, and other informal caregivers. Individuals in need of care have included persons with severe disabilities, adult and pediatric cancer patients, adults with dementia, adults suffering from a first episode of psychosis, children with autism, stroke survivors, and adolescents with traumatic brain injury. This application appears to be a particularly potent approach and one that is growing in number.

PST and Postpartum Depression

More recent, researchers have been interested in assessing the applicability and efficacy of PST for the treatment of perinatal and postpartum depression. The specific relevance of PST for these women, for example, is supported by a cross-sectional study of 150 postpartum women in Nigeria that found significant relationships between problem-orientation variables and postpartum depression (Danasabe & Elias, 2016). Unfortunately, the majority of published treatment studies addressing this population involve open trials and pilot studies. Although the results appear very promising, methodological concerns limit making definitive conclusions. It is interesting to note that these studies were conducted in countries outside the United States (Zimbabwe, Iran, Nigeria), in rural areas, or with low-income samples.

PST for Limited Cognitive/Executive Functioning

Multiple applications of PST have been conducted for populations that have limited cognitive and/or executive functioning capabilities. These include adults with intellectual disabilities (Ailey, Miller, & Fogg, 2014), older adults with executive dysfunction (Mackin et al., 2014), adolescents with traumatic brain injury (TBI; Wade et al., 2014), and active duty service members with combat-related mild TBI (Vuletic et al., 2016). These studies underscore the basic efficacy of PST, so it would appear that having "average intellectual/cognitive abilities" is not a requirement to benefit from this approach. Of related interest, Ailey, Friese, and Nezu (2012) provided a detailed description of how a PST program initially developed for adults was modified for individuals with intellectual disabilities who actually participated themselves in the adaptation.

PST Delivered via Telehealth Protocols

Perusal of Box 3.1 suggests that multiple PST programs were successfully delivered via a variety of telehealth approaches. These approaches include telephone (Lee et al., 2014), computerized interactive media (Sandoval et al.,

2017), and the Internet (Wade et al., 2012). Such protocols have been found to be generally efficacious, and a meta-analysis found that the method of PST delivery (i.e., in person vs. telehealth) did not moderate treatment outcome (Zhang et al., 2018), so it is likely that such methods will be increasingly applied in the future.

PST and Diverse Populations

Although there has been a significant increase in the application of PST for a variety of populations outside the United States (the Netherlands, Korea, Japan, Germany, Sweden, Mexico, Taiwan, Zimbabwe, Iran, Australia, Hong Kong, Canada, Spain, Iran, Tanzania, Turkey, Indonesia, South Africa) since our last book (Nezu, Nezu, and D'Zurilla, 2013) was published, there have been few studies focusing on other types of diverse populations. One important effort has focused on low-income adults (Alexopoulos et al., 2016; Choi et al., 2014; Lilly et al., 2014). With regard to a focus on ethnicity, one notable study was conducted by Reynolds et al. (2014) that included 90 Black individuals in a participant sample of 247 older adults. Their study was geared to prevent major depression among individuals experiencing subsyndromal depressive symptoms. General results indicated that PST was effective in preventing major depression in this population. Relevant to this discussion, no differences were found between White and Black individuals.

Dreer et al. (2016) reported the initial findings of a program that combined motivational interviewing with PST to enhance glaucoma medication adherence, specifically among an African American population. Results indicated patient satisfaction and acceptability to be high; adherence rates significantly increased and functional visual ocular symptoms significantly improved. Note that the program was designed to be culturally informed and relevant to this population. For example, these researchers conducted focus groups to better understand unique barriers to medication adherence; requested input from an African American consumer-based advisory board; and developed the program materials consistent with African American culture, beliefs, values, and language.

To comment on PST interventions focusing on Latino populations, we went through the relevant studies published before 2013. Most of these have tended to be embedded in larger collaborative care models. For example, in a study by Dwight-Johnson, Ell, and Lee (2005), Latina depressed cancer patients randomized to active treatment were initially provided the option of undergoing pharmacotherapy or PST. At 8 months postbaseline, PST participants were found to experience 4.5 times greater reduction in depression than the patients in the usual care condition. Additional studies demonstrating the efficacy of PST as part of a larger collaborative care model for reducing depression in Latino populations include Ell et al. (2008), which focused on low-income, depressed Latina women with cancer; Ell et al. (2010), which treated low-income, depressed Hispanic diabetic patients; and more recently, Wu et al. (2018), which included depressed Latina women with diabetes in primary care, safety-net systems. In addition, Areán et al. (2005) conducted subgroup analyses regarding the outcome of PST administered within a collaborative care model for certain minority groups. Of a sample of 1,801 older adults, 138 were Latino. Results of their subgroup evaluation indicated that such individuals experienced significant decreases in depression and health-related functional impairment compared with usual care participants.

Two open-trial studies further support the potential efficacy of PST as a treatment for depression. Schmaling and Hernandez (2008) provided eight sessions of PST to depressed Mexican Americans in primary care settings. Although depressive symptom scores decreased over time, only a minority of those individuals initially agreeing to participate in the study completed four or more sessions. However, this subgroup had greater reductions in depressive symptom severity than those participants completing three or fewer sessions. Camacho et al. (2015) focused on a sample of Hispanic/Latino patients of Mexican heritage attending a community health center near the California–Mexico border. Unlike the Schmaling and Hernandez study, these researchers attempted to develop and implement a culturally adapted PST intervention. Results indicated a significant reduction in depressive symptoms over a 6-month period.

SUMMARY

This chapter began with a description of multiple systematic reviews and meta-analyses of PST interventions. The number of studies evaluating PST has increased over the past decade, so more reviews have also been conducted. Although some of the reviews point to certain limitations of the empirical outcome literature, the overwhelming evidence supports the efficacy of PST across various age groups and targeted populations and problems. A listing of PST investigations published since our last book further supports the characterization of this approach as a transdiagnostic intervention, also demonstrating its flexibility of applications. Last, we highlighted certain aspects of the recent outcome literature featuring various clinical problems (e.g., health and behavioral health disorders), populations (e.g., older adults, children, ethnic minorities), and modes of delivery (e.g., telehealth).

REFERENCES

Ahmadizadeh, M. J., Ahmadi, K., Eskandari, H., Falsafinejad, M. R., Borjali, A., Anisi, J., & Teimoori, M. (2010). Improvement in quality of life after exposure therapy, problem solving and combined therapy in chronic war-related post traumatic stress disorder: Exposure therapy, problem solving and combined therapy in war-related PTSD. *Procedia-Social and Behavioral Sciences, 5,* 262–266. doi:10.1016/j.sbspro.2010.07.085

Ailey, S. H., Friese, T. R., & Nezu, A. M. (2012). Modifying a social problem-solving program with the input of individuals with intellectual disabilities and their staff. *Research in Nursing & Health, 35,* 610–623. doi:10.1002/nur.21497

Ailey, S. H., Miller, A. M., & Fogg, L. (2014). Social problem solving in staffed community homes among individuals with intellectual disabilities and their staff. *Journal of Mental Health Research in Intellectual Disabilities, 7,* 208–228. doi:10.1080/19315864.2013.814736

Alexopoulos, G. S., Raue, P. J., McCulloch, C., Kanellopoulos, D., Seirup, J. K., Sirey, J. A., … Areán, P. A. (2016). Clinical case management versus case management with problem-solving therapy in low-income, disabled elders with major depression: A randomized clinical trial. *American Journal of Geriatric Psychiatry, 24,* 50–59. doi:10.1016/j.jagp.2015.02.007

Areán, P. A., Ayalon, L., Hunkeler, E., Lin, E. H., Tang, L., Harpole, L., … Unützer, J. (2005). Improving depression care for older, minority patients in primary care. *Medical Care, 43,* 381–390. doi:10.1097/01.mlr.0000156852.09920.b1

Areán, P. A., Perri, M. G., Nezu, A. M., Schein, R. L., Christopher, F., & Joseph, T. X. (1993). Comparative effectiveness of social problem-solving therapy and reminiscence therapy as treatments for depression in older adults. *Journal of Consulting and Clinical Psychology, 61,* 1003. doi:10.1037/0022-006X.61.6.1003

Barnes, T. N., Wang, F., & O'Brien, K. M. (2018). A meta-analytic review of social problem-solving interventions in preschool settings. *Infant and Child Development,* e2095. doi:10.1002/icd.2095

Beaudreau, S. A., Gould, C. E., Mashal, N. M., Huh, J. T., & Fairchild, J. K. (in press). Application of problem solving therapy for late-life anxiety. *Cognitive and Behavioral Practice.* doi:10.1016/j.cbpra.2018.05.003

Bedford, L. A., Dietch, J. R., Taylor, D. J., Boals, A., & Zayfert, C. (in press). Computer-guided problem-solving treatment for depression, PTSD, and insomnia symptoms in student veterans: A pilot randomized controlled trial. *Behavior Therapy, 49,* 756–767. doi:10.1016/j.beth.2017.11.010

Bell, A. C., & D'Zurilla, T. J. (2009). Problem-solving therapy for depression: A meta-analysis. *Clinical Psychology Review, 29,* 348–353. doi:10.1016/j.cpr.2009.02.003

Bell, K. R., Fann, J. R., Brockway, J. A., Cole, W. R., Bush, N. E., Dikmen, S., … Temkin, N. (2017). Telephone problem solving for service members with mild traumatic brain injury: A randomized, clinical trial. *Journal of Neurotrauma, 34,* 313–321. doi:10.1089/neu.2016.4444

Berman, M. I., Buckey, J. C., Jr, Hull, J. G., Linardatos, E., Song, S. L., McLellan, R. K., & Hegel, M. T. (2014). Feasibility study of an interactive multimedia electronic problem solving treatment program for depression: A preliminary uncontrolled trial. *Behavior Therapy, 45,* 358–375. doi:10.1016/j.beth.2014.02.001

Berry, J. W., Elliott, T. R., Grant, J. S., Edwards, G., & Fine, P. R. (2012). Does problem-solving training for family caregivers benefit their care recipients with severe disabilities? A latent growth model of the Project CLUES randomized clinical trial. *Rehabilitation Psychology, 57,* 98–112. doi:10.1037/a0028229

Bevans, M., Wehrlen, L., Castro, K., Prince, P., Shelburne, N., Soeken, K., ... Wallen, G. R. (2014). A problem-solving education intervention in caregivers and patients during allogeneic hematopoietic stem cell transplantation. *Journal of Health Psychology, 19,* 602–617. doi:10.1177/1359105313475902

Bhat, A., Reed, S., Mao, J., Vredevoogd, M., Russo, J., Unger, J., ... Unützer, J. (2017). Delivering perinatal depression care in a rural obstetric setting: A mixed methods study of feasibility, acceptability and effectiveness. *Journal of Psychosomatic Obstetrics & Gynecology,* 1–8. doi:10 .1080/0167482X.2017.1367381

Bonete, S., Calero, M. D., & Fernández-Parra, A. (2015). Group training in interpersonal problem-solving skills for workplace adaptation of adolescents and adults with Asperger syndrome: A preliminary study. *Autism, 19,* 409–420. doi:10.1177/1362361314522354

Buntrock, C., Ebert, D. D., Lehr, D., Smit, F., Riper, H., Berking, M., & Cuijpers, P. (2016). Effect of a web-based guided self-help intervention for prevention of major depression in adults with subthreshold depression: A randomized clinical trial. *JAMA, 315,* 1854–1863. doi:10.1001/jama.2016.4326

Camacho, Á., González, P., Castañeda, S. F., Simmons, A., Buelna, C., Lemus, H., & Talavera, G. A. (2015). Improvement in depressive symptoms among Hispanic/Latinos receiving a culturally tailored impact and problem-solving intervention in a community health center. *Community Mental Health Journal, 51,* 385–392. doi:10.1007/s10597-014-9750-7

Cape, J., Whittington, C., Buszewicz, M., Wallace, P., & Underwood, L. (2010). Brief psychological therapies for anxiety and depression in primary care: Meta-analysis and meta-regression. *BMC Medicine, 8,* 38. doi:10.1186/1741-7015-8-38

Chan, D. C., Tsou, H. H., Yang, R. S., Tsauo, J. Y., Chen, C. Y., Hsiung, C. A., & Kuo, K. N. (2012). A pilot randomized controlled trial to improve geriatric frailty. *BMC Geriatrics, 12,* 58. doi:10.1186/1471-2318-12-58

Chibanda, D., Cowan, F., Verhey, R., Machando, D., Abas, M., & Lund, C. (2017). Lay health workers' experience of delivering a problem solving therapy intervention for common mental disorders among people living with HIV: A qualitative study from Zimbabwe. *Community Mental Health Journal, 53,* 143–153. doi:10.1007/s10597-016-0018-2

Chibanda, D., Shetty, A. K., Tshimanga, M., Woelk, G., Stranix-Chibanda, L., & Rusakaniko, S. (2014). Group problem-solving therapy for postnatal depression among HIV-positive and HIV-negative mothers in Zimbabwe. *Journal of the International Association of Providers of AIDS Care, 13,* 335–341.

Chien, W. T., Thompson, D. R., Lubman, D. I., & McCann, T. V. (2016). A randomized controlled trial of clinician-supported problem-solving bibliotherapy for family caregivers of people with first-episode psychosis. *Schizophrenia Bulletin, 42,* 1457–1466. doi:10.1093/schbul/sbw054

Chien, W. T., Yip, A. L., Liu, J. Y., & McMaster, T. W. (2016). The effectiveness of manual-guided, problem-solving-based self-learning programme for family caregivers of people with recent-onset psychosis: A randomised controlled trial with 6-month follow-up. *International Journal of Nursing Studies, 59,* 141–155. doi:10.1016/j.ijnurstu.2016.04.009

Chiu, M., Pauley, T., Wesson, V., Pushpakumar, D., & Sadavoy, J. (2015). Evaluation of a problem-solving (PS) techniques-based intervention for informal carers of patients with dementia receiving in-home care. *International Psychogeriatrics, 27,* 937–948. doi:10.1017/S1041610214002798

Choi, N. G., Hegel, M. T., Marti, C. N., Marinucci, M. L., Sirrianni, L., & Bruce, M. L. (2014). Telehealth problem-solving therapy for depressed low-income homebound older adults. *American Journal of Geriatric Psychiatry, 22,* 263–271. doi:10.1016/j.jagp.2013.01.037

Choi, N. G., Marti, C. N., & Conwell, Y. (2016). Effect of problem-solving therapy on depressed low-income homebound older adults' death/suicidal ideation and hopelessness. *Suicide and Life-Threatening Behavior, 46*, 323–336. doi:10.1111/sltb.12195

Cuijpers, P., de Wit, L., Kleiboer, A., Karyotaki, E., & Ebert, D. D. (2018). Problem-solving therapy for adult depression: An updated meta-analysis. *European Psychiatry, 48*, 27–37. doi:10.1016/j.eurpsy.2017.11.006

Cuijpers, P., van Straten, A., & Warmerdam, L. (2007). Problem solving therapies for depression: A meta-analysis. *European Psychiatry, 22*, 9–15. doi:10.1016/j.eurpsy.2006.11.001

D'Zurilla, T. J., & Goldfried, M. R. (1971). Problem solving and behavior modification. *Journal of Abnormal Psychology, 78*, 107–126. doi:10.1037/h0031360

Danasabe, M. (2017). Islamic problem solving therapy for postpartum depression among Muslim postpartum women in Nigeria. *Asian Journal of Multidisciplinary Studies, 5*(2), 69–79. Retrieved from http://www.ajms.co.in/sites/ajms2015/index.php/ajms/article/view/2330/pdf_380

Danasabe, M., & Elias, N. (2016). Relationship between postpartum depression and problem solving ability among postpartum women in Nigeria. *IOSR Journal of Humanities and Social Sciences, 21*, 81–89.

Dawson, K., Joscelyne, A., Meijer, C., Steel, Z., Silove, D., & Bryant, R. A. (2018). A controlled trial of trauma-focused therapy versus problem-solving in Islamic children affected by civil conflict and disaster in Aceh, Indonesia. *Australian & New Zealand Journal of Psychiatry, 52*, 253–261. doi:10.1177/0004867417714333

Dreer, L. E., Owsley, C., Campbell, L., Gao, L., Wood, A., & Girkin, C. A. (2016). Feasibility, patient acceptability, and preliminary efficacy of a culturally informed, health promotion program to improve glaucoma medication adherence among African Americans: "Glaucoma management optimism for a African Americans living with glaucoma" (GOAL). *Current Eye Research, 41*, 50–58. doi:10.3109/02713683.2014.1002045

Dwight-Johnson, M., Ell, K., & Lee, P. J. (2005). Can collaborative care address the needs of low-income Latinas with comorbid depression and cancer? Results from a randomized pilot study. *Psychosomatics, 46*, 224–232. doi:10.1176/appi.psy.46.3.224

Easom, L. R., Wang, K., Moore, R. H., Wang, H., & Bauer, L. (2018). Operation family caregiver: Problem-solving training for military caregivers in a community setting. *Journal of Clinical Psychology, 74*, 536–553. doi:10.1002/jclp.22536

Ebert, D. D., Lehr, D., Boß, L., Riper, H., Cuijpers, P., Andersson, G., … Berking, M. (2014). Efficacy of an internet-based problem-solving training for teachers: Results of a randomized controlled trial. *Scandinavian Journal of Work, Environment & Health, 40*, 582–596. doi:10.5271/sjweh.3449

Ell, K., Katon, W., Xie, B., Lee, P. J., Kapetanovic, S., Guterman, J., & Chou, C. P. (2010). Collaborative care management of major depression among low-income, predominantly Hispanics with diabetes: A randomized controlled trial. *Diabetes Care, 33*, 706–713. doi:10.2337/dc09-1711

Ell, K., Xie, B., Quon, B., Quinn, D. I., Dwight-Johnson, M., & Lee, P. J. (2008). Randomized controlled trial of collaborative care management of depression among low-income patients with cancer. *Journal of Clinical Oncology, 26*, 4488–4496. doi:10.1200/JCO.2008.16.6371

Erdley-Kass, S. D., Kass, D. S., Gellis, Z. D., Bogner, H. A., Berger, A., & Perkins, R. M. (2018). Using problem-solving therapy to improve problem-solving orientation, problem-solving skills and quality of life in older hemodialysis patients. *Clinical Gerontologist, 41*(5), 424–437. doi:10.1080/07317115.2017.1371819

Eskin, M., Kurt, I., & Demirkiran, F. (2012). Does social problem-solving training reduce psychological distress in nurses employed in an academic hospital. *Journal of Basic and Applied Scientific Research, 2,* 10450–10458.

Feinberg, E., Augustyn, M., Fitzgerald, E., Sandler, J., Ferreira-Cesar Suarez, Z., Chen, N., … Silverstein, M. (2014). Improving maternal mental health after a child's diagnosis of autism spectrum disorder: Results from a randomized clinical trial. *JAMA Pediatrics, 168,* 40–46. doi:10.1001/jamapediatrics.2013.3445

Ferré-Grau, C., Sevilla-Casado, M., Lleixá-Fortuño, M., Aparicio-Casals, M. R., Cid-Buera, D., Rodero-Sanchez, V., & Vives-Relats, C. (2014). Effectiveness of problem-solving technique in caring for family caregivers: A clinical trial study in an urban area of Catalonia (Spain). *Journal of Clinical Nursing, 23,* 288–295. doi:10.1111/jocn.12485

Fitzpatrick, S. L., Schumann, K. P., & Hill-Briggs, F. (2013). Problem solving interventions for diabetes self-management and control: A systematic review of the literature. *Diabetes Research and Clinical Practice, 100,* 145–161. doi:10.1016/j.diabres.2012.12.016

Garand, L., Rinaldo, D. E., Alberth, M. M., Delany, J., Beasock, S. L., Lopez, O. L., … Dew, M. A. (2014). Effects of problem solving therapy on mental health outcomes in family caregivers of persons with a new diagnosis of mild cognitive impairment or early dementia: A randomized controlled trial. *American Journal of Geriatric Psychiatry, 22,* 771–781. doi:10.1016/j.jagp.2013.07.007

Gellis, Z. D., Kenaley, B. L., & Ten Have, T. (2014). Integrated telehealth care for chronic illness and depression in geriatric home care patients: The Integrated Telehealth Education and Activation of Mood (I-TEAM) study. *Journal of the American Geriatrics Society, 62,* 889–895. doi:10.1111/jgs.12776

Gojani, M. G., Kordi, M., Asgharipour, N., Esmaeili, H., Amirian, M., & Eskandarnia, E. (2017). The effect of problem-solving skill training on mental health and the success of treatment of infertile women under intrauterine insemination treatment. *Journal of Education and Health Promotion, 6,* 107. doi:10.4103/jehp.jehp_20_17

Gross, R., Bellamy, S. L., Chapman, J., Han, X., O'Duor, J., Palmer, S. C., … Strom, B. L. (2013). Managed problem solving for antiretroviral therapy adherence: A randomized trial. *JAMA Internal Medicine, 173,* 300–306. doi:10.1001/jamainternmed.2013.2152

Gustavson, K. A., Alexopoulos, G. S., Niu, G. C., McCulloch, C., Meade, T., & Areán, P. A. (2016). Problem-solving therapy reduces suicidal ideation in depressed older adults with executive dysfunction. *American Journal of Geriatric Psychiatry, 24,* 11–17. doi:10.1016/j.jagp.2015.07.010

Habibi, M., Zamani, N., Abedini, S., & Jamshidnejad, N. (2015). Effectiveness of problem-solving training, exposure therapy, and the combined method on depression, anxiety, and stress in mothers of children with special needs. *International Journal of Educational and Psychological Researches, 1,* 246–252. doi:10.4103/2395-2296.163931

Hirai, K., Motooka, H., Ito, N., Wada, N., Yoshizaki, A., Shiozaki, M., … Akechi, T. (2012). Problem-solving therapy for psychological distress in Japanese early-stage breast cancer patients. *Japanese Journal of Clinical Oncology, 42,* 1168–1174. doi:10.1093/jjco/hys158

Holloway, E. E., Xie, J., Sturrock, B. A., Lamoureux, E. L., & Rees, G. (2015). Do problem-solving interventions improve psychosocial outcomes in vision impaired adults: A systematic review and meta-analysis. *Patient Education and Counseling, 98,* 553–564. doi:10.1016/j.pec.2015.01.013

Hopko, D. R., Funderburk, J. S., Shorey, R. C., McIndoo, C. C., Ryba, M. M., File, A. A., … Vitulano, M. (2013). Behavioral activation and problem-solving therapy for depressed breast cancer patients: Preliminary support for decreased suicidal ideation. *Behavior Modification, 37,* 747–767. doi:10.1177/0145445513501512

Junge, M. N., Lehr, D., Bockting, C. L., Berking, M., Riper, H., Cuijpers, P., & Ebert, D. D. (2015). For whom are internet-based occupational mental health interventions effective? Moderators of internet-based problem-solving training outcome. *Internet Interventions, 2,* 39–47. doi:10.1016/j.invent.2014.11.007

Kaaya, S. F., Blander, J., Antelman, G., Cyprian, F., Emmons, K. M., Matsumoto, K., … Smith Fawzi, M. C. (2013). Randomized controlled trial evaluating the effect of an interactive group counseling intervention for HIV-positive women on prenatal depression and disclosure of HIV status. *AIDS Care, 25,* 854–862. doi:10.1080/09540121.2013.763891

Karp, J. F., Gao, X., Wahed, A. S., Morse, J. Q., Rollman, B. L., Weiner, D. K., & Reynolds, C. F., III. (2018). Effect of problem-solving therapy versus supportive management in older adults with low back pain and depression while on antidepressant pharmacotherapy. *American Journal of Geriatric Psychiatry, 26,* 765–777. doi:10.1016/j.jagp.2018.01.004

Kasckow, J., Brown, C., Morse, J., Begley, A., Bensasi, S., & Reynolds, C. F., 3rd. (2012). Post-traumatic stress disorder symptoms in emotionally distressed individuals referred for a depression prevention intervention: Relationship to problem-solving skills. *International Journal of Geriatric Psychiatry, 27,* 1106–1111. doi:10.1002/gps.2826

Kasckow, J., Klaus, J., Morse, J., Oslin, D., Luther, J., Fox, L., … Haas, G. L. (2014). Using problem solving therapy to treat veterans with subsyndromal depression: A pilot study. *International Journal of Geriatric Psychiatry, 29,* 1255–1261. doi:10.1002/gps.4105

King, R. B., Hartke, R. J., Houle, T., Lee, J., Herring, G., Alexander-Peterson, B. S., & Raad, J. (2012). A problem-solving early intervention for stroke caregivers: One year follow-up. *Rehabilitation Nursing, 37,* 231–243. doi:10.1002/rnj.039

Kiosses, D. N., & Alexopoulos, G. S. (2014). Problem-solving therapy in the elderly. *Current Treatment Options in Psychiatry, 1,* 15–26. doi:10.1007/s40501-013-0003-0

Kirkham, J. G., Choi, N., & Seitz, D. P. (2016). Meta-analysis of problem solving therapy for the treatment of major depressive disorder in older adults. *International Journal of Geriatric Psychiatry, 31,* 526–535. doi:10.1002/gps.4358

Kleiboer, A., Donker, T., Seekles, W., van Straten, A., Riper, H., & Cuijpers, P. (2015). A randomized controlled trial on the role of support in Internet-based problem solving therapy for depression and anxiety. *Behaviour Research and Therapy, 72,* 63–71. doi:10.1016/j.brat.2015.06.013

Kurowski, B. G., Stancin, T., Taylor, H. G., McNally, K. A., Kirkwood, M. W., Cassedy, A., … Wade, S. L. (2018). Comparative effectiveness of family problem-solving therapy (F-PST) for adolescents after traumatic brain injury: Protocol for a randomized, multicenter, clinical trial. *Contemporary Clinical Trials Communications, 10,* 111–120. doi:10.1016/j.conctc.2018.04.001

Kurowski, B. G., Wade, S. L., Kirkwood, M. W., Brown, T. M., Stancin, T., & Taylor, H. G. (2014). Long-term benefits of an early online problem-solving intervention for executive dysfunction after traumatic brain injury in children: A randomized clinical trial. *JAMA Pediatrics, 168,* 523–531. doi:10.1001/jamapediatrics.2013.5070

Lakerveld, J., Bot, S. D., Chinapaw, M. J., van Tulder, M. W., Kostense, P. J., Dekker, J. M., & Nijpels, G. (2013). Motivational interviewing and problem solving treatment to reduce type 2 diabetes and cardiovascular disease risk in real life: A randomized controlled trial. *International Journal of Behavioral Nutrition and Physical Activity*, 10, 47. doi:10.1186/1479-5868-10-47

Law, E. F., Fales, J. L., Beals-Erickson, S. E., Failo, A., Logan, D., Randall, E., … Palermo, T. M. (2017). A single-arm feasibility trial of problem-solving skills training for parents of children with idiopathic chronic pain conditions receiving intensive pain rehabilitation. *Journal of Pediatric Psychology*, 42, 422–433. doi:10.1093/jpepsy/jsw087

Lee, H., Yoon, J. Y., Lim, Y., Jung, H., Kim, S., Yoo, Y., … Park, H. K. (2014). The effect of nurse-led problem-solving therapy on coping, self-efficacy and depressive symptoms for patients with chronic obstructive pulmonary disease: A randomised controlled trial. *Age and Ageing*, 44, 397–403. doi:10.1093/ageing/afu201

Lilly, C. L., Bryant, L. L., Leary, J. M., Vu, M. B., Hill-Briggs, F., Samuel-Hodge, C. D., … Keyserling, T. C. (2014). Evaluation of the effectiveness of a problem-solving intervention addressing barriers to cardiovascular disease prevention behaviors in 3 underserved populations: Colorado, North Carolina, West Virginia, 2009. *Preventing Chronic Disease*, 11, E32. doi:10.5888/pcd11.130249

Linde, K., Sigterman, K., Kriston, L., Rücker, G., Jamil, S., Meissner, K., & Schneider, A. (2015). Effectiveness of psychological treatments for depressive disorders in primary care: Systematic review and meta-analysis. *Annals of Family Medicine*, 13, 56–68. doi:10.1370/afm.1719

Linton, S. J., Boersma, K., Traczyk, M., Shaw, W., & Nicholas, M. (2016). Early workplace communication and problem solving to prevent back disability: Results of a randomized controlled trial among high-risk workers and their supervisors. *Journal of Occupational Rehabilitation*, 26, 150–159. doi:10.1007/s10926-015-9596-z

Mackie, C., Dunn, N., MacLean, S., Testa, V., Heisel, M., & Hatcher, S. (2017). A qualitative study of a blended therapy using problem solving therapy with a customised smartphone app in men who present to hospital with intentional self-harm. *Evidence-Based Mental Health*, 20(4), 118–122. doi:10.1136/eb-2017-102764

Mackin, R. S., Nelson, J. C., Delucchi, K., Raue, P., Byers, A., Barnes, D., … Arean, P. A. (2014). Cognitive outcomes after psychotherapeutic interventions for major depression in older adults with executive dysfunction. *American Journal of Geriatric Psychiatry*, 22, 1496–1503. doi:10.1016/j.jagp.2013.11.002

Malouff, J. M., Thorsteinsson, E. B., & Schutte, N. S. (2007). The efficacy of problem solving therapy in reducing mental and physical health problems: A meta-analysis. *Clinical Psychology Review*, 27, 46–57. doi:10.1016/j.cpr.2005.12.005

McCann, T. V., Cotton, S. M., & Lubman, D. I. (2017). Social problem solving in carers of young people with a first episode of psychosis: A randomized controlled trial. *Early Intervention in Psychiatry*, 11, 346–350. doi:10.1111/eip.12301

Merrill, K. L., Smith, S. W., Cumming, M. M., & Daunic, A. P. (2017). A review of social problem-solving interventions: Past findings, current status, and future directions. *Review of Educational Research*, 87, 71–102. doi:10.3102/0034654316652943

Mikami, K., Jorge, R. E., Moser, D. J., Arndt, S., Jang, M., Solodkin, A., … Robinson, R. G. (2013). Prevention of poststroke apathy using escitalopram or problem-solving therapy. *American Journal of Geriatric Psychiatry*, 21, 855–862. doi:10.1016/j.jagp.2012.07.003

Nasiri, S., Kordi, M., Gharavi, M. M., & Lotfabadi, M. K. (2018). Effect of problem-solving therapy and relaxation on the severity of postpartum depressive symptoms: A randomized controlled trial. *Nursing and Midwifery Studies*, 7, 6–11. doi:10.4103/nms.nms_35_17

Nezu, A. M., Nezu, C. M., & D'Zurilla, T. J. (2013). *Problem-solving therapy: A treatment manual.* New York, NY: Springer Publishing.

Nguyen, C. M., Chen, K. H., & Denburg, N. L. (2018). The use of problem-solving therapy for primary care to enhance complex decision-making in healthy community-dwelling older adults. *Frontiers in Psychology, 9,* 870. doi:10.3389/fpsyg.2018.00870

Nguyen, C. T., Fairclough, D. L., & Noll, R. B. (2016). Problem-solving skills training for mothers of children recently diagnosed with autism spectrum disorder: A pilot feasibility study. *Autism, 20,* 55–64. doi:10.1177/1362361314567134

Nieuwsma, J. A., Trivedi, R. B., McDuffie, J., Kronish, I., Benjamin, D., & Williams, J. W. (2012). Brief psychotherapy for depression: A systematic review and meta-analysis. *International Journal of Psychiatry in Medicine, 43,* 129–151. doi:10.2190/PM.43.2.c

Palermo, T. M., Law, E. F., Essner, B., Jessen-Fiddick, T., & Eccleston, C. (2014). Adaptation of problem-solving skills training (PSST) for parent caregivers of youth with chronic pain. *Clinical Practice in Pediatric Psychology, 2,* 212–223. doi:10.1037/cpp0000067

Pech, M., & O'Kearney, R. (2013). A randomized controlled trial of problem-solving therapy compared to cognitive therapy for the treatment of insomnia in adults. *Sleep, 36,* 739–749. doi:10.5665/sleep.2640

Pfeiffer, K., Beische, D., Hautzinger, M., Berry, J. W., Wengert, J., Hoffrichter, R., ... Elliott, T. R. (2014). Telephone-based problem-solving intervention for family caregivers of stroke survivors: A randomized controlled trial. *Journal of Consulting and Clinical Psychology, 82,* 628–643. doi:10.1037/a0036987

Pugliese, C. E., & White, S. W. (2014). Brief report: Problem solving therapy in college students with autism spectrum disorders: Feasibility and preliminary efficacy. *Journal of Autism and Developmental Disorders, 44,* 719–729. doi:10.1007/s10803-013-1914-8

Raj, S. P., Zhang, N., Kirkwood, M. W., Taylor, H. G., Stancin, T., Brown, T. M., & Wade, S. L. (2018). Online family problem solving for pediatric traumatic brain injury: Influences of parental marital status and participation on adolescent outcomes. *Journal of Head Trauma Rehabilitation, 33,* 158–166. doi:10.1097/HTR.0000000000000331

Rees, G., O'Hare, F., Saeed, M., Sudholz, B., Sturrock, B. A., Xie, J., ... Lamoureux, E. L. (2017). Problem-solving therapy for adults with diabetic retinopathy and diabetes-specific distress: A pilot randomized controlled trial. *BMJ Open Diabetes Research and Care, 5,* e000307. doi:10.1136/bmjdrc-2016-000307

Reinhardt, J. P., Horowitz, A., Cimarolli, V. R., Eimicke, J. P., & Teresi, J. A. (2014). Addressing depression in a long-term care setting: A phase II pilot of problem-solving treatment. *Clinical Therapeutics, 36,* 1531–1537. doi:10.1016/j.clinthera.2014.10.005

Reynolds, C. F., III, Thomas, S. B., Morse, J. Q., Anderson, S. J., Albert, S., Dew, M. A., ... Quinn, S. C. (2014). Early intervention to preempt major depression among older black and white adults. *Psychiatric Services, 65,* 765–773. doi:10.1176/appi.ps.201300216

Robinson, R. G., Jorge, R. E., & Long, J. (2017). Prevention of poststroke mortality using problem-solving therapy or escitalopram. *American Journal of Geriatric Psychiatry, 25,* 512–519. doi:10.1016/j.jagp.2016.10.001

Robinson, R. G., Jorge, R. E., Moser, D. J., Acion, L., Solodkin, A., Small, S. L., ... Arndt, S. (2008). Escitalopram and problem-solving therapy for prevention of poststroke depression: A randomized controlled trial. *Journal of the American Medical Association, 299,* 2391–2400. doi:10.1001/jama.299.20.2391

Rosen, D., Engel, R. J., McCall, J., & Greenhouse, J. (2017). Using problem-solving therapy to reduce depressive symptom severity among older adult methadone clients: A randomized clinical trial. *Research on Social Work Practice*. doi:10.1177/1049731516686692

Rovner, B. W., Casten, R. J., Hegel, M. T., Massof, R. W., Leiby, B. E., Ho, A. C., & Tasman, W. S. (2013). Improving function in age-related macular degeneration: A randomized clinical trial. *Ophthalmology, 120*, 1649–1655. doi:10.1016/j.ophtha.2013.01.022

Sahler, O. J., Dolgin, M. J., Phipps, S., Fairclough, D. L., Askins, M. A., Katz, E. R., ... Butler, R. W. (2013). Specificity of problem-solving skills training in mothers of children newly diagnosed with cancer: Results of a multisite randomized clinical trial. *Journal of Clinical Oncology, 31*, 1329–1335. doi:10.1200/JCO.2011.39.1870

Sampson, M., Villarreal, Y., & Rubin, A. (2016). A problem-solving therapy intervention for low-income, pregnant women at risk for postpartum depression. *Research on Social Work Practice, 26*, 236–242. doi:10.1177/1049731514551143

Sandoval, L. R., Buckey, J. C., Ainslie, R., Tombari, M., Stone, W., & Hegel, M. T. (2017). Randomized controlled trial of a computerized interactive media-based problem solving treatment for depression. *Behavior Therapy, 48*, 413–425. doi:10.1016/j.beth.2016.04.001

Schmaling, K. B., & Hernandez, D. V. (2008). Problem-solving treatment for depression among Mexican Americans in primary care. *Journal of Health Care for the Poor and Underserved, 19*, 466–477. doi:10.1353/hpu.0.0032

Simon, S. S., Cordás, T. A., & Bottino, C. M. (2015). Cognitive behavioral therapies in older adults with depression and cognitive deficits: A systematic review. *International Journal of Geriatric Psychiatry, 30*, 223–233. doi:10.1002/gps.4239

Sorsdahl, K., Myers, B., Ward, C. L., Matzopoulos, R., Mtukushe, B., Nicol, A., ... Stein, D. J. (2015). Adapting a blended motivational interviewing and problem-solving intervention to address risky substance use amongst South Africans. *Psychotherapy Research, 25*, 435–444. doi:10.1080/10503307.2014.897770

Stahl, S. T., Albert, S. M., Dew, M. A., Anderson, S., Karp, J. F., Gildengers, A. G., ... Reynolds, C. F., III. (2017). Measuring participant effort in a depression prevention trial: Who engages in problem-solving therapy? *American Journal of Geriatric Psychiatry, 25*, 909–916. doi:10.1016/j.jagp.2017.03.005

Sturrock, B. A., Holloway, E., Keefe, J., Hegel, M., Casten, R., Mellor, D., & Rees, G. (2016). Rehabilitation staff perspectives on training for problem-solving therapy for primary care in a low vision service. *British Journal of Visual Impairment, 34*, 26–41. doi:10.1177/0264619615610159

Syrjala, K. L., Jean, C. Y., Artherholt, S. B., Romano, J. M., Crouch, M. L., Fiscalini, A. S., ... Leisenring, W. M. (2018). An online randomized controlled trial, with or without problem-solving treatment, for long-term cancer survivors after hematopoietic cell transplantation. *Journal of Cancer Survivorship, 12*, 560–570. doi:10.1007/s11764-018-0693-9

Tenhula, W. N., Nezu, A. M., Nezu, C. M., Stewart, M. O., Miller, S. A., Steele, J., & Karlin, B. E. (2014). Moving Forward: A problem-solving training program to foster veteran resilience. *Professional Psychology: Research and Practice, 45*, 416–424. doi:10.1037/a0037150

Van Loan, C. L., Garwood, J. D., Smith, S. W., & Daunic, A. P. (2018). Take CHARGE!: A randomized controlled trial of a social problem-solving curriculum to support students with emotional and behavioral disorders. *Journal of Emotional and Behavioral Disorders*, 1–11. doi:10.1177/1063426617754083

Vázquez González, F. L., Otero Otero, P., Torres Iglesias, A., Hermida, García, E., Blanco Seoane, V., & Díaz Fernández, O. (2013). A brief problem-solving indicated-prevention intervention for prevention of depression in nonprofessional caregivers. *Psicothema, 25,* 87–92. doi:10.7334/psicothema2012.89

Villamil-Salcedo, V., Vargas-Terrez, B. E., Caraveo-Anduaga, J., González-Olvera, J., Díaz-Anzaldúa, A., Cortés-Sotres, J., & Pérez-Ávila, M. (2018). Glucose and cholesterol stabilization in patients with type 2 diabetes mellitus with depressive and anxiety symptoms by problem-solving therapy in primary care centers in Mexico City. *Primary Health Care Research & Development, 19,* 33–41. doi:10.1017/S1463423617000512

Visser, M. M., Heijenbrok-Kal, M. H., Spijker, A. V., Oostra, K. M., Busschbach, J. J., & Ribbers, G. M. (2015). Coping, problem solving, depression, and health-related quality of life in patients receiving outpatient stroke rehabilitation. *Archives of Physical Medicine and Rehabilitation, 96,* 1492–1498. doi:10.1016/j.apmr.2015.04.007

Vuletic, S., Bell, K. R., Jain, S., Bush, N., Temkin, N., Fann, J. R., ... Gahm, G. A. (2016). Telephone problem-solving treatment improves sleep quality in service members with combat-related mild traumatic brain injury: Results from a randomized clinical trial. *Journal of Head Trauma Rehabilitation, 31,* 147–157. doi:10.1097/HTR.0000000000000221

Wade, S. L., Cassedy, A. E., Shultz, E. L., Zang, H., Zhang, N., Kirkwood, M. W., ... Taylor, H. G. (2017). Randomized clinical trial of online parent training for behavior problems after early brain injury. *Journal of the American Academy of Child & Adolescent Psychiatry, 56,* 930–939. doi:10.1016/j.jaac.2017.09.413

Wade, S. L., Kurowski, B. G., Kirkwood, M. W., Zhang, N., Cassedy, A., Brown, T. M., ... Taylor, H. G. (2015). Online problem-solving therapy after traumatic brain injury: A randomized controlled trial. *Pediatrics, 135,* e487–e495. doi:10.1542/peds.2014-1386

Wade, S. L., Stancin, T., Kirkwood, M., Brown, T. M., McMullen, K. M., & Taylor, H. G. (2014). Counselor-assisted problem solving (CAPS) improves behavioral outcomes in older adolescents with complicated mild to severe TBI. *Journal of Head Trauma Rehabilitation, 29,* 198–207. doi:10.1097/HTR.0b013e31828f9fe8

Wade, S. L., Walz, N. C., Carey, J., McMullen, K. M., Cass, J., Mark, E., & Yeates, K. O. (2012). A randomized trial of teen online problem solving: Efficacy in improving caregiver outcomes after brain injury. *Health Psychology, 31,* 767–776. doi:10.1037/a0028440

Wu, S., Ell, K., Jin, H., Vidyanti, I., Chou, C. P., Lee, P. J., ... Guterman, J. (2018). Comparative effectiveness of a technology-facilitated depression care management model in safety-net primary care patients with type 2 diabetes: 6-month outcome of a large clinical trial. *Journal of Medical Internet Research, 20,* e147. doi:10.2196/jmir.7692

Yoon, H., Kim, Y., Choi, K., Lim, Y. O., Nam, I., Kim, W., & Ham, H. (2018). The effectiveness of problem-solving therapy program intervention in reducing depression of older cancer patients. *Korean Journal of Health Promotion, 18,* 60–70. doi:10.15384/kjhp.2018.18.1.60

Zhang, A., Park, S., Sullivan, J. E., & Jing, S. (2018). The effectiveness of problem-solving therapy for primary care patients' depressive and/or anxiety disorders: A systematic review and meta-analysis. *Journal of the American Board of Family Medicine, 31,* 139–150. doi:10.3122/jabfm.2018.01.170270

ASSESSMENT, CLINICAL, AND TREATMENT PLANNING CONSIDERATIONS AND EC-PST "METAMESSAGES"

4

ASSESSMENT AND TREATMENT PLANNING CONSIDERATIONS

We begin this chapter by describing various practical assessment issues related to the effective implementation of emotion-centered problem-solving therapy (EC-PST). Readers who may be interested in learning about broader conceptual, theoretical, and/or research issues related to the assessment and evaluation of the construct of social problem solving (SPS) are referred to other sources (D'Zurilla & Nezu, 1990, 2007; Maydeu-Olivares & D'Zurilla, 1995). The second part of this chapter provides treatment guidelines to assist the reader to best determine what form or version of EC-PST (e.g., full-blown EC-PST vs. problem-solving skills training) or training sequence (i.e., which tool kits to teach initially and in what order) should be implemented with a given individual.

SOCIAL PROBLEM-SOLVING ASSESSMENT

Major areas of clinical assessment relevant to EC-PST include the following:

- Assessment of general SPS abilities and attitudes
- Assessment of current and previous SPS activities
- Assessment of problems, stressful difficulties, major negative life events, and/or traumatic events recently or currently experienced by a given client or client population
- Assessment of outcome variables related to presenting problems and emotion reactivity vulnerabilities

ASSESSMENT OF SOCIAL PROBLEM-SOLVING ABILITIES AND ATTITUDES

This type of evaluation can be useful for three general purposes:

- Determining whether EC-PST would be a useful intervention for a given individual
- Obtaining a detailed clinical picture of a person's overall and specific problem-solving abilities and beliefs to determine his or her strengths and limitations
- Assessing changes in problem-solving abilities as a function of engaging in EC-PST or other forms of therapy

Social Problem-Solving Inventory–Revised

A measure that we developed to address the aforementioned goals is the Social Problem-Solving Inventory–Revised (SPSI–R; D'Zurilla, Nezu, & Maydeu-Olivares, 2002). This is a revision of the 70-item, Social Problem-Solving Inventory (SPSI), which was initially developed on the basis of social problem-solving theory (D'Zurilla & Nezu, 1990). The current measure was revised on the basis of a series of factor-analytic studies (Maydeu-Olivares & D'Zurilla, 1995, 1996) and includes two major versions—a long form (SPSI–R:L) and a short form (SPSI–R:S). The SPSI–R:L contains 52 items and is a Likert-type, self-report questionnaire that provides a total score as well as scale scores representing the following five major scales that map onto the two problem-orientation dimensions and the three problem-solving styles described earlier in Chapter 1:

- *Positive Problem Orientation Scale* (*PPO*; 5 items; e.g., "Whenever I have a problem, I believe it can be solved")
- *Negative Problem Orientation Scale* (*NPO*; 10 items; e.g., "Difficult problems make me very upset")
- *Rational Problem-Solving Scale* (*RPS*; 20 items; e.g., "Before I try to solve a problem, I set a specific goal so that I know exactly what I want to accomplish")
- *Impulsivity/Carelessness Style Scale* (*ICS*; 10 items; e.g., "When I am attempting to solve a problem, I act on the first idea that comes to mind")
- *Avoidance Style Scale* (*AS*; 7 items; e.g., "I wait to see if a problem will resolve itself first before trying to solve it myself")

The items of the RPS Scale are further divided into four subscales (each with five items) corresponding to the four rational or planful problem-solving skills:

- Problem Definition and Formulation (PDF)
- Generation of Alternatives (GOA)
- Decision Making (DM)
- Solution Implementation and Verification (SIV)

An initial evaluation has provided substantial support indicating that the SPSI–R:L has strong psychometric properties (see SPSI–R test manual; D'Zurilla et al., 2002). For example, estimates of internal consistency across multiple samples ($N > 1,800$) for the total SPSI–R score range from 0.85 to 0.96. Test–retest reliability has been estimated to be 0.87 for the total score. In addition, studies have demonstrated the SPSI–R to have strong structural, concurrent, predictive, convergent, and discriminant validity properties. It is also sensitive to the effects of problem-solving–based interventions and is not correlated with general measures of intelligence. Normative data are available for both men and women older than 13 years and divided into four normal samples: adolescents, young adults, middle-aged adults, and older adults (see D'Zurilla et al.'s 2002 test manual). In addition, normative data are provided for select distressed populations, including psychiatric adults, psychiatric adolescents, distressed adult cancer patients, depressed outpatients, and suicidal adult inpatients.

In addition to the SPSI–R:L, the short form contains 25 items and measures the five major SPS dimensions. However, it does not assess the specific skills within the RPS Scale (e.g., PDF). This short form is recommended for research purposes or for circumstances in which length of testing time is an issue. The 52-item version generally requires about 15 to 20 minutes to complete, whereas the short form can be completed in about 10 minutes.

Several researchers have translated the SPSI–R into various languages. These include Spanish (Maydeu-Olivares, Rodríguez-Fornells, Gómez-Benito, & D'Zurilla, 2000), Chinese (Siu & Shek, 2005), German (Graf, 2003), Japanese (Sato et al., 2006), and two South African languages—Afrikaans and isiXhosa (Sorsdahl, Stein, & Myers, 2017). In each case, the five-factor model was cross-validated, providing support for the universal existence of this model of SPS. It has also been translated into Hungarian (Kasik, 2015). In addition, a version specific to assessing SPS among adolescents was developed on the basis of the original SPSI (Frauenknecht & Black, 1995).

Moreover, other researchers have validated this model focusing on additional select populations, including a sample of 325 Spanish-speaking North American Hispanic adults (De La Torre, Morera, & Wood, 2010), 219 Australian university students (Hawkins, Sofronoff, & Sheffield, 2009), 499 adult male sexual offenders in the United Kingdom (Wakeling, 2007), 699 Native American rural youth (Yetter & Foutch, 2014), and 90 adults with moderate and severe traumatic brain injury (Li, Waid-Ebbs, Velozo, & Heaton, 2016).

When comparing an individual's SPSI–R scores with the normative data provided in the manual (D'Zurilla et al., 2002), raw scores are converted to standard scores such that the SPSI–R total score as well as each of the five major scale and four subscale scores have a mean of 100 with a standard deviation of 15. Using this conversion, one can determine a client's particular problem-solving strengths and limitations in relation to his or her relevant group (e.g., 1 standard deviation above or below the mean in the appropriate direction). For example, if a patient has a score of 120 on the NPO scale (higher scores on NPO indicate more dysfunctional or poorer problem-solving attitudes and beliefs), it can be said that he or she is above the normed group average, suggesting a potential problem-solving concern or area in need of focused intervention. Scores more than 2 standard deviations from one's group norms are indicative of a significant limitation. On the contrary, a score of 132, for example, on the RPS scale, represents a particular strength for a given individual, in that it is 2 standard deviations above the mean of his or her comparison group.

Converting raw scores into standard scores clinically helps to identify areas of relative strengths and limitations that might affect a person's current and/or future functioning. It also can help determine the presence of vulnerabilities that may suggest the need for different levels of treatment. For example, identifying a particular SPS limitation suggests that the EC-PST therapist focus more heavily on this area.

The SPSI–R can also be applied as a means of assessing progress (or lack thereof) for an individual receiving EC-PST or other forms of related psychotherapy in which changes in SPS abilities and skills would be predicted if the person is improving. From an evidence-based perspective, one would expect improvements in SPS to *precede* improvements in a targeted outcome, such as depression. Thus, assessing changes (or lack thereof) in SPSI–R scores can be helpful in determining the success of the intervention at various points during treatment. For example, after several months of EC-PST, if either the ultimate outcome (e.g., depressive symptoms) or SPS abilities (e.g., SPSI–R scores) do not improve, then the clinician may need to reassess the appropriateness of a given intervention.

Social Problem-Solving Test

A similar measure we developed, called the *Social Problem-Solving Test*, was originally intended to be used as a self-help guide for individuals to use to be able to obtain a ballpark estimate of their real-life problem-solving abilities (A. M. Nezu, Nezu, & D'Zurilla, 2007). Although it is based on the SPSI–R to some degree, it is important to note that *it has not been subjected to any psychometric scrutiny or evaluation to date*. This self-help test contains 25 items, shown in Box 4.1.

BOX 4.1 ■ PROBLEM-SOLVING TEST

Instructions. Read each statement carefully and choose one of the following numbers (1 through 5) that best describes how much that statement is true of you regarding how you handle real-life problems. Respond as you *usually* think, feel, and act when faced with a real-life problem these days.

1 = *Not at all true of me*
2 = *Somewhat true of me*
3 = *Moderately true of me*
4 = *True of me*
5 = *Very true of me*

1. I feel afraid when I have an important problem to solve.
2. When making decisions, I think carefully about my many options.
3. I get nervous and unsure of myself when I have to make an important decision.
4. When my first efforts to solve a problem fail, I give up quickly, because finding a solution is too difficult.
5. Sometimes even difficult problems can have a way of moving my life forward in positive ways.
6. If I avoid problems, they will generally take care of themselves.
7. When I am unsuccessful at solving a problem, I get very frustrated.
8. If I work at it, I can learn to solve difficult problems effectively.
9. When faced with a problem, before deciding what to do, I carefully try to understand why it is a problem by sorting it out, breaking it down, and defining it.
10. I try to do anything I can to avoid problems in my life.
11. Difficult problems make me very emotional.
12. When I have a decision to make, I take the time to try to predict the positive and negative consequences of each possible option before I act.
13. When I am trying to solve a problem, I often rely on instinct and choose the first good idea that comes to mind.
14. When I am upset, I just want to run away and be left alone.
15. I can make important decisions on my own.
16. I frequently react before I have all the facts about a problem.
17. After coming up with an idea of how to solve a problem, I work out a plan to carry it out successfully.
18. I am very creative about coming up with ideas when solving problems.
19. I spend more time worrying about problems than actually solving them.
20. My goal for solving problems is to stop negative feelings as quickly as I can.
21. I try to avoid any trouble with others to keep problems to a minimum.
22. As soon as someone upsets me or hurts my feelings, I always react the same way.
23. When I am trying to figure out a problem, it helps me to stick to the facts of the situation.
24. In my opinion, being systematic and planful with personal problems seems too cold or "businesslike."
25. I understand that emotions, even bad ones, can actually be helpful to my efforts at problem solving.

(continued)

BOX 4.1 ■ PROBLEM-SOLVING TEST *(continued)*

INSTRUCTIONS FOR SCORING

Scales of Effective Problem Solving

1. Positive Problem Orientation (PPO)
   • Add scores for items: 5, 8, 15, 23, and 25.
2. Planful Problem Solving (PPS)
   • Add scores for items: 2, 9, 12, 17, and 18.

Explanation of Scores

• For both scales, scores less than 12 suggest that this individual requires problem-solving education, training, and practice to improve his or her psychological resilience to deal with the stress of daily problems.
• Scores between 12 and 18 indicate that he or she has some strengths, but can probably benefit from some training to improve.
• Scores greater than 18 indicate that this individual has strong positive attitudes and/or strong planful problem-solving skills.

Scales of Ineffective Problem Solving

1. Negative Problem Orientation (NPO)
   • Add scores for items: 1, 3, 7, 11, and 16.
2. Impulsive/Careless (IC)
   • Add scores for items: 4, 13, 20, 22, and 24.
3. Avoidance (AV)
   • Add scores for items: 6, 10, 14, 19, and 21.

Explanation of Scores

• For all these three scales, note that higher scores are indicative of a higher level in that scale (i.e., the higher the NPO score, the more negative one's orientation; the higher the IC score, the more he or she is impulsive/careless; the higher the AV score, the more avoidant the person).
• Scores greater than 12 indicate that one has some characteristic way(s) of dealing with problems that can frequently get in the way of his or her problem-solving efforts. Scores lower than 12 on any of these scales suggest the absence of any concerns regarding these areas.
• A Negative Orientation score of 12 or higher indicates that one has the tendency to think about problems in ways that are inaccurate, as well as experiencing difficulty managing the emotions that are often present when under stress. The higher the score above 12, the more negative the person's orientation.
• An Impulsive/Careless score of 12 or higher indicates that these individuals may not have the tendency to "look before he or she leaps" and may often make decisions that are not in his or her best interest. The higher the score above 12, the more impulsive the person.
• An Avoidance score of 12 or higher indicates that one has the tendency to avoid problems. This is the type of individual who often withdraws or leaves the room when engaged in an interpersonal argument, or pushes thoughts and feelings out of his or her head when worried or sad. Scores higher than 12 are suggestive of particular difficulties with avoidance.

The scoring key and brief explanation of the test scores are given to aid therapists whose clients will benefit by completing this test. However, clinicians should remember that this test has unknown psychometric properties and caution should be used when attempting to interpret the scores. A copy of the test is included in the Client Workbook (for availability, see the Preface of this book).

ASSESSMENT OF CURRENT SOCIAL PROBLEM-SOLVING ACTIVITIES

In addition to the SPSI–R, another means of assessing extant problem-solving abilities and attitudes, before conducting EC-PST, can involve a self-description of the actual activities in which an individual engages when attempting to handle or solve a real-life problem. During the initial intake or evaluation period, the clinician can request that clients complete a *Social Problem-Solving Self-Monitoring (SPSSM)* form (or something similar) that provides for a self-description in response to the following questions regarding a particular real-life problem. Box 4.2 contains the different pieces of information requested by the SPSSM regarding a recent problem.

This information, in combination with the person's SPSI–R results, can provide the therapist with important information about a given individual's overall and specific problem-solving attitudes and reactions to a specific problem. Moreover, it can serve as a springboard for further assessment questions. It would also be noteworthy to compare individuals' actual problem-solving actions regarding a specific problem to their responses to the SPSI–R, in an attempt to determine how close their self-report matches their actual attempts in real life.

Another important assessment issue would be to request that a client complete more than one self-monitoring form, specifically requesting him or

---

BOX 4.2 ■ SOCIAL PROBLEM-SOLVING SELF-MONITORING FORM

- *What was the problem?* (Describe the situation; be sure to indicate who was involved, why it was a problem for you, and your goal or objectives in the situation.)
- *What was your emotional reaction to the problem?* (Be sure to note your initial feelings, as well as your emotions throughout—did they change?)
- *What did you do to handle the problem?* (Describe what you tried to do to solve or cope with the problem; try to be as specific as possible, describing your thoughts and actions.)
- *What was the outcome?* (Describe what happened after you tried to handle the problem; be sure to indicate your emotional reactions to this outcome, how satisfied you were with this outcome, and whether you believe the problem was "solved.")

her to select different types of problems. As noted in Chapter 1, we suggested that it is possible that an individual may be characterized as holding a positive orientation when dealing with certain types of problems (e.g., achievement-oriented situations such as those involving work, career, or school), while additionally having the opposite type of orientation when reacting to other types of problems (e.g., interpersonally oriented situations such as those involving romantic relationships, friendships, or social interactions) or vice versa. Thus, having the client complete at least two differing SPSSM forms, one for an achievement-oriented problem and one for an interpersonal or relationship-oriented problem, can provide insight into his or her problem-specific, problem-solving strengths and limitations.

It can also be helpful if clients are requested to complete an additional SPSSM form with specific regard to one of the most difficult or traumatic experiences they have had in the past. This assessment can provide for a better understanding of how significant (or even extreme) stress has affected individuals. Moreover, as Chapter 2 strongly indicated, early childhood stress is a significant predictor of future distress. Obtaining a fuller history of a client's early experience with stressful events can be useful when attempting to explain to him or her how certain current distress symptoms have arisen.

ASSESSMENT OF CURRENT PROBLEMS

A third area of assessment involves obtaining a clinical picture of the type of problems a client is currently experiencing. Although such information can be obtained via a semistructured interview, at times it is more expedient to use various problem checklists or inventories. For example, four different versions of the Mooney Problem Checklist (Mooney & Gordon, 1950) exist that contain myriad age-specific problems (i.e., junior high school, high school, college, and adults) that can be helpful as a quick means of gathering initial intake information.

If the referral problem is specific (e.g., distressed cancer patient), or if EC-PST is being provided to a group that was constituted around a common diagnosis (e.g., depressed heart failure patients or distressed caregivers of patients with traumatic brain injury), other checklists may exist or can be developed that include common problems related to that diagnosis or group theme. Examples of such checklists are given in Box 4.3 (General Problem Checklist), Box 4.4 (Work-Related Problem Checklist), Box 4.5 (Cancer-Related Problem Checklist adapted from our work with adult cancer patients; A. M. Nezu, Nezu, Felgoise, McClure, & Houts, 2003), Box 4.6 (Heart Failure-Related Problem Checklist adapted from our work with adults diagnosed with heart failure; A. M. Nezu et al., 2011), and Box 4.7 (Common Problems Experienced by U.S. Veterans on the basis of our EC-PST–based Moving Forward program [Tenhula et al., 2014]).

BOX 4.3 ■ "GENERAL" PROBLEM CHECKLIST

Job or career problem
Drug problem
Marriage problem
Time-management problem
Problem with children or adolescents
Self-discipline problem
Low self-esteem
Academic problem
Emotional problem
Conflict between job and family responsibilities
Moral conflict
Religious problem
Conflict between academic and family
  responsibilities
Legal problem
Lack of recreation or leisure activities
Housekeeping or home maintenance problem
Transportation problem
Problem with parents or other relatives

Concern about the neighborhood
Concern about the community
Lack of social relationships
Concern about the environment
Interpersonal conflicts
Problems with business products or
  services
Sexual problem
Sleep problem
Problem with professional services
Financial problem
Illness or disability problem
Problem with social or government
  services
Lack of exercise
Weight problem
Concern about world problems
Drinking problem

BOX 4.4 ■ WORK-RELATED PROBLEMS

Problem finding a job
Not enough job autonomy
Job-interview problem
Limited opportunity for advancement
Inadequate job performance
Absenteeism or tardiness
Unsafe practices
Poor communication with superiors
Too much work
Too little work
Work not challenging enough
Poor communication with subordinates
Work too difficult or complex
Ambiguous job demands
Poor relationships with peers
Ambiguous job goals
Interpersonal disputes

Conflicting job demands
Ineffective delegation or lack of
  assertiveness
Too much responsibility
Too little responsibility
Lack of recognition
Lack of opportunity to participate in decision-
  making, which affects the job
Aversive or unhealthy work
  environment
Inadequate pay or benefits
Procrastination
Poor job security
Unproductive meetings
Commuting problems
Wasting time
Too much traveling for the job

BOX 4.5 ■ CANCER-RELATED PROBLEM CHECKLIST

Physical Distress

I have trouble walking.
I have difficulty with household chores.
I cannot engage in recreational activities anymore.
I am losing weight.
I am having problems working.
I have lots of pain.

Psychological Distress

I am ashamed of the way my body looks.
I worry more than ever now.
I cannot seem to think straight.
I have problems making decisions.
I have difficulty talking to my friends.
Most of my friends shun me.
I feel sad all the time.
I have trouble sleeping.

Marital and Family Interactions

We are not talking a lot lately.
There is too little affection between us.
My family will not leave me alone.
There is a change in family roles.

Interactions With Healthcare Team

I cannot get the information I want.
I cannot seem to communicate with the medical team.
I do not like feeling out of control.
I get nervous asking questions.
I get very angry waiting for so long to talk to the doctor for just a few minutes.
I feel like I am just a patient, not a real person.

Sexual Distress

I lost interest in sex.
Sex is difficult for me.
My partner does not want to have sex with me anymore.
I feel so unattractive.
Sex is now very painful.
I cannot let my husband see my surgical scars.

Requesting that clients complete such brief checklists can not only provide the therapist with important intake information in a timely manner but also helps to foster a patient's awareness and relief that other people also experience similar types of problems (i.e., normalizing and validating the experience of problems).

BOX 4.6 ■ HEART FAILURE-RELATED PROBLEMS

I feel tired all the time.
I have difficulty asking questions to my doctors.
I have difficulty doing things around the house.
I feel dizzy a lot.
I do not like the way I look since my heart problems.
I am bothered by the side effects of the medications.
I have difficulty understanding what the healthcare team tells me.
I find that doctors do not explain things that well to me.
I cannot go places or travel like I used to.
I have difficulty getting around physically.
I worry about my heart problems all the time.
I feel helpless because of my heart condition.
I feel angry a lot of the time.
I have difficulty sleeping.
I feel sad a lot of the time.
I worry that I will die.
I do not feel sexually attractive.
I have memory difficulties.
I do not feel good about myself.
I have financial problems.
I have problems sticking to a healthy diet.
I have difficulty talking with friends/family members about my health.
I find that friends/family members ignore or avoid me since being diagnosed.
I do not feel that people really understand my situation.
I feel my life has changed for the worse.
I do not feel interested in having sex any more.
I do not get along with people, including family, as well as I used to.
I have difficulty asking people for help.
I feel like a burden to my family and friends.
I often forget to take my medications.
I find it difficult to exercise.

ASSESSMENT OF OUTCOME VARIABLES AND EMOTION REACTIVITY

It is rather obvious that therapists need to include measures of those variables or factors related to the reasons why someone is seeking treatment or that are relevant to the goals of an intervention. For example, if clients are coming to therapy because they are depressed or anxious, then measuring symptom severity of the depression or anxiety would be crucial to determine the course and outcome of treatment.

BOX 4.7 ■ COMMON PROBLEMS EXPERIENCED BY U.S. VETERANS

Problems with a spouse/partner
Confusion about the future
Sense of powerlessness/limited control
Medical problems or pain
Anger
Sadness and depression
Stress of becoming a new parent
Not being understood by people
Difficulty finding a job
Financial problems/limited income
Hard to transition back to civilian life
Pressures of school/training
Getting stuck in a rut
Handling physical limitations
Memory or cognitive problems
Gaining or losing weight
Ethical conflicts

Frequent relocations and redeployments
Feeling lonely
Family problems
Spiritual/religious concerns
Negative memories of combat experiences
Trouble sleeping
Job dissatisfaction
Problems with coworkers, boss, or someone
  in your unit
Dissatisfied with neighborhood or location
Dissatisfied with deployment living conditions
Relying too much on alcohol or drugs
Feeling overloaded/overwhelmed
Feeling irritable or anxious
Hard to engage in social activities
Difficulty keeping "molehills" from becoming
  "mountains"

In addition to such measures, we advocate the inclusion of a measure of emotion reactivity to allow for a more comprehensive picture of individuals' general reactions to stressful events. As noted earlier, we indicated that individual differences in emotion reactivity can serve as one important factor accounting for variability among people regarding their responses to the same stressful problem. Including such a measure can allow the EC-PST therapist to obtain information about a client's particular vulnerability to react emotionally to problems that make it more difficult to manage or regulate. Two such measures to our knowledge currently exist—the Emotion Reactivity Scale (ERS; Nock, Wedig, Holmberg, & Hooley, 2008) and the Perth Emotional Reactivity Scale (PERS; Becerra, Preece, Campitelli, & Scott-Pillow, 2017). The ERS measures emotion sensitivity (e.g., "Even the littlest things make me emotional"), intensity (e.g., "I experience emotions very strongly"), and persistence (e.g., "If I have a disagreement with someone, it takes a long time for me to get over it"), whereas the PERS assesses very similar constructs, ease of activation (e.g., "I tend to get upset very easily"), intensity (e.g., "I experience the feeling of frustration very deeply"), and duration (e.g., "Once in a negative mood, it's hard to snap out of it"), but does so for negative and positive emotions separately (item examples listed refer to negative emotions).

In essence, the assessment protocol suggested in the preceding paragraph allows the therapist to obtain a more comprehensive picture of a client's particular strengths and limitations across general SPS abilities, SPS activities regarding specific types of problems, and general vulnerabilities concerning emotion reactivity to stressors. Having such information can help guide individual treatment planning and clinical decision making.

TREATMENT-PLANNING CONSIDERATIONS

To foster effective treatment planning and clinical decision-making specific to EC-PST, this section provides for a series of "FAQs" (frequently asked questions) for therapists unfamiliar with this approach.

Is EC-PST appropriate for my client?
Chapter 3 provides strong support that EC-PST has been found to be effective for a wide range of psychological problems and difficulties. In fact, as indicated, such a list is continuously growing, which underscores the versatility of this approach. Moreover, research has suggested that problem-solving–based protocols are well received by potential patients as acceptable interventions to help treat their emotional problems (Kasckow et al., 2010). In addition, various tools within EC-PST can provide for a more positive psychological approach that can be applied to foster a person's ability to "flourish" and/or attain more meaningful life goals rather than only being geared to decreasing or minimizing psychopathology (see Chapter 12).

What form of EC-PST should I conduct?
Taking a case formulation approach to clinical decision making (i.e., where results of an individualized assessment inform treatment planning decisions; see C. M. Nezu & Nezu, 1995) in addressing this question suggests that the following dimensions need to be considered:

- The client's overall SPS strengths and limitations
- The seriousness of one's emotion reactivity vulnerabilities
- The intensity of his or her predominant symptomatology (e.g., depression, anxiety, anger)
- The presence of recent major negative life events or trauma

According to the aforementioned list of considerations, the more significant a client's problem-solving deficits, and/or the greater the severity of his or her emotional distress or functional problems, and/or the more sensitive, intense, and pervasive his or her emotion reactivity is in general to negative stressful events, the more likely that the treatment provider should implement a more comprehensive version of EC-PST. In other words, all four tool kits should be taught, including substantial opportunities to practice the various skills across multiple problem areas. The one exception would be the situation in which the individual might not be experiencing emotional distress at clinically significant levels at the present time, he or she has recently experienced a major negative life stressor (e.g., diagnosis of a significant medical illness, divorce, losing a job, losing a close friend or family member) that is likely to increase his or her vulnerability to experiencing such significant distress in the near future, especially if an assessment of his or her general emotion reactivity identifies that as a risk factor.

An example of this latter approach involves Moving Forward, a four-session group program conducted in a classroom setting, which we developed (A. M. Nezu & Nezu, 2012) specifically for veterans of recent military campaigns overseas (i.e., Operation Enduring Freedom, Operation Iraqi Freedom, Operation New Dawn). This EC-PST program is currently being implemented across the United States in multiple Veterans Health Administration medical centers as a preventive approach. More specifically, it is geared to helping veterans better readjust to civilian life by dealing with stressful problems by applying various problem-solving strategies. The goal is to decrease the likelihood that such individuals would eventually experience significant psychological problems and require less medical and psychiatric care. A systematic program evaluation of this approach that included 621 veterans identified statistically and clinically significant improvements in their depression, general emotional distress, social functioning, SPS, and resilience to future stress (Tenhula et al., 2014).

Less comprehensive forms of EC-PST might entail bibliotherapy (e.g., self-help manuals and handouts, such as those provided within the Moving Forward program or a book based on an earlier version of EC-PST written for the lay public [A. M. Nezu et al., 2007]), problem-solving skills training (less emphasis on the orientation or emotion regulation treatment components), or an EC-PST workshop (e.g., classroom setting). These types of approaches may be particularly appropriate for primary care or other medical settings, whereby initial EC-PST–based psychoeducational materials can be provided to aid medical patients to (a) better adjust to the experience of a chronic illness (e.g., diabetes, heart disease), and/or (b) improve their ability to adhere to certain medical treatment regimens, such as complex medication prescriptions (see A. M. Nezu, Nezu, & Perri, 2006).

Last, if time is an issue, depending on results from a more formal assessment of an individual's problem-solving strengths and limitations (e.g., SPSI–R findings plus clinical interviews), EC-PST can be tailored to emphasize those areas where deficits are identified while de-emphasizing training in those areas that represent his or her problem-solving strengths.

Which tool kit should I start treatment with?
On the basis of a provider's initial case formulation conducted during the first session, Table 4.1 can be used to develop an initial treatment plan (i.e., which tool kit to train first and how much emphasis should be placed on training a given tool kit). Note that this plan can change as a function of how the therapy is progressing.

Guidelines to consider (Table 4.1):

1. If the participant appears to be motivated, only mildly distressed, and cognitively stable, the provider should consider beginning with Tool kit #1.

2. If the participant feels very hopeless, initially consider training Tool kit #3.

3. If the participant is experiencing significant emotional distress or appears at moderate to high suicide risk, begin with Tool kit #4.

4. In general, teach Tool kit #2 after training Tool kit #1 unless #2 or #3 is valid.

Can I conduct EC-PST in a group format?
EC-PST has previously been applied successfully in group settings (A. M. Nezu & Perri, 1989). Group treatment can be preferable in those situations in which multiple clients are able to serve as sources of feedback to each other regarding both problem-solving skill acquisition and implementation. In addition, group members can share ideas and experiences as well as serve as models and sources of social support and reinforcement. This approach can be particularly effective if structured around a specific clinical population or client problem to foster a sense of normalization. Conducting EC-PST in a group format can also serve as a more efficient use of therapists' time. It can also provide for a meaningful analogue to everyday life (i.e., representing numerous interpersonal interactions) in which new ways of coping can be encouraged.

How much time will EC-PST take?
Similar to many other forms of directive psychotherapy, there is little research that directly answers this type of question. Randomized controlled trials (RCTs) evaluating EC-PST represented by good outcome have included a range of eight to 20 sessions. Many of these sessions have been between 1 to 1.5 hours in length. Clinically, it would seem fair to suggest that the more

TABLE 4.1 ▪ GUIDE TO TREATMENT PLANNING: WHEN TO IMPLEMENT THE VARIOUS EC-PST TOOLS

Tool	When to Use
Tool kit #1: Planful Problem Solving	Applicable for everyday problems, decisions, or dilemmas; these are the basic set of tools to help one solve any problem or achieve any goal.
Tool kit #2: Problem-Solving Multitasking	Applicable for problems that are more complex and require more focused attention (i.e., helps manage "cognitive overload").
Tool kit #3: Enhancing Motivation for Action	Applicable for times when one is either (a) "sitting on the fence" regarding carrying out an action plan or (b) feeling that there is "no light at the end of the tunnel" and the individual just wants to "give up."
Tool kit #4: "Stop and Slow Down"	Applicable for times when the problem is becoming more stressful and one is having trouble handling negative feelings, such as sadness, anxiety, worry, and anger, that interfere with his or her problem solving; very likely to be applicable as a first-order intervention for individuals at moderate to high risk for suicide.

EC-PST, emotion-centered problem-solving therapy.

intense the negative symptomatology (e.g., moderate vs. severe depression), the more likely that EC-PST will take longer. Certain patient populations (e.g., those with chronic illness, traumatic brain injury, or developmental disabilities) may also require more lengthy treatment. In most outpatient settings, the overall length of treatment may be dictated more by insurance considerations than by the clinical issues. Given that EC-PST has been found to be effective across multiple settings and venues, it is likely that the basic therapy process can be tailored to fit the needs of a patient population within the restraints of various provider care limitations in most circumstances.

My patient is asking if his spouse can be included in EC-PST, although there are no marital problems. Is this a good idea?
We believe that if both members of a dyad (e.g., married couples, same-sex couples, couples living with each other) are willing, having both individuals included can potentially enhance treatment efficacy. This recommendation is directly supported by multiple studies identified in Chapter 3 where

treatment included both a patient and a caregiver. Moreover, in a study we conducted with adults coping with cancer, titled "Project Genesis" (A. M. Nezu et al., 2003), the inclusion of a significant other/caregiver led to statistically and clinically significant improvement beyond that achieved by having only the cancer patient receive treatment. In certain situations, we believe that such an invitation can also be extended to other family members or adult friends as well.

The significant other can serve as a problem-solving coach and cheerleader. In such a role, these individuals can help motivate, guide, and support the patient. He or she can reinforce the identified client when he or she is actively using a skill and can suggest the use of specific skills (i.e., reminders) when this individual is experiencing distress and not using the skills effectively.

Although the primary focus would be for the significant other to be a support person, it is important to provide these individuals with a personal benefit from EC-PST as well. Thus, caution should be exercised never to ignore the personal needs of the family members or support person. In addition, some patients may come to treatment experiencing guilt and a sense of burden to their families as a function of the difficulties he or she has been experiencing. Significant others, caregivers, and other family members may also feel particularly guilty or hesitant to talk about their feelings of burden. Caregivers or individuals engaged as coaches may feel additionally burdened by homework or practice assignments or other requirements of the EC-PST intervention. Thus, it is important to communicate to the support person that his or her participation in EC-PST can help improve her or his own quality of life as well. At times, the problems addressed in treatment may well focus on improving family relationships and communication patterns.

My patient is having severe anxiety and depression problems. I want to apply EC-PST, but I also think it would be a good idea to use other cognitive and behavioral strategies as well. Is this okay?
The astute clinician will easily note that various overlaps exist among EC-PST and other cognitive behavioral therapy (CBT) interventions. For example, both cognitive therapy and dialectic behavior therapy include training in problem solving as standard components of treatment. Thus, there exists a strong compatibility among these therapies regarding philosophy, common features, and at times, specific strategies. Also, EC-PST can easily be combined in conjunction with multiple other types of CBT approaches within a more comprehensive overall treatment plan. For example, EC-PST and various behavioral stress-management strategies can be effective in treating a variety of stress and anxiety-related disorders, where EC-PST is included to help an individual better cope with extant stressful problems

and events, and stress-management techniques are geared to aid in reducing an individual's negative physiological arousal occurring in reaction to such stressors. As another example, EC-PST and behavioral activation strategies can be a powerful means of treating clinical depression by simultaneously addressing two critical depression-related difficulties (i.e., coping with stress as well as difficulties eliciting and enjoying positive events in one's life). Note that the program developed by Dreer et al. (2016) combines psychoeducation, motivational interviewing, and problem solving to enhance glaucoma medication adherence. Many of the studies supporting the efficacy of problem-solving–based protocols have, in fact, combined it with other treatment components to maximize the efficacy of a larger treatment package.

I work with a lot of Latina/Latino clients as well as African Americans and Black persons. Has EC-PST been found to be effective for these populations as well? Similar to many other evidence-based psychosocial interventions, EC-PST has not been extensively validated with individuals of diverse ethnic backgrounds. However, it has been found to be effective in several studies when provided to Latino and Black individuals (see Chapter 3). Thus, although substantial research has not yet been conducted with individuals of a variety of diverse backgrounds, the extant research does underscore the potential applicability and efficacy of EC-PST with such individuals. Note also the increase in applications of problem-solving–based protocols in countries outside of the United States.

Some of the planful problem-solving strategies reminds me of what I do as a therapist in trying to develop treatment plans for various clients. Is there a way that I can use these principles in this way more formally?
We have previously developed a model of clinical decision making and case formulation for cognitive and behavioral therapies that is based on various problem-solving principles (A. M. Nezu, Nezu, & Cos, 2007; A. M. Nezu, Nezu, & Lombardo, 2004). For example, various principles and activities related to helping individuals better understand the nature of a stressful real-life problem can easily be thought of as relevant to conducting a comprehensive assessment for developing an individualized case formulation model of a given client's problems. For example, the generation-of-alternatives process can foster the assessment (e.g., identifying alternative ways of obtaining clinical information), treatment planning (e.g., identifying alternative treatment strategies to help reach a goal), and evaluation (e.g., identifying alternative means of determining whether treatment is working) phases of therapy. The decision-making set of tasks taught to a client can also be used by a clinician, such as predicting the

possible outcomes if a particular cognitive and/or behavioral strategy is implemented, conducting a cost–benefit analysis among the various identified treatment alternatives to determine which ones to carry out, and developing an overall treatment plan based on such decisions. The solution-implementation-and-verification steps would involve the clinician determining whether treatment was being optimally conducted as well as assessing whether it is leading to its predicted outcome.

The relevance for using such problem-solving steps in case formulation and treatment planning increases with the complexity of a given case. Because all patients experiencing the same problem (e.g., depression) are "not created equal," such an approach is highly recommended. In other words, multiple individual-difference variables, as well as environmental and social context dimensions, are likely to exist and significantly distinguish among such individuals, thus leading to the need for the therapist to explore how he or she can optimally personalize or tailor EC-PST treatment to a specific client. Readers interested in learning more about the use of problem-solving principles in this context are directed to A. M. Nezu, Nezu, and Cos (2007) and A. M. Nezu, Nezu, and Lombardo (2004).

SUMMARY

This chapter first described several major assessment tasks that can help guide EC-PST: assessment of SPS abilities and attitudes, assessment of current problem-solving activities, assessment of stressors the individual is currently experiencing, and assessment of relevant outcome variables and emotion reactivity vulnerabilities. Several inventories and questionnaires were identified to help the therapist conduct such assessments, including the SPSI–R, the Problem-Solving Test, the SPSSM form, various Mooney Problem Checklists, and a variety of problem-specific checklists. A second goal of this chapter was to address a variety of questions regarding treatment planning issues. These were presented as answers to several FAQs that a therapist beginning to learn this approach might ask.

REFERENCES

Becerra, R., Preece, D., Campitelli, G., & Scott-Pillow, G. (2017). The assessment of emotional reactivity across negative and positive emotions: Development and validation of the Perth Emotional Reactivity Scale (PERS). *Assessment*. Advance online publication. doi:10.1177/1073191117694455

D'Zurilla, T. J., & Nezu, A. M. (1990). Development and preliminary evaluation of the Social Problem-Solving Inventory (SPSI). *Psychological Assessment: A Journal of Consulting and Clinical Psychology, 2*, 156–163. doi:10.1037/1040-3590.2.2.156

D'Zurilla, T. J., & Nezu, A. M. (2007). *Problem-solving therapy: A positive approach to clinical intervention* (3rd ed.). New York, NY: Springer Publishing.

D'Zurilla, T. J., Nezu, A. M., & Maydeu-Olivares, A. (2002). *Manual for the Social Problem-Solving Inventory–Revised.* North Tonawanda, NY: Multi-Health Systems.

De La Torre, M. T., Morera, O. F., & Wood, J. M. (2010). Measuring social problem solving using the Spanish Version for Hispanics of the Social Problem Solving Inventory–Revised. *Cultural Diversity and Ethnic Minority Psychology, 16,* 501–506. doi:10.1037/a0021372

Dreer, L. E., Owsley, C., Campbell, L., Gao, L., Wood, A., & Girkin, C. A. (2016). Feasibility, patient acceptability, and preliminary efficacy of a culturally informed, health promotion program to improve glaucoma medication adherence among African Americans: "Glaucoma management optimism for a African Americans living with glaucoma" (GOAL). *Current Eye Research, 41,* 50–58. doi:10.3109/02713683.2014.1002045

Frauenknecht, M., & Black, D. R. (1995). Social Problem-Solving Inventory for Adolescents (SPSI-A): Development and preliminary psychometric evaluation. *Journal of Personality Assessment, 64,* 522–539. doi:10.1207/s15327752jpa6403_10

Graf, A. (2003). A psychometric test of a German version of the SPSI-R. *Zeitschrift für Differentielle und Diagnostische Psychologie, 24,* 277–291. doi:10.1024/0170-1789.24.4.277

Hawkins, D., Sofronoff, K., & Sheffield, J. K. (2009). Psychometric properties of the social problem solving inventory-revised short-form: Is the short form a valid and reliable measure for young adults? *Cognitive Therapy and Research, 33,* 462–470. doi:10.1007/s10608-008-9209-7

Kasckow, J., Brown, C., Morse, J. Q., Karpov, I., Bensasi, S., Thomas, S. B., ... Reynolds, C. (2010). Racial preferences for participation in a depression prevention trial involving problem-solving therapy. *Psychiatric Services, 61,* 722–724. doi:10.1176/ps.2010.61.7.722

Kasik, L. (2015). Development of social problem solving—A longitudinal study (2009–2011) in a Hungarian context. *European Journal of Developmental Psychology, 12,* 142–157. doi:10.1080/17405629.2014.969702

Li, C. Y., Waid-Ebbs, J., Velozo, C. A., & Heaton, S. C. (2016). Factor structure and item level psychometrics of the Social Problem Solving Inventory–Revised: Short Form in traumatic brain injury. *Neuropsychological Rehabilitation, 26,* 446–463. doi:10.1080/09602011.2015.1044458

Maydeu-Olivares, A., & D'Zurilla, T. J. (1995). A factor analysis of the Social Problem-Solving Inventory using polychoric correlations. *European Journal of Psychological Assessment, 11,* 98–107. doi:10.1027/1015-5759.11.2.98

Maydeu-Olivares, A., & D'Zurilla, T. J. (1996). A factor-analytic study of the Social Problem-Solving Inventory: An integration of theory and data. *Cognitive Therapy and Research, 20,* 115–133. doi:10.1007/BF02228030

Maydeu-Olivares, A., Rodríguez-Fornells, A., Gómez-Benito, J., & D'Zurilla, T. J. (2000). Psychometric properties of the Spanish adaptation of the Social Problem-Solving Inventory–Revised (SPSI-R). *Personality and Individual Differences, 29,* 699–708. doi:10.1016/S0191-8869(99)00226-3

Mooney, R. L., & Gordon, L. V. (1950). *The Mooney manual: Problem checklist.* New York, NY: Psychological Corporation.

Nezu, A. M., & Nezu, C. M. (2012, April). *Moving Forward: A problem-solving approach to achieving life's goals.* Workshop presented at the Department of Veterans Affairs Education/Training Conference, Philadelphia, PA.

Nezu, A. M., Nezu, C. M., & Cos, T. A. (2007). Case formulation for the behavioral and cognitive therapies: A problem-solving perspective. In T. D. Eells (Ed.), *Handbook of psychotherapy case formulation* (2nd ed., pp. 349–378). New York, NY: Guilford Press.

Nezu, A. M., Nezu, C. M., & D'Zurilla, T. J. (2007). *Solving life's problems: A 5-step guide to enhanced well-being.* New York, NY: Springer Publishing.

Nezu, A. M., Nezu, C. M., Felgoise, S. H., McClure, K. S., & Houts, P. S. (2003). Project Genesis: Assessing the efficacy of problem-solving therapy for distressed adult cancer patients. *Journal of Consulting and Clinical Psychology, 71,* 1036–1048. doi:10.1037/0022-006X.71.6.1036

Nezu, A. M., Nezu, C. M., Lee, M., Haggerty, K., Salber, K. E., Greenberg, L. M., … Foster, E. (2011, November). *Social problem solving as a mediator of posttraumatic growth and quality of life among patients with heart failure.* Paper presented at the Annual Convention of the Association of Behavioral and Cognitive Therapies, Toronto, ON, Canada.

Nezu, A. M., Nezu, C. M., & Lombardo, E. R. (2004). *Cognitive-behavioral case formulation and treatment design: A problem-solving approach.* New York, NY: Springer Publishing.

Nezu, A. M., Nezu, C. M., & Perri, M. G. (2006). Problem solving to promote treatment adherence. In W. T. O'Donohue & E. R. Levensky (Eds.), *Promoting treatment adherence: A practical handbook for health care providers* (pp. 135–148). New York, NY: Sage Publications.

Nezu, A. M., & Perri, M. G. (1989). Social problem-solving therapy for unipolar depression: An initial dismantling investigation. *Journal of Consulting and Clinical Psychology, 57,* 408–413. doi:10.1037/0022-006X.57.3.408

Nezu, C. M., & Nezu, A. M. (1995). Clinical decision making in everyday practice: The science in the art. *Cognitive and Behavioral Practice, 2,* 5–25. doi:10.1016/S1077-7229(05)80003-3

Nock, M. K., Wedig, M. M., Holmberg, E. B., & Hooley, J. M. (2008). The emotion reactivity scale: Development, evaluation, and relation to self-injurious thoughts and behaviors. *Behavior therapy, 39,* 107–116. doi:10.1016/j.beth.2007.05.005

Sato, H., Takahashi, F., Matsuo, M., Sakai, M., Shimada, H., Chen, J., … Sakano, Y. (2006). Development of the Japanese version of the Social Problem-Solving Inventory-Revised and examination of its reliability and validity. *Japanese Journal of Behavior Therapy, 32,* 15–30.

Siu, A. M., & Shek, D. T. (2005). The Chinese version of the social problem-solving inventory: Some initial results on reliability and validity. *Journal of Clinical Psychology, 61,* 347–360. doi:10.1002/jclp.20023

Sorsdahl, K., Stein, D. J., & Myers, B. (2017). Psychometric properties of the Social Problem Solving Inventory–Revised Short-Form in a South African population. *International Journal of Psychology, 52,* 154–162. doi:10.1002/ijop.12192

Tenhula, W. N., Nezu, A. M., Nezu, C. M., Stewart, M. O., Miller, S. A., Steele, J., & Karlin, B. E. (2014). Moving Forward: A problem-solving training program to foster veteran resilience. *Professional Psychology: Research and Practice, 45,* 416–424. doi:10.1037/a0037150

Wakeling, H. C. (2007). The psychometric validation of the Social Problem-Solving Inventory–Revised with UK incarcerated sexual offenders. *Sex Abuse, 19,* 217–236. doi:10.1177/107906320701900304

Yetter, G., & Foutch, V. (2014). Exploration of the structural and convergent validity of the Social Problem-Solving Inventory–Revised with Native American youth. *Cultural Diversity and Ethnic Minority Psychology, 20,* 276–282. doi:10.1037/a0034349

EC-PST METAMESSAGES AND OTHER IMPORTANT CLINICAL CONSIDERATIONS

This chapter addresses a variety of important treatment issues regarding the effective implementation of emotion-centered problem-solving therapy (EC-PST). We begin by discussing various EC-PST "metamessages," which are inherent principles that define and characterize the "essence" of this approach. Moreover, such precepts provide a meaningful framework and context within which this approach can be maximally effective. We urge therapists to attempt to incorporate these messages into both the manner in which they conduct treatment and to repeatedly remind clients about the importance of such ideas.

Next, we briefly describe and emphasize the importance of the therapist–client relationship. This is followed by a discussion of a variety of adjunctive therapy strategies and instructional guidelines that can be applied by the EC-PST clinician to enhance a client's overall problem-solving learning and skill acquisition. We realize that the experienced clinician may find some of this material rather basic, but we also believe it should be included to remind all of us of the importance of such issues. The last topic provides a list of "dos and don'ts" specifically related to the effective implementation of EC-PST.

EC-PST METAMESSAGES
The Equivalent Role of Affect, Cognition, and Behavior

Various therapy orientations tend to ascribe primacy to certain factors regarding the etiology of psychopathology or emotional distress. For example, according to a cognitive therapy perspective, various cognitive factors, such as cognitive distortions, are the primary cause of one's difficulties. A behavioral activation approach would suggest that one major difficulty that leads to distress involves behaviorally avoiding previously reinforcing activities. Emotion-focused therapies tend to underscore the predominant importance of focusing on the emotional experience in treatment. Although these characterizations are obviously somewhat superficial, what we are suggesting is that many forms of therapy often prescribe what a clinician should initially and predominantly focus on, attend to, and gear treatment strategies toward effect change in these predetermined factors. EC-PST, on the contrary, assumes equal clinical importance and function of various affective, cognitive, and behavioral factors. Although significant commonalities exist as a simple function of people being human, individual differences do exist and need to be addressed. Thus, on the basis of this conceptualization, EC-PST therapists should apply the clinical decision-making guidelines given in Chapter 4 based on what an overall assessment protocol points to as initial salient factors to target for a given client. For example, if a client initially presents to therapy with significant emotional distress related to a recent stressful problem or series of problems (e.g., breakup of an important romantic relationship), rather than attempt to teach him or her rational or planful problem-solving skills, we would argue that what needs to be attended to initially is to help this person better understand and manage the emotional distress. Such intense affect would certainly interfere greatly with his ability to effectively engage in rational or logical thinking and probably lead to frustration or even early termination. Equally important is the notion that one's emotions represent important information about oneself.

EC-PST Therapists Need to Understand and Accurately Convey the Social Problem Solving Model of Stress/Distress

For EC-PST to be maximally effective across clients, we strongly posit that clinicians implementing this approach should be well versed in the areas of social problem solving, stress, emotional regulation, brain–behavior relationships, and the various details of a variety of health and mental health problems as given in Chapter 2. A reasonable amount of preparation and understanding of these areas is required to convey to the patient a sense of expertise and competence. More important, in our opinion, is the notion that this also helps the client to better understand how he or she is currently having these types of difficulties. Providing a context or etiological framework within which clients can better understand the nature and cause of their problems can foster clarity regarding therapy goals and the means by which to achieve them. Snyder (2002) defines *hope* as the belief that people can find pathways to their desired goals and become motivated to use such pathways. Within this context, providing the client with a brief overview of the social problem-solving model of stress/distress not only suggests which pathways led him or her to the current state of distress, but, more important, also creates hope by outlining how he or she can identify more effective pathways to reach more positive goals. In essence, we argue that it is insufficient for clinicians to be competent in the implementation of EC-PST (e.g., competent in teaching a client to use the visualization tool); rather, they should be able to understand *why* such strategies are important to teach to a given client. We suggest explaining to clients that as a function of the combination of various biological/genetic factors and early and current learning experiences, their "brain and body" have come to react to stress in certain predictable ways. Moreover, this combination can be very different for different people. An analogy we find helpful is to characterize one's brain as "computer hardware," whereas psychological factors, including learning experiences, sociocultural factors, and personality characteristics, function as one's current "software." Although one cannot go out to a "brain store" and purchase new equipment, because of the brain's plasticity, new software (i.e., EC-PST tools) can both improve current software and enhance the hardware's capabilities (i.e., increase in activity in certain relevant parts of the brain, increase in cell connections, increase in grey matter in the brain). As part of the rationale of EC-PST, we suggest to clients that this approach, in part, is to help "retrain" the brain to react differently than before.

In addition, we argue that it is important to convey to clients that we do not wish to "eradicate" negative emotions, rather to minimize the negative impact these emotions may have on their overall well-being and functioning. Once again, we suggest that emotions play an important role in ultimately adapting well to stress—that is, they represent information or signals that something in one's life is "not right." In other words, negative emotions inform us "that a problem exists." As a means of explaining this concept, we often use the analogy posed by the rare genetic disease of congenital analgesia. This disease, present from birth, results in a complete insensitivity to physical pain. One's initial reaction to hearing about this at times is the wish to not be able to feel emotional pain. But we then ask clients what would happen to such people when they fall down. Of course the notion is that if they cannot feel the pain, they would be unable to determine the presence and/or extent of any damage. Thus, they may continue to walk with a broken foot, only to increase the damage. Also, not experiencing negative emotions inhibits greatly people's ability to recognize when problems occur. Without such recognition, problems are likely to become worse and exact increased negative impact. In this manner, we suggest that clients develop the framework that it is important to combine cognitive strengths with emotional reactions to best cope with stressful events in their lives.

Encourage Adoption of EC-PST Terminology

In keeping with the aforementioned notion underscoring the importance of conveying the just-mentioned conceptual framework to clients, we also suggest that therapists encourage clients to adopt EC-PST language when possible. For example, when directing clients to record or write down information, therapists should repeatedly note that this is an example of "externalization" or the strategy of "getting thoughts or images out of one's head onto paper" (see Chapter 8). Using EC-PST language can foster increased learning and understanding and promote effective applications of the skills.

EC-PST Therapists Need to Apply These Tools to Themselves

On the basis of training of thousands of clinicians during the past few decades in problem-solving programs, we believe that the most effective therapists for this approach are those who use problem-solving strategies in their own lives as a means of coping with stressful situations. This is why we request workshop participants to apply the various tools to one or more of their own personal/professional difficulties to foster a better understanding. Doing so is especially poignant if the stressful situation actually involves conducting EC-PST for the first time. For example, we have frequently observed beginning therapists demonstrate a predictable naiveté in their initial approach when addressing certain problem-orientation variables. Armed with a plethora of information concerning the types of selective thinking processes and negative appraisals and attributions associated with disorders such as depression and anxiety, student therapists often report surprise and frustration when clients resist changing these beliefs. They wonder why their clients are so stubborn or resistive. These students, however, are often wrestling with their own self-evaluations of competency and desire to be helpful and successful. Using the EC-PST perspective allows the beginning therapist to see how these fears are predictable problems in their own training that need to be solved.

In addition, an effective EC-PST therapist is one who also uses these strategies and principles as a guide to his or her clinical decision making and judgment. As introduced in Chapter 4, we have previously developed a comprehensive model of clinical decision-making based on a problem-solving formulation (Nezu & Nezu, 1989; Nezu, Nezu, & Cos, 2007). In essence, this model posits that a therapist needs to be flexible about developing individualized client treatment plans as well as being aware of the types of biases inherent in all human judgment. Use of the various problem-solving strategies, such as brainstorming a list of treatment strategies for a given client with a given set of symptoms, rather than engaging in a knee-jerk prescription based on the (possibly false) similarity between this client and others experiencing similar symptoms, can increase the likelihood that treatment will be ultimately effective.

EC-PST Emphasizes the Importance of Fostering Client's "Inner Awareness"

As indicated in Chapter 2, many emotions, and the reasons why we experience them (i.e., the person-specific stimulus that serves as a trigger of the affective reaction), often occur nonconsciously. In other words, the person can initially feel some form of arousal *prior* to being able to identify both the affect itself and the cause of the reaction. Thus, until individuals are more adept at recognizing such stimulus triggers and the subsequent types of reactions that usually occur, they may have minimal ability to attenuate the arousal, unfortunately, allowing the "emotional train to leave the station," that is, the emotions become more intense and thus, more difficult to regulate. Therefore, part of the goal of the "Stop and Slow Down" set of tools is to foster clients' abilities to focus on their inner emotional experiences as a means to better recognize when various (affective, cognitive, physical) changes occur so that they can subsequently better manage these changes/reactions—depressive, angry, anxious, and so forth in nature—and allow them to ultimately engage in a behavior (e.g., planful problem solving) that is more adaptive and appropriate.

EC-PST Encourages Exposure Versus Avoidance

As with most directive types of therapies, EC-PST encourages clients to "try something different" when attempting to deal with stressful problems. In other words, rather than avoiding such situations, this approach advocates having clients expose themselves to active attempts to cope with stressors. However, this may be a process of graduated steps working on problems that engender little distress and then continuously focusing on increasingly more difficult problems. What is crucial is the learning of the various EC-PST tools to apply them at a later point in time. We do not wish to teach people "how to swim when they are in the process of drowning." But we do want them to begin "dipping their feet in the water as an initial step toward learning to swim in the ocean."

EC-PST Emphasizes the Importance of Experiential Learning

Although a substantial aspect of EC-PST involves teaching new skills, as well as assisting clients to learn to apply "old skills in new ways," we strongly wish to underscore the importance of experiential learning. In other words, rather than simply convey or didactically teach the various tools, it is extremely important for clients to practice the skills in session, as well as via practice (i.e., homework) assignments between sessions. We argue that it is only in this manner that clients are actually able to apply the tools in an effective manner. As an analogy, a tennis coach does not hope that his or her student will learn to play simply by listening to various lectures. Rather, it is important for that student to practice (across different types of tennis courts) the various tennis skills to enhance his or her ability to actually play competently. Similarly, we encourage therapists to create multiple opportunities within each session for both didactics and practice activities.

THE THERAPIST–CLIENT RELATIONSHIP IN EC-PST

It is likely that most clinicians would argue that, in general, it is important for therapists to be perceived by their clients as warm, empathetic, trustworthy, and genuine. Such is the case with EC-PST. However, these types of characteristics, within the context of EC-PST, should be viewed as representing minimally required, but not sufficient, therapist skill areas. The EC-PST clinician is attempting to change long-term patterns of unsuccessful attempts at coping with stress, so it is possible that clients may perceive the therapist's attempts to do so as an attack upon their personality (i.e., it is their poor problem solving that is at fault). Thus, it is essential that the EC-PST clinician communicate an acceptance and respect for the individual, while explaining why certain habits or patterns may actually be working against his or her goals. Therapists must also realize that when attempting to change such well-learned behaviors, many people may experience fear, frustration, and anger. Such reactions can be directed toward the therapist and the therapy approach itself. In practicing the philosophy of EC-PST, the clinician needs to remain objective in observing, understanding, and analyzing these types of reactions (i.e., effective and appropriate problem definition techniques).

As in other forms of psychotherapy, the therapist–client relationship is important for a problem-solving approach. Although EC-PST can be thought of as consisting of various training modules, ignoring the importance of the therapist–client relationship can have a severe impact on the overall effectiveness of this approach. Particularly when clients are fearful of being independent because of poor self-esteem, they may have difficulties with learning strategies that will increase their self-efficacy and help them to function more independently. There may be less anxiety, initially, for such an individual to engage in a counseling approach that relies more on the therapist's problem-solving abilities that provide for a strong sense of social support. The approach that we believe communicates the most respect for a client is one in which the therapist approaches the case with confidence as a scientist to observe, question, test, and synthesize information, and *not* to fix everything.

In addition, the EC-PST clinician should attempt to strike a meaningful balance between being an active and directive practitioner and conveying a sense of collaboration with the client. Owing to the inherent psychoeducational flavor of EC-PST, we often present our role of the EC-PST therapist as a teacher, coach, or educator. Moreover, analogies, such as becoming a team of investigative reporters, detectives, or personal scientists, are often useful in characterizing this collaborative relationship. In other words, they help convey a sense of mutual exploration into the nature of a client's problems and experience of distress by creating a framework of being active members of a team working toward a mutual goal of getting to the bottom of the story, solving a mystery, or testing certain scientific hypotheses.

BUILDING A POSITIVE AND COLLABORATIVE TRAINING RELATIONSHIP

Some general guidelines that we have found helpful in developing a positive therapist–client relationship within the context of EC-PST are described in the following sections.

Display Warmth, Empathy, and Genuineness

Although many psychotherapies incorporate these positive therapeutic characteristics, there are certain applications to EC-PST interventions that make them particularly important. In addition to showing that one cares about a participant's well-being, expressing warmth by way of kind, gentle, and patient guidance through this new and uncertain way of coping can do much to reduce the tendency for the client to reject a new learning experience because it may represent unchartered territory. Empathy expressed through careful listening when clients describe their problems and concerns, recognizing their feelings, and communicating one's understanding of such problems and concerns can serve as important steps toward increasing hopefulness that learning these EC-PST skills will be relevant and effective for them. It is also important for the clinician to identify a given client's strengths and to convey that these strengths will serve as "building blocks" upon which to build further skills. One can show genuineness by being a "real person" in the relationship; using self-disclosure, if and when appropriate (i.e., one's own problem-solving mistakes and successes), and answering a client's questions and concerns honestly and respectfully without being patronizing or condescending. It is important to be genuine regarding the realistic ways in which problem solving may help the person's life. For example, if coping somewhat more flexibly and creatively can improve one's life satisfaction by 10%, 20%, or 50% (vs. perfectly), the philosophy to instill is as follows—"Why reject the opportunity to improve your well-being?"

Convey Enthusiasm and Belief in the Intervention

To maximize feelings of hope and expectations of benefit in participants, it is important to emphasize the relevance and effectiveness of problem-solving training for a given individual's life. Thus, it is helpful if the therapist is familiar with the relevant EC-PST outcome literature such as that given in Chapter 3. In addition, conveying confidence in this approach is often best communicated by therapists who actually use and have personal confidence in problem solving. The clinician should explain that this approach can help them cope more effectively with stressful problems and reduce the negative impact of stress on their emotional and physical well-being to better achieve their life goals. It is important to convey to the client that EC-PST is *not* just for people who are poor problem solvers. In other words, one should emphasize the fact that it helps good problem solvers to become even *better* problem solvers, as well as better teachers of problem solving (e.g., teaching their children to become effective problem solvers), and that it helps clients learn how to apply their problem-solving strengths (e.g., those applied to a work situation) to new (e.g., those required to improve a relationship) problems.

Encourage Participation

Although much didactics do occur in this approach, the therapist needs to conduct EC-PST in an interactive manner that encourages as much participation by the client as possible. This is in keeping with the metamessage that EC-PST should foster experiential learning. The major training methods for encouraging participation include in vivo rehearsal and role playing, as well as between-session practice assignments. Rehearsal involves guided practice in solving hypothetical and real problems in the training sessions, and practice assignments involve supervised practice in applying the various tools to real-life current problems. We strongly emphasize the wisdom of the old Chinese adage regarding the most effective teaching approach:

> *Tell me, and I will probably forget.*
> *Show me, and I might remember.*
> *Involve me, and I will understand.*

BASIC EC-PST TRAINING STRATEGIES

Similar to many other directive forms of psychotherapy or counseling, in particular those under a cognitive and behavioral umbrella, the success of EC-PST to a large degree depends on the effectiveness of the manner in which it is actually implemented. Therefore, in this section, we describe several general instructional or training principles regarding how to optimally conduct EC-PST.

Psychoeducation/Didactics

EC-PST involves imparting substantial psychoeducational knowledge, using verbal instructions and written materials, while also making use of the Socratic approach to instruction, which emphasizes questions and discussions that encourage clients to think for themselves and formulate their own conclusions, deductions, and elaborations. Such instruction is consistent with the overall problem-solving goal of facilitating independent productive thinking.

Coaching

Coaching primarily involves verbal prompting, such as asking leading questions, providing suggestions, and offering instructions. For example, the EC-PST therapist can prompt a client during a brainstorming exercise to begin the process of generating alternative solutions or ask the client about times when he or she applied a given problem-solving skill during a stressful situation.

Modeling

This includes written and verbal problem-solving examples and demonstrations conducted by the therapist, using hypothetical as well as real problems, presented by the client. This can be done in vivo, through filmed or pictorial presentation, or through role-plays. On occasion, EC-PST clinicians have found it helpful in group settings to use brief movie or film clips that illustrate how certain characters engage in effective and/or ineffective problem-solving attempts. To facilitate learning and to help clients discriminate more effectively, it is important at times to model both correct *and* incorrect ways of applying various problem-solving principles.

Shaping

This can involve specific training in the various tools in progressive steps, with each new step being contingent on successful performance in the previous step. In addition, it can be useful to develop a hierarchy of a client's problems, on the basis of dimensions of severity or complexity, such that less intense or difficult problems may then be used as relevant examples early in treatment. Once the client has mastered certain prerequisite EC-PST skills, more difficult problems can then be addressed. Shaping can also refer to the therapist providing more guidance in the beginning of the intervention and then requiring the client to become more involved in a given task, such as generating alternative solutions to a problem.

Rehearsal and Practice

These techniques involve EC-PST practice in in-session and between-session exercises. In addition to written exercises and assignments, rehearsal may involve role-playing, practice in imagination (covert rehearsal), and practice with real-life problematic situations. The use of visualization, one of the foundational multitasking skills in EC-PST, can be useful when applied to rehearsing newly learned skills. In addition, practice assignments are a particularly important feature of any skill acquisition program. Without practice, the ability to actually implement the various EC-PST tools in real life can be compromised.

Performance Feedback

Feedback about a client's in-session and outside-of-session activities should be provided on an ongoing basis. These include activities documented in the client's self-monitoring and self-evaluation forms, including practice forms.

Positive Reinforcement

This includes the therapist's positive feedback for trying to apply various EC-PST tools in general as well as specific reinforcement of a given act, even if not perfect. For example, although clients may continue to react to a problem with worry or a high degree of emotional distress (i.e., negative problem orientation), they may also be simultaneously attempting to brainstorm creative solutions. The specific act of generating alternatives should be reinforced and accompanied with feedback that a more positive orientation could further enhance the benefits of applying that specific skill.

Use of Analogies and Metaphors

Using analogies and metaphors (where appropriate) can be very helpful as a means of better illustrating various points or ideas. For example, the therapist can use skills or knowledge bases (e.g., sports, cooking, driving, hobbies) as a means of explaining the concept that skills, such as problem solving, often take time to learn and that practice is usually required before someone becomes competent or expert in that skill. Another example we frequently use involves American football. We ask clients (who are familiar with this sport): "What is the better play to use when you are one touchdown away from winning the game and there are only 2 minutes left in the game—a running play or a passing play?" We are usually met with various "it depends" statements—that is, it depends on a wide range of considerations, such as how talented the various players are, who is on the opposite team, how many timeouts one has left, what are the weather conditions? We use this answer and context to help explain that real-life problems frequently are like this question—there are a number of "it depends" considerations that ultimately require application of the various tools to obtain "the best answer," rather than acting impulsively.

PROBLEM-SOLVING THERAPY DOS AND DON'TS

The following list of EC-PST dos and don'ts is offered as important considerations based on decades of experience conducting and training various problem-solving–based programs, both in clinical and research settings. Many of these are consistent with the metamessages described earlier.

1. *DO NOT present EC-PST in a mechanistic manner.*—EC-PST should be as interactive as possible. Consider this type of therapy as an opportunity for individuals to discover, share, learn, and grow. "Dryly" teaching the various problem-solving skills is likely to be received poorly—although EC-PST is learning experience, it should not be purely academic, but experiential.

2. *DO make EC-PST relevant to a particular client or group.*—Training examples should be specific and relevant to the participant(s) at hand. Do not deliver a canned treatment that does not incorporate relevant life experiences of a given individual or group. This is why it is important to conduct a sufficiently comprehensive assessment early during therapy. For example, when initially explaining the SPS model of stress/distress, it is very helpful to elicit personal and relevant examples from the client's life. This should be conducted in an atmosphere of respecting the client's values.

3. *DO include opportunities to practice the skills in session and between sessions.*—As mentioned earlier, practice is an important component of EC-PST; clients should be encouraged to practice as much as possible between EC-PST sessions. However, note that with certain individuals,

the term *homework* can be negatively associated with tedious school assignments. Terms such as *opportunities to practice, personal missions,* or *assignments* (or other creative terms) will likely garner a better reception.

4. *DO focus on the client as well as the treatment itself.*—Although correctly implementing EC-PST is important to ensure its effectiveness, the client himself or herself should always be the primary focus of attention. Consistently demonstrate respect for clients' feelings and foster the idea that they can use negative emotions as important information that can help them clarify what is important to their lives.

5. *DO NOT focus only on "superficial" problems.*—The therapist needs to use his or her own clinical decision-making skills to assess whether the problems being discussed are in fact the most crucial for a given client; otherwise, the effectiveness of treatment will be limited. For example, a superficial problem might involve helping a client to get more dates, when the more important or core issue might entail coping with the fear of committing to an intimate relationship.

6. *DO remember that even creative and effective solution ideas require a solid action plan that needs to be carried out.*—The client should be encouraged to implement the solution plan (or parts thereof) to obtain the best feedback possible (i.e., problem resolution).

7. *DO NOT equate problem-focused coping with problem-solving coping.*— We define *problem-solving coping* as the more general process of dealing with stressful situations. Problem-solving coping entails both *problem-focused* coping (i.e., strategies to change the nature of the situation so that it no longer represents a problem) and *emotion-focused* coping (i.e., strategies geared to minimize emotional distress related to the problem and enhance emotional regulation). Clients should be encouraged to be aware of their emotions as useful information concerning their goals and important values. In addition, the therapist needs to convey to clients that both forms of coping are advisable depending on the nature of the situation. For instance, if a problem is perceived as unchangeable (e.g., the other person involved in an interpersonal problem is unwilling to change), a potentially viable and effective solution alternative might be understanding that the situation will not change and to foster one's acceptance of that perspective. Often, problems require both types of problem-solving

strategies. For example, the individual who is experiencing problems with a difficult coworker may need to identify several goals, such as (a) acknowledging and managing one's own emotional reactions, (b) changing one's current interpretations that the fellow employee is "out to get me," and (c) brainstorming ways to change the nature of his or her interpersonal interactions.

8. *DO use handouts as adjuncts to training.*—Written handouts help clients to remember and practice the skills between sessions. Often it may be useful to encourage the participants to purchase a loose-leaf–type notebook to store the handouts for current and future reference. Again, it would be important to adapt such handouts to be relevant to a given target population. We have found handouts to be an extremely useful and effective training tool in both our research and clinical work.

9. *DO conduct an adequate assessment of a client's problem-solving strengths and limitations.*—Do not assume that "all clients are equal" and conduct EC-PST accordingly (unless required as part of a controlled clinical research study).

10. *BE SURE to address each participant's concerns if conducting EC-PST in a group format.*—It is possible that there may be one or two individuals within the group who tend to monopolize the session. Others may be very quiet and hesitant to participate. Be sure to manage the group such that all members can benefit equally from a group venue. Encourage all members to participate and limit those who tend to dominate.

SUMMARY

This chapter was geared to provide an overall context within which to conduct EC-PST as a means of maximizing its efficacy. This began with a discussion of various metamessages that represent important principles and precepts of the EC-PST approach to treatment. This was followed by a description of how to foster a positive therapist–client relationship. Next, we provided a number of adjunctive instructional strategies and guidelines that can be used to enhance clients' overall learning and skill acquisition. Last, on the basis of our research and clinical practice involving EC-PST, we provided a listing of dos and don'ts that we believe greatly enhance the efficacy of this approach.

REFERENCES

Nezu, A. M., & Nezu, C. M. (Eds.). (1989). *Clinical decision making in behavior therapy: A problem-solving perspective*. Champaign, IL: Research Press.

Nezu, A. M., Nezu, C. M., & Cos, T. A. (2007). Case formulation for the behavioral and cognitive therapies: A problem-solving perspective. In T. D. Eells (Ed.), *Handbook of psychotherapy case formulation* (2nd ed., pp. 349–378). New York, NY: Guilford Press.

Snyder, C. R. (2002). Hope theory: Rainbows in the mind. *Psychological Inquiry, 13*, 249–275. doi:10.1207/S15327965PLI1304_01

OVERVIEW OF THE EC-PST THERAPY PROCESS, INTRODUCTORY SESSIONS, AND THE CASES OF "MEGAN," "DAVID," AND "MARK"

6

This chapter represents the beginning of our revised emotion-centered problem-solving therapy (EC-PST) manual. We start by delineating the components comprising the overall therapy process, followed by a description of the introductory remarks that includes treatment rationales. Last, we provide brief summaries of three clients—"Megan," "David," and "Mark"—whom we follow throughout the manual to illustrate a variety of training strategies and tools comprising EC-PST.[1]

ADJUNCTIVE RESOURCES

Note that the first chapter of the Client Workbook, "Solving Life's Problems: A Guide to Becoming a More Effective Problem Solver," can be given to a client as an adjunct to face-to-face treatment (see the Preface of this book for information on obtaining the Client Workbook). Moreover, it can be provided to clients as material that can be reviewed at home to reinforce the philosophy that effective learning and skill acquisition require active between-session activities and effort.

Additional resources for clients include a web-based course titled, Moving Forward, which is based on our work (Nezu, Nezu, & D'Zurilla, 2013) and was developed for the Department of Veterans Affairs (www.veterantraining.va.gov),

---

[1]Although these three individuals represent actual clients, their names and essential demographic characteristics were changed to protect their confidentiality. In addition, samples of client dialogues contained throughout the manual have also been modified to both more efficiently illustrate a point and continue to preserve anonymity.

as well as a smartphone app also titled Moving Forward that is available at the app store. Although the free web course was originally designed to be used by U.S. veterans and active service members, it can be used by anyone interested in learning to apply the basic EC-PST principles. The smartphone app, also free, is geared more for the general public. Both programs can be used as adjuncts to formal therapy or counseling.

THE PROBLEM-SOLVING THERAPY PROCESS

EC-PST encompasses the following major intervention components across the overall course of treatment:

1. Assessment and Treatment Planning
2. Introductory Session(s)
3. Training in Tool Kit #1—Planful Problem Solving: Fostering Effective Problem Solving
4. Training in Tool Kit #2—Problem-Solving Multitasking: Overcoming "Brain Overload"
5. Training in Tool Kit #3—Enhancing Motivation for Action: Overcoming Reduced Motivation and Feelings of Hopelessness
6. Training in Tool Kit #4—"Stop and Slow Down": Overcoming Emotional Dysregulation
7. Guided Practice
8. Future Forecasting and Termination

The order of training in these tool kits represents our recommendations for use in research (e.g., clinical trials) and structured group programs. If providing training to an individual, we strongly recommend following the clinical decision-making guidelines delineated in Chapter 4 (see Table 4.1). This would require that therapists conduct a comprehensive assessment to best understand an individual's clinical picture. As also noted in Chapter 4, this involves the following four EC-PST–specific assessments:

*   Assessment of general SPS abilities and attitudes
*   Assessment of current and previous SPS activities
*   Assessment of problems, stressful difficulties, major negative life events, and/or traumatic events recently or currently experienced by a given client or client population

- Assessment of outcome variables related to presenting problems and emotion reactivity vulnerabilities

On the basis of the results of this assessment process, in conjunction with findings from the typical evaluation of additional standard demographic and clinical areas (e.g., daily functioning, client's stated treatment goals), the clinician can begin to determine whether EC-PST is an appropriate treatment option for a given individual (see Chapter 4 for EC-PST–related treatment planning considerations). Assuming this assessment leads the therapist to recommend EC-PST to clients and assuming that they agree to this, the next step in treatment involves providing them with a more complete rationale for EC-PST while establishing a positive rapport.

INTRODUCTORY SESSIONS

Introductory Sessions: Therapeutic Goals

The goals of the introductory session (or sessions) in EC-PST include the following:

- To foster a positive therapist–client relationship
- To present an overview and rationale of EC-PST
- To encourage optimism

Establishing a Positive Relationship

Using the guidelines presented in Chapter 5, during the initial sessions with a new client it is important to develop a positive therapeutic relationship. Therapists should begin by introducing themselves (e.g., one's professional background and current role regarding this client's overall treatment) and presenting a brief overview of anticipated activities (e.g., "you and I will be working together to try to reduce some of the distress that you are currently experiencing"). A useful initial starting point is to ask clients about their "story." In other words, what is currently occurring in their lives that has led them to seek help. We have found it helpful in the beginning sessions to ask the following set of questions—"What do you hope to see happen by coming here?" (i.e., global goals), and "What is currently happening in your life that prevents or makes it difficult for you to get there without a therapist's help?" (i.e., extant obstacles to such goals). This "story" provides a context that will be repeated throughout EC-PST; that is, it conceptualizes the overall therapy process as a mutual effort to "solve the person's problem(s)."

Another area of early inquiry involves identifying recent major stressors that the individual may have experienced (e.g., divorce, rape, traffic accident, loss of job, chronic illness). If individuals were referred by a medical team for psychosocial complications (e.g., depression, pain) related to a physical illness, it is important to ask them about their subjective experience (e.g., "Tell me about your experiences—how has [e.g., cancer] affected your life thus far?" vs. "Give me the specifics of your medical treatment"). This approach has been reported by clients as comforting because of the relief that someone is willing to discuss the impact of an illness, such as cancer or heart failure, when so many friends and family members may have been avoidant and fearful of discussing such topics.

In addition, when discussing clients' experience of a major stressor, it is important to ask questions regarding how their life has *changed* (e.g., what are their predominant reactions, the reactions of the family, or the effects on their job and friends). This information can be augmented by data gleaned from previously completed questionnaires or inventories, especially those addressing the nature and type of problems that individuals are currently experiencing (e.g., problem checklists). It is helpful at this stage to elicit from the person whether and how the major stressful event, such as loss of a job, has exacerbated negative emotional reactions to existing daily stressors (e.g., traffic jams, long lines at the grocery store, or minor arguments with family members), as well as creating new stressful problems (e.g., reduced resources for the family, inability to pay rent, or negative image of self).

During a client's responses to these types of inquiries, it is important to use counseling strategies geared to enhance the therapist–client relationship (e.g., reflection of content and feeling—"It sounds like you felt your whole world fell apart when this happened"). Finally, as in almost all treatment approaches, it is critical for any therapeutic relationship that the clinician display warmth, support, genuine interest, and a sense of commitment to the client.

If clients also have a comorbid medical illness, it is possible that such individuals may be reluctant to see the need for a "mental health professional" even when referred by a medical team when the self-perception is that they only have a physical illness. Therefore, it may be helpful to emphasize one's role as a teacher or coach (i.e., to help clients sort through this experience and acquire new skills to foster their ability to cope with the illness), rather than conducting intensive psychotherapy or analysis. In addition, the therapist should underscore the notion of teamwork and mutual respect (e.g., "You will help me to understand how your life has changed and the new problems you have encountered, and I will teach you how people can learn to become more effective at coping with many of these types of difficulties created by this medical illness").

Presenting the Rationale

After obtaining a brief version of the client's story, it becomes important early in treatment to provide an overview of EC-PST that includes a rationale for why it is relevant to, and potentially effective for, *this* individual. Providing a rationale increases the likelihood that both the therapist and client be "on the same page" (i.e., where the client understands and agrees with the underlying precepts and philosophy of EC-PST) and, thus, can enhance the likelihood that this treatment will be successful. In doing so, the rationale should be presented in "lay terms," with the clinician mindful of avoiding jargon and being a "talking head" lecturer. Instead, the information about EC-PST and its potential effectiveness needs to be conveyed within a therapeutic context and with many examples drawn from the real world (e.g., other clients) as well as *this* client's real world (i.e., using examples previously provided by the individual to illustrate various points, such as how major life events can create additional problems). Moreover, it is important for the therapist to appropriately adapt words and language in concert with the client's developmental, educational, and cultural background.

We believe the following to be concepts and issues that are critical to include in the rationale provided to all clients. How much time is devoted to any one topic is heavily dependent on the relevance for a particular individual. (The reader is directed to Chapters 1 through 3 for more specific information.)

- The impact of early life stress on current reactions to difficult problems (emphasize the *stress sensitization* hypothesis)
- The negative effects of stressful events, including major negative life changes, chronic daily stressors, and traumatic events on one's health and mental health (emphasize the *stress generation* hypothesis)
- How the body is evolutionarily geared to react to stress (i.e., threats to one's well-being) with a "fight, flight, or freeze" reaction, but few threats exist in one's current life that are life-threatening
- How continuous stress, if left unchecked, can have significant negative effects on several parts of *everyone's* body and brain (i.e., emphasize the ubiquity of such responses), such that the ultimate reaction is likely to be clinical levels of distress (e.g., depression, anxiety)

- How our brains are hardwired to react to emotional stimuli in such a way that at times results in misperceived threats

- How the brain can be rewired via new learning experiences to become more resilient to stress

- How improving one's coping ability (via EC-PST skills) can decrease the negative impact of life stress

- How research has demonstrated that this approach, as a means of improving one's coping ability, has a strong scientific support base

- The skills taught in this intervention are similar to other types of skills (e.g., driving, sports, music, cooking) in that, similar to other skills, beginners are likely to feel awkward, nervous, and potentially skeptical; to become competent (and even expert) at such skills, one needs to practice

An example of a therapist's rationale follows. Note that this description should always include multiple pauses to provide frequent opportunities for the client to ask questions or render reactions. However, *note that this sample is not meant to imply that the therapist memorize the "script."* Rather, it provides a sample flow of how to present information important to the rationale. More important, pieces of the following rationale should be presented throughout in a conversational manner, rather than as a lecture.

Sample Treatment Rationale

This approach, called, emotion-centered problem-solving therapy, or EC-PST, *is based on the notion that one major reason why people experience long-lasting depression, anxiety, anger, and other forms of emotional distress is the overwhelming effects of stress on one's physical and emotional health. Lots of research has demonstrated that stress has very significant and specific effects on one's body, brain, and emotional well-being.*

Stress can take the form of major events, traumatic events, as well as daily hassles that can collectively add up to become a much larger source of stress. [Note: Insert here specific examples already discussed by the client.] *Often major negative events create new minor problems; for instance, the loss of a job can lead to many additional problems, such as loss of income, negative self-esteem, and needing to obtain a new job.*

On the contrary, someone experiencing many smaller, but continuous problems, such as arguments with a spouse, financial hassles, and parent–child relationship difficulties, can eventually experience a major negative life event, such as getting a divorce, because of the chronic nature of the problems. [Note: Again, if possible, the therapist should try to illustrate these points using examples directly from the client's life.]

Let's think about divorce as an example. It is not only a difficult major life change, which is stressful in and of itself, but also frequently creates additional stressful problems, including the possibility of having to move one's home, potentially having to find new schools for one's children, having to find new resources (e.g., bank, grocery store, drug store), feeling lonely and wanting companionship, and so forth. Furthermore, emotions are often mixed and involve multiple people. Problems with finances and extended family members are also common. These can all be very, very stressful.

Unfortunately, such stress can lead to more distress. Moreover, increases in distress will lead to increases in stressful problems. For example, being upset by a divorce can lead to inappropriate parenting behaviors, which can then lead to additional parent–child relationship problems. This stress–distress downward spiral can eventually lead to despair and hopelessness. As an ancient Persian proverb suggests—"If fortune turns against you, even jelly can break your teeth."

Bottom line, stress can lead to more stress, as well as more distress. We refer to this process as stress generation. *In other words, when we have difficulty handling or coping with stress, more stressful problems can occur.* [Note: If relevant, include the following: "This is especially true if the major event is the onset and treatment of a serious medical illness, such as cancer, heart disease, or diabetes, as this usually leads to multiple stressful problems beyond the illness itself."]

Moreover, depending on how much stress we may have had earlier in our lives while growing up, our bodies and brains can react in a way that becomes more sensitive to further stress. For example, sometimes having a bruise or broken leg makes that area of the body more sensitive to touch or additional trauma. Therefore, it takes less stress to make us upset, tense, annoyed, or uptight than not having the bruise or broken leg from the beginning. This is called stress sensitivity. *In other words, if we experienced a lot of stress earlier in our lives, it can make our bodies and brains more sensitive to stress later on, and consequently, we react more strongly to even less intense levels of stress that we are experiencing now. In other words, early stress can make our bodies and brains more vulnerable and it takes less stress to get us upset.* (Note: If relevant, the therapist should illustrate these points using examples from the client's earlier experiences. In addition, if appropriate, the clinician can illustrate how this has occurred for this client by connecting his or her Emotion Reactivity scores to his or her current distress.)

Does this mean you are crazy or weak or stupid? Of course not! At times, for a variety of reasons, the amount of stress we experience can be so great that it overwhelms us and we are unable to know exactly what to do. Sometimes we want to run away and hide or at other times we try to "attack" the source of stress in an impulsive way just to make it go away. This is a common reaction.

Specifically, when our brains become aware of a threat, our bodies react in a way that alerts us to that threat in an extremely fast manner, and begin to undergo various changes as a means of helping us to get ready to deal with the threat. This is called the fight, flight, or freeze response. *Our bodies are getting ready to either fight the threat or run away to get out of harm's way. Sometimes we are stunned and feel that we are unable to move, either emotionally or physically—that is, we freeze!*

Under stress, the heart begins to pump faster to get the blood flowing throughout the body, our immune system sends out certain types of cells to be prepared for an enemy's (e.g., germs) attack, and our breathing gets faster and shallower because our lungs are trying to get in more oxygen to supply the body. Unfortunately, most often, the threats in everyday life are not combat warfare, or dinosaurs, or tigers trying to eat us. Rather, they often represent psychological and emotional threats, such as frustration from being in a bad traffic jam; not having enough money to pay this month's rent or mortgage; having to listen to a supervisor yell at us for a mistake we made; or having constant arguments with a coworker, family member, or spouse.

Despite the differences in the objective nature of the threats, nevertheless, our bodies react the same. When the stress is continuous, the body's reaction is also continuous. Unfortunately, our bodies are not made to sustain such constant stress reactions. Continuous stress puts a major strain on our bodies and brains. If nothing helps to change this situation, negative consequences can occur, including health problems, such as heart disease, and emotional problems, such as depression and anxiety.

So what can we do? What we need to do is to "rewire" our brains to be able to become more resistant to stress. We need to be able to become better able to cope with stress so that it no longer leads to emotional difficulties or physical problems. The good news is that this is possible! In other words, research has shown that through different learning experiences, we can actually rewire our brains to become more resilient to stress!

What can help reduce this stress? There are many things that can help reduce, minimize, or prevent stress from turning into distress. These can include the types of resources we have access to. For example, having family and friends can provide a strong source of social support to help us handle the stress. A second very significant factor is the manner in which we cope with stress. Different people find various coping strategies to be helpful. These can include prayer, humor, exercise, and relaxation exercises. This program involves teaching you a variety of problem-solving tools to help you deal more effectively with stress.

*Problem solving can be thought of as a set of skills or tools that people use to handle, cope with, or resolve difficult situations encountered in life. The type of problem solving I am talking about here is often referred to as **social** problem solving, to highlight the notion that there are different skills involved in attempting to solve stressful problems in real life versus the kinds of intellectual or purely academic problems that we had to solve on tests in school. That's because real-life problems that are stressful usually are connected to strong* *emotions. The parts of the brain needed to solve stressful problems can differ from the parts of the brain needed to solve arithmetic problems or crossword puzzles.*

Research has demonstrated that social problem solving is composed of two major components. The first is called problem orientation. *This involves people's beliefs and attitudes about stressful problems and their ability to deal with them. In a way, think of it as one's worldview about problems or the type of glasses one sees through when looking at the world and thinking about problems. There are two types of orientations—one is positive in nature and one is negative. The second major component is referred to as one's* problem-solving style. *This involves the general way that people attempt to deal with stressful problems. The most effective style is called* planful *problem solving, in which the approach is mainly thoughtful and systematic in nature. Two other general styles have been identified—both being ineffective—an avoidant problem-solving style and an impulsive or careless problem-solving style.*

The therapist should next describe the two different types of orientations (Box 6.1) at this point, as well as the three types of problem-solving styles

---

BOX 6.1 ■ CHARACTERISTICS OF A POSITIVE AND NEGATIVE PROBLEM ORIENTATION

Positive Orientation (the "Optimist")
Involves the tendency for individuals to:
- Appraise problems as challenges.
- Be optimistic in believing that problems are solvable.
- Have a strong sense of self-efficacy regarding their ability to cope with problems.
- Understand that successful problem solving involves time and effort.
- View negative emotions as an integral part of the overall problem-solving process, which can ultimately be helpful in coping with stressful problems.

Negative Orientation (the "Pessimist")
Involves the tendency for individuals to:
- View problems as threats.
- Expect problems to be unsolvable.
- Have doubts about one's ability to cope with problems successfully.
- Become particularly frustrated and upset when faced with problems or confronted with negative emotions.

(Box 6.2). The clinician should also describe the differences between an overall "effective" problem solver (i.e., one who has a positive orientation and primarily uses a planful problem-solving approach) versus an overall "ineffective" problem solver (i.e., one who is represented by a negative problem orientation and uses an impulsive problem-solving style, an avoidant style, or both). Next, the therapist should begin to describe the major components of social problem solving, how they are related to negative health and mental health problems, and how they can be translated into training modules all geared toward improving the individual's ability to cope more effectively

---

BOX 6.2 ■ CHARACTERISTICS OF THE THREE PROBLEM-SOLVING STYLES

Planful Problem Solving (the "Planful Problem Solver")
This is a constructive problem-solving style, which involves systematic and thoughtful application of the following set of specific skills:
- *Problem Definition* (clarifying the nature of a problem, setting realistic goals, identifying those obstacles that prevent one from reaching such goals)
- *Generation of Alternatives* (thinking of a range of possible solution strategies geared to overcome the identified obstacles)
- *Decision-Making* (predicting the likely consequences of these various alternatives, conducting a cost–benefit analysis based on these identified outcomes, developing a solution plan that is geared to achieve the problem-solving goals)
- *Solution Implementation and Verification* (carrying out the solution plan, monitoring and evaluating the consequences of the plan, determining whether one's problem-solving efforts have been successful or need to continue)

Impulsive/Careless Style (the "Quick Fixer")
This is a maladaptive problem-solving approach that involves impulsive or careless attempts at problem resolution. Such attempts are narrow, hurried, and incomplete. Such individuals typically consider only a few solution alternatives, often impulsively going with the first idea that comes to mind. In addition, they scan alternative solutions and consequences quickly, carelessly, and unsystematically, and monitor solution outcomes carelessly and inadequately.

Avoidant Style ("the Avoider")
This dysfunctional pattern is characterized by procrastination, passivity, inaction, and dependency on others. This "type" of problem solver prefers to avoid problems rather than confronting them "head on," puts off problem solving for as long as possible, waits for problems to resolve on their own, and attempts to shift the responsibility for solving problems to other people.

with stress as a means of decreasing extant emotional and health problems. The following is a sample therapist presentation:

The importance of focusing on one's social problem-solving skills and abilities can be especially understood when looking at the research about differences between effective problem solvers and ineffective problem solvers. Basically, ineffective problem solving has been found to be strongly associated with high levels of depression, anxiety, suicidal thinking and attempts, hopelessness, pessimism, anger proneness, substance abuse, criminal activities, poor self-esteem, work stress, pain, and worsening of medical symptoms.

On the contrary, effective problem solving has been linked to more effective overall coping, higher levels of optimism, social adjustment, positive mood, better life satisfaction, higher levels of hope, more motivation, and better overall well-being. Given these findings, I am suggesting that you and I work together to help you become a better problem solver and to more effectively manage all the stress in your life.

In general, this treatment approach can help you to learn how to do the following: How to think of problems as challenges rather than aversive threats, how to approach problems in an adaptive manner (i.e., a head-on approach vs. avoidance), how to improve your problem-solving style (i.e., planful vs. impulsive and avoidant), how to define problems and set goals, how to understand why the situation is a problem, how to accurately identify major obstacles, how to set realistic goals, how to invent and to create new solutions to problems, how to make effective decisions, how to carry out a solution or action plan, and how to validate the outcome of the solution.

In addition, this program teaches you how to become more aware of, better understand, and more effectively manage your negative emotions. In essence, we suggest that negative emotions serve a very important role in your life—to let you know that something is "not right in your life"—it may feel silly to state this when you are feeling upset to begin with and you know that, What I am suggesting is how your automatic emotional reactions often "dictate" how you continue to feel, to think, and to act. Negative arousal often makes it difficult to think logically and rationally. When you are very upset, how do you react when someone says, "Just calm down"? You probably get more upset and your thinking gets cloudy. The last thing you can do is be a good problem solver. So, I can also teach you skills to help you better manage these emotions—not to get rid of them—as I said before, as they are important sources of information, but to minimize the negative impact they may have on your ability to make good decisions and cope with difficult situations.

I view all of these skills as an important way of successfully approaching and coping with life's problems—the types of problems that led you to see someone like me. In essence, you will learn a set of skills that can be applied to all types of problems—those that you are currently experiencing and those that you might encounter in the future. To a large extent, it's like the old saying—"Give a person a fish, he eats for a day ... teach a person to fish, he eats for a lifetime." This program is like learning to fish—you will be able to use these skills throughout your lifetime.

What Kind of Problem Solver Are You?

At this point, it can be helpful for the therapist to engage in a discussion that basically asks clients to self-identify the orientation and style they believe matches their own past and current beliefs and actions, as well as to note any situation-behavior variability (i.e., differences in one's orientation or style depending on the situation). If clients have previously completed a Social Problem-Solving Inventory–Revised (SPSI–R; see Chapter 4), the therapist can provide an overview of the results and discuss their meanings. During this general discussion, it is important to highlight the following:

- Knowing one's orientation and style at this point is helpful to better understand one's strengths and areas in need of improvement. We advocate using the expression that "knowledge is power" (Sir Francis Bacon).

- Some people have differing orientations and/or styles depending on the nature of the problem—one aspect of EC-PST can be geared toward helping individuals "transfer" their effective coping strategies to other areas of one's life (i.e., successful use of problem-solving at work can be applied to difficulties in relationships).

- Having emotional and/or psychosocial difficulties at present does not imply that a person is or has always been an ineffective problem solver; rather, sometimes the stress is so overwhelming or the problem is very new or complex such that additional teaching, training, and practice in how to cope with such stress becomes necessary.

- One's problem orientation and/or style(s) do not represent personality traits. Rather, they represent long-standing patterns of coping that can be changed and improved.

In conducting such a discussion, the therapist can refer to parts of the Client Workbook (for availability, see the Preface of this book). For example, in helping clients to better understand their problem-solving orientation and style, they are guided to think about a recent problem as a means of "matching" attitudes and actions to these problem-solving dimensions.

One activity that can be helpful here is to ask the client to describe how different types of problem solvers might react to a variety of different hypothetical situations (see sample problems in the subsequent text). This type of discussion can lead to additional insight into the client's understanding of these concepts as well as to provide further learning opportunities.

Sample problems (the therapist is encouraged to think of additional sample problems, especially those that are relevant to a given client):

- *Football*: A team with a rather weak offense is currently in the "red zone" and the score is tied. The other team is known to have a very strong offense. It is the fourth quarter, third down, and time is running out.

- *Traffic:* A counselor, Jane, lives 90 minutes away from the medical center. She is stuck in traffic because of a serious car accident that just happened and is at least an hour away from work. Traffic is totally stopped. She has an 8:00 a.m. appointment with a seriously ill client.

- *Rent:* John's rent is due tomorrow, but he has no means of paying for it. This is not the first time, and he is worried that he may be evicted. While walking outside, he finds a wallet with $150 in it as well as the person's ID.

In addition, results from any formal assessments previously conducted, such as a completed Social Problem-Solving Self-Monitoring (SPSSM) form, the SPSI–R, or the Problem-Solving Test (see Chapter 4 and the Client Workbook) can augment this discussion. Of particular importance is to determine whether the client has accurately identified his or her correct orientation and style when compared with these more objective results. If there is a significant discrepancy, this should be pointed out with an ensuing discussion to determine why such a discrepancy occurred.

Overview of the Four Problem-Solving "Tool Kits"

Part of the rationale should include a brief overview of the four EC-PST tool kits. We use the term *tool kit* to underscore the notion that we are teaching a set of skills and providing individuals with a set of tools that can help them cope more effectively with stressful problems as a means of reducing extant negative symptoms. On the contrary, if the therapist feels more comfortable using other language (e.g., therapy components) or believes that the client would be more accepting of differing language, we have no inherent reason to insist that such language be used.

In describing these tool kits for the first time, the therapist should provide a brief rationale for why these specific strategies are included. In essence, EC-PST provides tools to help an individual reach a set of goals, including solving a variety of stressful problems. We conceptualize the four tool kits as the means by which we can help people overcome certain general obstacles that often prevent or make it difficult to reach such goals. The four major sets of obstacles to reaching one's goals, which the four tool kits map onto, are as follows:

- Ineffective problem solving (Tool Kit #1—*Planful Problem Solving*)
- Stimulus overload (Tool Kit #2—*Problem-Solving Multitasking: Overcoming "Brain Overload"*)
- Low motivation and feelings of hopelessness (Tool Kit #3—*Enhancing Motivation for Action : Overcoming Low Motivation and Feelings of Hopelessness*)
- Emotional dysregulation under stress (Tool Kit #4—*"Stop and Slow Down": Overcoming Emotional Dysregulation*)

As suggested earlier in Chapter 4, whether all strategies in all tool kits are taught and emphasized is greatly dependent on the assessment of a client's problem-solving and emotion regulation strengths and limitations, as well as the therapist's clinical judgment regarding the relevance and importance of other related factors, such as the anticipated length of treatment, the severity of negative symptoms, and the subsequent progress (or lack thereof) being made by the individual. In clinical settings (compared to research protocols that require consistency), it is not mandatory to engage in all training activities across all four tool kits. Rather, the therapist should use assessment and outcome data to inform various treatment decisions.

In addition, for purposes of presentation, we describe each of the four tool kits in sequence. However, the EC-PST therapist may wish to apply certain EC-PST strategies in a different order, based on the specifics of a given case as explained in Chapter 4 (Box 4.7). The following is a sample presentation of these tools:

> *Let me explain what this approach will actually entail. Years of research and clinical experience have identified four major obstacles to successful coping with real-life, stressful situations. These are the factors that make it difficult getting from point "A," which is where you are now, to point "B," which is where you would like to get to—that is, reaching your goals. These include ineffective problem-solving strategies, brain overload, low motivation and feelings of hopelessness, and difficulties managing negative emotions. EC-PST has been developed specifically to help you overcome these four obstacles by providing you with specific tools to deal with each barrier. So, over the next several weeks, I will serve in many roles—teacher, coach, therapist, counselor, and problem-solving cheerleader. During this time, I will teach you a set of skills and strategies to help you overcome those obstacles. As noted, through rigorous science this approach has been shown to be effective for large numbers of people, experiencing a wide range of problems.*

Encourage Optimism and a Sense of Control

During these initial sessions, it is also important to facilitate clients' sense of optimism and belief that they can regain control of their lives. Therapists should try to identify and point to examples of effective problem-solving attempts that clients have engaged in previously. It should be emphasized that our overall response to problems can either work *for* or *against* us; the goal of EC-PST is to increase the chance that our problem-solving reactions will work *for* us.

In addition, it is important to reinforce a person's current competencies in various areas of living to enhance motivation for optimally engaging in EC-PST. For example, the therapist can point out areas where the person is currently engaging in effective problem solving and coping as a means of highlighting various strengths. However, if the individual appears very pessimistic in the beginning, the therapist may wish to move to Tool Kit #3 and engage in the *positive visualization* activity as a means of enhancing motivation at this early stage of treatment.

Ground Rules and Therapy Expectations

A final point about the introductory sessions. Many individuals may not be familiar with a directive or skill development approach to psychotherapy or counseling and subsequently may have different expectations. Thus, it is important to discuss with the client several ground rules of the approach, along with other standard therapy issues, such as confidentiality and informed consent. We have found it useful to include such a discussion of session timing and frequency, as well as expectations of practice assignments between sessions, as part of EC-PST "ground rules." It can additionally be useful to obtain mutual agreement with clients concerning joint responsibilities. These include the following:

> *Therapist responsibilities.* The therapist should agree to draw upon all training, knowledge of the scientific literature, and clinical experience to best help the client.
>
> *Client responsibilities.* The client needs to agree to "give it his or her best shot," to engage in between-session activities, practice skills, and keep appointments and let the therapist know of problems or disappointments with treatment.

THE CASES OF MEGAN, DAVID, AND MARK

In this section, we present the cases of "Megan," "David," and "Mark" (note that all identifying information has been changed to protect their confidentiality). These three clients underwent an EC-PST approach to treatment with one of the authors (C.M.N.). These cases are used as a means of providing a context for meaningful clinical illustrations and examples of how to apply various EC-PST strategies. To begin with, we provide a summary of information gleaned from the initial assessment sessions with each client in the subsequent text as a means of introducing them. These cases have been revisited throughout the remaining chapters in this manual, highlighting how the various tool kits were helpful in the course of their treatments.

The Case of Megan: The One Who Decided It Was Too Early to Quit on Life

Megan was a 27-year-old woman who approached psychotherapy by stating, "I've reached a point in my life where I am re-evaluating my lifestyle. I feel anxious and detached and can't tell if it's me or due to my past alcohol abuse.

Sometimes I wonder if I can't change my feelings of worry and depression or ever change my life for the better."

She stated that her problems began in high school and continued in college. Her college years were marked by choice of an "easy" major (Italian) and weekends of heavy drinking and socializing. After college, she drifted from job to job and maintained a pattern of completing her required work duties during the week, followed by heavy drinking, eating, and socializing with friends during the weekends. She had occasional brief sexual encounters when drinking, which usually occurred during an alcohol-induced blackout. She stated that she has had almost no "sober" sexual relationships, reported no history of sexual abuse or trauma, but described both sex and masturbatory activities as "boring."

Approximately 3 months before her first appointment, she stopped drinking alcohol following a blackout and implemented a self-directed abstinence. The day after this blackout, she had frightening sensory experiences (i.e., hypervigilance and seeing movement out of the corner of her eye), concentration difficulties, episodes of panic, a sense of detachment, and a fear of losing control of her thoughts. She attended a few Alcoholics Anonymous meetings, but considered the organization a bad match for her. She committed to stopping drinking on her own with the support of her sister and a close friend. Over the 3 months before entering therapy, the episodes of panic and limited sensory hallucinatory experiences had diminished. However, her fears concerning the loss of control, anhedonia, low motivation, and sense of detachment from others had remained particularly troublesome. In addition, she experienced a fear of her roommate, because of this person's continued drinking, casual sexual encounters with men she brought home to the shared apartment, and the knowledge that her roommate owned a firearm (although Megan had never seen it or been threatened by her roommate in any way).

Megan was currently working as an administrative assistant at a biotechnology firm and performed her work duties well. She had no absenteeism and had recently received a promotion. Megan stated, however, that despite her recent successes, she experienced no joy or motivation for her work, and also felt disconnected from her coworkers, as well as those with whom she socialized. Her few friendships had remained the same, and she indicated that there were times when she felt lonely because she no longer frequented the neighborhood bar where her familiar group of friends congregated on Friday evenings.

Megan reported few social supports. However, the individuals she did identify as helpful provided her with a sense of safety and enjoyment. These included her older sister and one male friend. She described her family background and early home life as giving her and her siblings a "good" upbringing, citing many activities and trips as a family. She initially described herself as a "basically happy kid" in her early years without many challenges in school. However, Megan reported that her family home also had an undercurrent of tension between her parents. For example, when she was in high school, her parents separated and divorced, only to live near each other for several years and then remarried some years later. There was a family history of anxiety among Megan's two sisters, and her older sister had been diagnosed with bipolar disorder.

Megan's initial assessment involved a comprehensive evaluation that included a series of clinical interviews, communication with her primary care physician, completion of several diagnostic screening measures (for a range of clinical problems, including bipolar disorder), psychological testing, symptom checklists, and the SPSI–R. In general, the results of this overall assessment protocol indicated that Megan met criteria for generalized anxiety disorder with a history of alcohol abuse, plus subclinical levels of depressive symptoms. In addition, she reported binge-eating episodes and a significant alcohol abuse history. Her primary care physician reported her current health as generally good. However, she exhibited mild hypertension and smoked approximately one pack of cigarettes daily. She expressed a strong desire to reduce her symptoms and improve her life without the use of drugs.

Concerning standardized testing, Megan's scores confirmed a diagnosis of anxiety disorder and ruled out a diagnosis of personality disorders or bipolar disorder. Her response to other self-report measures indicated lifelong maladaptive schemas concerning hypervigilance and emotional inhibitions, suggesting that her home environment tended to place emphasis on suppressing feelings, impulses, and choices. Furthermore, her family tended to foster and support various rigid rules and expectations. Verbal reports of her early life were consistent with the self-report measures, as she reported an undercurrent of pessimism and worry in the home.

The SPSI–R revealed striking areas specific to her strengths and vulnerabilities in solving real-life problems. Specifically, her positive problem orientation responses were consistent with scores of individuals in the normative, nonpsychiatric group. This reflected her optimism and desire to seek help for the significant symptoms and fears that she was currently experiencing. However, the scores regarding her negative orientation were more than 2 standard deviations above the average normed score, reflecting her significant worry and intense fears of not coping well with life. Her concentration difficulties, feelings of detachment, recent experiences of depersonalization while withdrawing from alcohol use, and continual worry about her roommate's behavior when drinking, all left her feeling hypervigilant and chronically anxious and tearful. These served as barriers to her being able to benefit from her optimism.

Megan's scores on the various components of planful problem solving (i.e., the Rational Problem-Solving [RPS] scale score) indicated that she had strengths concerning her ability to define problems clearly, but revealed more limited abilities concerning flexibility and creativity in generating solutions, weighing alternatives, and following through on intended plans of thoughtful action. One example of the latter was her intention to eat better, organize her home, and exercise. She believed that if she could just "get started," she would follow through with what she needed to do. However, she reported her motivation to start was poor. Her total RPS scale score reflected the cumulative challenges she had concerning her problem-solving ability and was within the area of scores more similar to those of psychiatric outpatient sample groups. Her scores with regard to the Impulsive/Careless Style scale was a full standard deviation beyond the average nonpsychiatric patient. Finally, her scores concerning avoidant responding were only slightly, but nonsignificantly, above average. Overall, her total SPSI–R score was 2 standard deviations below the average score for nonpsychiatric samples, indicating significant problem-solving deficits and limitations.

Consistent with our EC-PST philosophy of clinical decision making, Megan's therapist shared her case formulation with her. Rather than focus on the diagnostic labels or descriptions of her difficulties, her therapist presented this case formulation to explain Megan's "life story"; more specifically, how her stressful early emotional learning experiences had contributed to the types of implicit emotional and cognitive responses that comprised her reactions to current stressors, as well as various explicit concerns, triggers, learned behavior, and desire for change. In addition, Megan's strengths were underscored as one initial means of instilling hope and reinforcing constructive approaches to life problems. In sharing her understanding of Megan's "life story," the therapist also identified possible targets for change that would have the most significant impact on her current ultimate goals for treatment. These appeared to be improved management of anxiety, reduction of feelings of interpersonal detachment and sadness, and improved enjoyment in living.

It is useful to note that we have found that simultaneously sharing the case formulation with a client, using a visual depiction of both the factors influencing his or her current level of distress and highlighting how social problem solving is an essential mediator of the stress–distress relationship, is a useful way to underscore the relevance of EC-PST for a given individual. Also, this activity provides an extra boost to the therapeutic alliance, as clients such as Megan have the opportunity to understand how the use of effective problem-solving and emotion regulation skills, as well as other new learning experiences, can impact their effective management of life problems.

Megan responded very positively to hearing her case formulation shared in this manner, reporting that it provided a "different way" of looking at her current problems and symptoms. Moreover, she indicated that she felt "listened to and respected." Specifically, she felt the therapist understood how hard she was trying to manage her distress and to do the best she could. While discussing this case formulation, Megan volunteered additional information, describing that the tension and uncertainty in her childhood home concerning her parents' disagreements had given her the feeling that "something bad was going to happen," but not knowing what. As a function of this discussion, Megan began to understand that these early childhood stressful experiences had likely contributed to her current hypervigilance and reactivity when under stress (i.e., stress sensitization). In addition, because her sister had been formally diagnosed with bipolar disorder, it was suggested that it was possible that Megan may have a genetic vulnerability concerning the stress–depression association (as described in Chapter 2). Furthermore, she was able to see how these attempts at managing the current stress in her life—that is, heavy drinking—served to help her avoid, rather than confront, problems. Moreover, she realized that such "ineffective solutions" served only to engender further worries regarding her health and overall well-being and create new problems (i.e., stress generation). Her sense of hopelessness, the inability to experience pleasure, and low motivation were some of the significant symptoms of her subclinical depression. As part of the case formulation, it was explained to Megan that she had been drinking for so long that she had learned few alternative ways by which she could begin to challenge her worries and hypervigilance, as well as her avoidance of feelings and social confrontation, and current concerns with regard to her roommate's behavior.

As suggested earlier, it was described to Megan how problem-solving ability was related to stress. It was further explained how learning EC-PST skills could provide her with a new way of becoming more aware of, and consequently, more able to manage negative feelings, think planfully, and ultimately motivate herself to put more positive strategies into action. This would ultimately involve a new overall learning experience concerning her reactions to herself and others and a different way of coping with life's problems.

Megan's initial reaction to this rationale was positive, indicating that she found this approach helpful, because it provided her with a view of herself as having certain reactive habits, albeit maladaptive, that were learned earlier in life compared with "that's just my messed up alcoholic brain!" She also realized that by drinking, she missed multiple opportunities to learn how to cope more effectively with life's difficulties and that the EC-PST tool kits might now provide such experiences. Moreover, she indicated that the case formulation convinced her that she had a future and that she was "not on the brink of a mental crash!"

One final note regarding Megan's initial case formulation—as part of providing a rationale for EC-PST, her therapist also indicated that at times it might be prudent to incorporate additional empirically based strategies in her overall treatment plan. This was to underscore the point that an EC-PST framework and intervention do not require an exclusive manual-driven implementation when applied in real-world settings. However, in this book, when we revisit Megan, we only discuss case material specific to examples related to EC-PST strategies and techniques.

The Case of David: The Man Who Appeared to "Have It All"

The following is a brief description of David and how EC-PST was applied to his treatment for anxiety, depression, anger, hopelessness, and elevated risk for suicide.

David was a 40-year-old male who was referred by a coworker from a university medical center. He is a White male who described himself as Catholic and ethnically "German Irish." David was a neurologist and a medical officer in the U.S. military. At the time of the referral, he was serving active duty at a major military medical center. He was married, recently became a new father, and to the outside world, appeared to "have it all." However, his close colleague, a civilian psychiatrist, experienced a growing concern that David was depressed, hostile, and isolated, and had made statements that suggested increased suicidal risk. Although he had been previously avoidant of seeking psychotherapy, David relented in response to his friend's supportive suggestions.

Almost a year before David entered treatment, his father had committed suicide by suffocation. David blamed himself for this tragedy, stating that he knew that his father (whom he described as a "brilliant cognitive scientist") was increasingly depressed and had a long history of threatening to kill himself. As a result, this client expressed a strong sense of guilt stating, "I knew it was coming and should have done something to save him."

David's first session indicated that he was extremely depressed and hopeless. Despite his apparent success, David disclosed a history of hiding a painful inner life with periods of intense anxiety and significant depression. He described a challenging childhood and the relentless stress of "knowing" that his father was chronically depressed and suicidal. David was raised in a mid-Atlantic state and attended a state university. He credits his success with being provided the structure of the Reserve Officers' Training Corps (ROTC) while in college and later in the military. He is the oldest of four children and described his nuclear family as closed off emotionally, stating that they never discussed in any meaningful way the loss of their father or any other family problems that occurred over the years. As stated, David was married and recently became a parent. His wife was currently at home to care for their baby son.

Despite his successful career, David's distress continued to interfere with his work as a physician. His anxiety concerning his nuclear family was ever present, and his guilt and self-blame for his father's death were continuously painful. Moreover, he recently experienced a growing belief that his wife was also disappointed in him. Although not at immediate risk of a suicide attempt, it appeared that David at times thought of developing a plan. His increased risk worsened because of the upcoming anniversary of his father's death, approximately 6 weeks from his initial session.

An assessment protocol was aimed at developing an initial case formulation that could help create a treatment plan specific to David. This included both quantitative (e.g., self-report questionnaires) and qualitative strategies (e.g., interview questions, use of visualization exercises). In addition to confirming elevated levels of clinical depression, anxiety, and moderate suicidal risk, additional clinical interview material—along with his responses to the SPSI–R—suggested that David had a strong negative problem orientation related to his personal life. This negativity was beginning to impact his view of his work activities and future, which made him particularly concerned and increasingly more depressed and hopeless. Also, it appeared that although his planful problem-solving abilities had been sufficiently effective in helping him to achieve a meaningful career as a physician in the military, he did not apply such skills to problems encountered in his personal life. Moreover, as an adult, he continued to engage in avoidant problem-solving strategies that developed during his childhood and adolescence, particularly involving his nuclear family and his wife.

As a standard part of EC-PST, the case formulation was shared with David. His emotional learning history was particularly stressful as it was characterized by having a chronically depressed father, a family that avoided open acknowledgment or discussions about emotions, and by prioritizing academic and career goals to the exclusion of a balance with his relationship and personal goals as a means of emotion regulation. David's academic and military goals provided him with a focus and structure that enabled him to avoid attempts to better understand and deal with several of his early life challenges. Chief among those included the incident in which his father had unsuccessfully attempted to kill himself in David's presence when David was only 10 years old. David's significant lifelong stress collectively led to his chronic symptoms of depression and hopelessness concerning his personal problems. Predictable current stressors that emanated from his work as a physician, as well as being anxious about the possibility of failing as a father to his recently born son, further exacerbated such difficulties.

Alternatively, it appeared that a significant strength characterizing David was his ability to be sufficiently effective in his work environment, which included positive relationships with a few coworkers, supervisors, and clients. Avoidance and suppression of his negative orientation and emotions, particularly concerning his father's suicide and his subsequent feelings of guilt, while serving him well in one area of his life, simultaneously led to increasing difficulties outside of work. For example, others considered David as someone whom everyone at work perceived to be "friendly and self-confident." However, he would come home only to reveal a low threshold for any perceived criticism. Although the majority of his negative affect involved depression, he frequently became enraged and withdrawn when his wife attempted to tease him playfully about even a minor flaw. David reported that he was experiencing persistent emotional and psychological pain, viewed himself as disconnected emotionally from others, and believed that his guilt regarding his father's death was both relentless and hopeless to change.

On the basis of numerous discussions with his therapist, David defined his reasons for seeking treatment as decreasing his feelings of depression and improving his relationship with his wife. However, his intense guilt over his father's death and relationships with his family were significant, and he was hopeless regarding the possibility that these problems could improve or that therapeutic involvement would be helpful. He did appear to experience a mild connection to therapy during the initial session and stated that before this point in his life, no one knew the level of pain or shame he wrestled with on a daily basis. At the same time, this presented a risk, in that the anniversary of his father's death would occur in about 6 weeks.

On the basis of the initial assessment, in consideration of the degree of hopelessness he experienced, the upcoming anniversary of his father's death, and the significant deficits exhibited in both avoidance and negative orientation scales of the SPSI–R, David's treatment plan was prescribed as follows and conducted in the following order:

Overcome feelings of hopelessness. Use of Tool Kit #3, designed to enhance hope and motivation, which involved the use of visualization to overcome feelings of hopelessness, appeared critical to David's improvement. This tool kit was used initially to help him become more hopeful and foster directing his efforts toward using the various other EC-PST tools. It was explained that applying these tools could help him more effectively manage his strong feelings related to his father's death, ultimately reduce his emotional pain, and improve his overall quality of life.

Improve emotion regulation. Despite his ability to function successfully in his work environment, David had significant difficulty in understanding and regulating negative emotions pertaining to his personal life. It was important for David to apply the "Stop and Slow Down" tools in Tool Kit #4 to increase his awareness and better manage his reactions to both interoceptive and external cues that served as his unique triggers for negative emotions.

Planful problem solving. More formal training in these skills using Tool Kit #1 would follow the aforementioned approaches with the specific application of a problem-solving approach that would demonstrate how such tools could be helpful across life problems and not just tied to academic and career arenas.

Overcoming brain overload. Training in Tool Kit #2 was closely tied to the emotion regulation training, because in the past, when David has felt overwhelmed with stressful stimuli, he had tended to become intensely sad, angry, anxious, flooded with negative memories, and unable to remain focused on the stressful situation that required his planful problem-solving strengths.

The Case of Mark: The Artist Who Dared to Be "Normal"

Mark was a 25-year-old single Latino American man who presented with concerns of low self-esteem, doubts about himself, depression, anxiety, inattentiveness, past suicidal thoughts, and experiences of depersonalization. A coworker at the coffee shop where Mark worked provided the referral. Mark described his job as basically "something to do to pay the rent," while he continued to develop his work as an artist (painting, photography). For the past 5 years, since graduating from a local university for the arts, it had been his goal to achieve commercial success as an artist, sufficient to sustain a satisfactory income.

Mark reported that his reason for seeking psychotherapy was that he wanted to be more comfortable around other people, especially women, to feel less lonely, and "find a better balance between my emotional state and self-concept."

Mark was born and raised in the Midwest. His White, American-born mother and Cuban-born father divorced when he was young (8 years old). He has one sibling, a 19-year-old brother, who was in the military. Mark described his mother as reacting in extreme ways to his behavior when he was young—treating him as a family scapegoat, becoming angry with him for expressing sadness or depression, spoiling him when she felt sorry for her behavior, or becoming anxious and critical when he acted in peculiar ways. He described his father as having a flat and disinterested mood or being very "anxious with a short temper." His father's anger when Mark was younger took the form of both physical violence (on at least two occasions) and abandonment (when his father drove him to a place and left him there with no mention of when he would be back). After a particularly violent instance of abuse, when his father punched him with car keys in his fist, Mark did not see his father for 18 months. This was a particularly troublesome period for him. However,

Mark described getting along better with his father than his mother at present, but stated that his parents "hate" each other. Mark endorsed having some happy memories of his childhood (such as family vacations), but also many unhappy memories (e.g., his experiences of abuse and the deaths of family members, including his grandparents). Possessing a slight build, he described being bullied in junior high school.

At the time of the initial assessment, Mark lived alone in a studio apartment in an East Coast city. He was not dating anyone at the time, but did mention certain women in whom he was interested. He stated that one of his primary reasons for coming to therapy was that he becomes "shy around attractive women." He indicated experiencing some painful breakups in the past and that he tends to date women with "cold" personalities that "sting" him. He stated that he has "masochistic tendencies" concerning relationships, but he is uncomfortable with this pattern. Note that it was not surprising that Mark had appealed to some of his past girlfriends in that he can appear dark, distant, and brooding.

With regard to his medical and psychiatric history, Mark reported having asthma, as well as stomach pain and headache and a past diagnosis of attention deficit hyperactivity disorder (ADHD) since grammar school. However, he was not in or seeking treatment for this problem. Family medical history is significant for Alzheimer's disease both in his paternal grandmother and uncle, as well as an aunt with a reported history of bipolar disorder.

Mark reported that he had seen many therapists ("too many to name") over the years for various problems. He indicated that he had a particularly good experience with at least one therapist, who unfortunately died in 2013, while Mark was finishing college. He described this loss as "traumatic." Mark also reported that he was diagnosed with posttraumatic stress disorder after an incident of abuse in high school when his father punched him while holding keys. He also stated that in the past, he had been diagnosed, at least provisionally, with ADHD, bipolar disorder, panic disorder, other anxiety disorders, and depression.

Mark had been hospitalized twice for psychiatric concerns. The first hospitalization occurred when he was in 4th grade. He described being hospitalized because of his mother being "hypersensitive" to his outbursts of temper, particularly after he pushed a shopping cart into her. In the hospital, he recalls sharing a room with a boy with schizophrenia. In early high school, during the period when he was not seeing his father, he described engaging in nonsuicidal self-injury at that time to alleviate emotional pain. He also reported "acting out" in other ways (e.g., reportedly cutting and dying his hair in a "Mohawk" haircut and wearing the same t-shirt every day). He voluntarily committed himself to a psychiatric hospital because of suicidal thoughts, which he described as a "terrible" experience. He that he felt "disrespected" and not at all helped during this hospitalization, feeling as if he was "in prison." He stated that he vowed never to go back and that he would "do away with myself" before being hospitalized again. In addition, he reported a phobic avoidance of hospitals that often prevented him from following through with medical appointments.

Mark's clinical assessment indicated that he was experiencing significant social anxiety, depressed mood, and instability of interpersonal behavior in which he would behave provocatively, seek approval, then mistrust, avoid and ultimately reject other people. He did not endorse the presence of current suicidal ideation, although he had experienced this in the past, and he currently experienced urges to engage in nonsuicidal self-mutilation.

A comprehensive evaluation with a combination of self-report, clinician-administered and standardized tests, resulted in the following clinical impressions: Mark experienced extreme difficulty regulating his emotions and often experienced anger, disgust, or feelings of emptiness toward others. His relationships were best described as chaotic and involved past suicide attempts, self-harm, shame, and fears of abandonment when experiencing relationship stress. He had an unstable sense of himself, and his behavior was often impulsive.

Mark attended grade and high school in a Midwest city. After he graduated high school, he matriculated to an urban university for fine arts, where he studied painting and photography. With regard to his art, he performed well in school and received an award with a cash stipend of $100 for one of his paintings. However, he had always been very self-critical of his work and doubted his professors' favorable opinions of it. Thus, it was difficult to determine his actual level of performance from the content of his statements. As noted before, he holds a job as a barista in the city, where he reportedly performs his work well. However, he indicated that he needs to "wear a mask" at work to be accepted by his coworkers and customers, and that he does not fully trust his coworkers, including one whom he has known for many years. In general, Mark appears to be a committed, hard worker (especially with his art), but is "not easily satisfied" with much of what he produces.

Mark reported clear concerns related to his social life and endorsed that although he has a small social circle, it was "nowhere near" as satisfying as those friendships he had prior to moving to his current location for college. He stated that he often views himself as "without a clique" and that others do not "take me seriously." He stated that with his friends from his art program, there was a subtle atmosphere of competition. He endorsed that he does not make friends easily, but does keep the friends he has. Loneliness has been a major concern in his life, especially on weekends. However, Mark also values his personal, private time, and even prefers isolation when working on his art, which he states is "allowed and accepted" in the art world. He currently experiences significant discomfort both in a social context and in isolation and stated that one of his goals for therapy was to learn to feel "okay," whether he is socially engaged or by himself. Specifically, when he is alone and engaged in his artwork, he continually compares himself to others and ruminates about whether he is "good enough to make it" in the world of art. He states that he experiences social gatherings as "torture" and that he spends most of the time at a social event worrying about what to say next or making critical comments to himself about others in the room.

Mark further stated that his sexual experiences were limited to two fellow art students that he dated during the time he was in college. He reports that he "knew" neither of these relationships would work out, because of the lack of warmth or connection he experienced with either woman. He states that his preference is to date women (vs. men), but also states that many men "hit on me" in the coffee shop where he works. As a function of these types of events, he has occasionally wondered if he might be sexually attracted to men.

Mark decided to engage in therapy to try to understand why "I am how I am" and to try to decide whether he should continue his artwork or take his life on a different course.

Following this overall assessment, it was determined that Mark was currently experiencing significant distress, which he mainly attributed to strained familial relationships and a lack of available social support. He described symptoms consistent with social anxiety disorder and mild depression, but also revealed long-term interpersonal difficulties that included emotional dysregulation, an unstable identity, a fear of abandonment, and impulsive acts to "relieve" his emotional pain. Among the more significant historical sources of his distress were experiencing victimization (abuse and abandonment) as a child with resulting schemas of abandonment, and inconsistent reinforcement of his "acting out" behavior, which he reported took the form of tantrums and aggressive pushing or throwing of objects. He had developed a pattern of setting very high standards for himself, which he believed applies only to his artwork, but may appear in other areas. He was quite critical of himself when he failed to meet these ambitions.

Although Mark's assessment revealed many areas of strength (e.g., perseverance in work and school, sensitivity, willingness to seek help, and good rational problem-solving skills), his lack of a stable personal identity rendered it difficult for him to apply these skills to make major life changes in valued directions (e.g., social relationships). Mark's self-concept was also somewhat fragile and varied widely and rapidly, from a self-described "narcissism" to depressive states marked by loneliness, regret, and self-doubt. At times his more "dark" characteristics and mood, as well as his provocative behavior, appeared to provide him with an identity, albeit one of a brooding artist, outside the mainstream of society. This resulted in a self-image of one who chose to be different or idiosyncratic versus viewing these characteristics as being out of his control.

Although he developed a range of ways to cope with his stress, anxiety, and depression, these were often successful only in the short term. For example, he would seek to be isolated at times, stating that he preferred to be alone, but then experienced intense loneliness and alienation from others. At such times, he had impulsively sought reassurance or help from people on whom he was dependent. These erratic and impulsive requests for help often resulted in attempts from others to aid him that competed with each other. These competing attempts of others to help actually resulted in confusion or counterproductivity and impeded help from any one source. Ultimately, Mark was viewed by others (as well as himself) as fragile and emotionally incompetent.

The patterns just described created a clinical diagnostic picture of an individual with a borderline personality disorder, social anxiety, and dysthymia. He had a very low tolerance for negative feelings and emotional pain, unrealistic expectations for himself, a lack of clarification regarding personal values and a personal identity, and a schema-driven need to get help from others. However, his adherence to the help or advice that was given was poor, often to the point of positioning one source of help to contradict or disagree with another. His social isolation and anxiety presented chronic barriers to his overall quality of life. His depressive symptoms appeared labile and tied to acute environmental triggers, such as receiving criticism of his artwork or being bored. Partially a function of the stress Mark experienced when he was young, he had developed a strong sense of mistrust and fear of becoming close with others. His choices of previous women with whom he had a relationship seemed to reinforce his expectation that others would ultimately be cold and uncaring. This mistrust was evident in his perception of other's view of his artwork despite positive feedback. The identity of a dark and unusual artist may have provided him with an expectation of rejection that provided him with a false perception of control.

It was determined that Mark's vague goals and perceived fragility would benefit from an initial focus on emotion regulation principles, and the structure provided through training in planful problem solving would help direct him more toward both identifying and ultimately reaching certain goals. These could initially provide Mark with specific coping skills to use, particularly when under stress. His treatment plan initially centered on providing a direct and structured focus that might help him to achieve small goals one at a time, slowly building resilience that would allow him to slowly and cautiously let go of the identity he was wearing and "dare to be normal."

SUMMARY

This chapter began with identifying the major intervention components of EC-PST, which include assessment and treatment planning, providing a treatment rationale, fostering a positive therapist–client relationship, training in the four major tool kits, guided practice, and "future forecasting" and termination. It was emphasized that ongoing clinical assessment of a client's problem-solving strengths and limitations, as well as improvement in symptoms and goal achievement (or lack thereof), should inform treatment planning, particularly with regard to the choice, emphasis, and timing of training in the various EC-PST strategies and guidelines.

It was suggested that in describing EC-PST, the therapist should provide an overview of the four EC-PST tool kits, which involves specific skills and guidelines geared to help overcome four major barriers to effective problem solving: (a) ineffective problem-solving strategies, (b) stimulus overload, (c) reduced motivation and feelings of hopelessness, and (d) emotional dysregulation.

Last, to provide an ongoing context to illustrate various EC-PST exercises and strategies, we presented cases of three clients—Megan, David, and Mark. In the following chapters that describe in detail the various treatment components of EC-PST, these cases have been revisited to provide relevant examples of certain EC-PST training activities.

REFERENCE

Nezu, A. M., Nezu, C. M., & D'Zurilla, T. J. (2013). *Problem-solving therapy: A treatment manual.* New York, NY: Springer Publishing.

EMOTION-CENTERED PROBLEM-SOLVING THERAPY: TREATMENT GUIDELINES

TOOL KIT #1—PLANFUL PROBLEM SOLVING: FOSTERING EFFECTIVE PROBLEM SOLVING

> *By failing to prepare, you are preparing to fail.*
>
> —Benjamin Franklin

> *A good plan is like a road map—it shows the final destination and usually the best way to get there.*
>
> —H. Stanley Judd

This chapter describes the first emotion-centered problem-solving therapy (EC-PST) tool kit—Planful Problem Solving. EC-PST consistently involves active participation by the client, so many of the tools found throughout this therapy manual require clients to "externalize." This is explained in more detail in Chapter 8 as a strategy to help people better handle stimulus overload, especially under stress. It is described in the Client Workbook in the following manner:

> *When we recommend that you externalize, we want you to "take your thoughts out of your head and put them down on paper" so that (a) you won't forget them, (b) you will have a record and be able to view them at any time, and (c) you can add to them to reorganize or change them. Some of you may work with a computer or a laptop—that's another great way to externalize using a word-processing program. For those of you who have a tablet or a smartphone, there is a free app available called* Moving Forward, *which is based on this program of EC-PST. This app can be useful to help externalize your thoughts, as well as to*

© Springer Publishing Company DOI: 10/1891/9780826143167.0007

provide additional information about becoming a better problem solver.

As with many of the training activities, clients are requested to externalize their responses. Therefore, it is important to encourage clients early in treatment to purchase a notebook or journal or to use their computer/laptop for this purpose.

PLANFUL PROBLEM-SOLVING TASKS

This tool kit focuses on teaching individuals the following four sets of planful problem-solving skills:

- *Problem definition* (i.e., clarifying the nature of a problem, delineating a realistic problem-solving goal, and identifying those obstacles that prevent one from reaching such goals)

- *Generation of alternatives* (i.e., thinking of a range of possible solution ideas geared to overcome the identified obstacles)

- *Decision making* (i.e., predicting the likely consequences of these various alternatives, conducting a cost–benefit analysis based on these identified outcomes, and developing an action plan that is geared toward achieving the problem-solving goal)

- *Solution implementation and verification* (i.e., carrying out the action plan, monitoring and evaluating the consequences of the plan, and determining whether one's problem-solving efforts have been successful or need to continue)

RATIONALE

The basic rationale for teaching these tools is largely based on the notion that such skills are characteristic of individuals who are effective problem solvers, in addition to the positive outcomes associated with effective problem solving (see Chapter 1). Training in these tools is useful for individuals who (a) have difficulty coping with stressful problems because they have never learned effective problem-solving strategies, (b) have difficulty applying effective problem-solving skills to *all* areas of their lives, and/or (c) have experienced significant stress (e.g., trauma) that has inhibited their ability to fully use their effective problem-solving skills as a means of coping. Note also that individuals may have particular strengths in some areas (e.g., ability to generate alternative solution ideas), but limitations in others (e.g., making decisions). Similar to previous recommendations, the degree to which training in a given planful problem-solving tool is emphasized is largely determined by information gleaned from continuous formal (e.g., results from the 52-item version of the Social Problem-Solving Inventory–Revised [SPSI–R]) and informal (e.g., clinical interviews, material from completed Social Problem-Solving Self-Monitoring forms) evaluations.

Such assessments early in treatment can help the therapist decide which of two approaches to take in teaching these tools:

- "Brief" Planful Problem-Solving Training
- "Intensive" Planful Problem-Solving Training

BRIEF PLANFUL PROBLEM-SOLVING TRAINING

For clients who appear to have only minor planful problem-solving deficits, if EC-PST is being provided to a particular population as more of a preventive approach, or if time constraints exist, we recommend that this briefer version of training in planful problem solving be implemented. This would initially involve providing an overview of the four planful problem-solving skills and training in the use of the Problem-Solving Worksheet.

Problem-Solving Worksheet

As a means of guiding one's approach to solving a real-life problem (i.e., applying the planful problem-solving steps), clients are requested to attempt to resolve a given problem using a Problem-Solving Worksheet. The following are the types of information that are requested and grouped according to the four basic problem-solving tasks:

Problem Definition

- What is the problem (try to be specific)?
- What is your problem-solving goal?
- What are the major obstacles to achieving your goal at this time?

Generating Alternative Solutions

- What are some specific things you can do to help you reach your goal (try to think of at least three to five different ways; be creative; be specific)?

Decision-Making

- What are the major "pros" or positive consequences of these alternatives?

- What are some of the "cons" or negative consequences?

- Which ones do you think will be the best to help you achieve your goal? Decide which alternatives are the best by choosing the ones with the best *positive* consequences and few *negative* consequences. Write down a specific action plan.

Carrying Out the Plan and Determining Whether It Worked

- After you carry out the plan, observe the consequences: Are you satisfied that your plan worked?

When initially describing how to use this worksheet, it is a good idea for the client to choose to address a problem that is lower within the hierarchy of extant stressful problems to minimize emotional arousal that may be distracting to the learning process. We recommend that an initial "go through" of the worksheet be geared mostly toward increasing the client's familiarity with the form as well as with the various steps. This is also an opportunity for the therapist to assess the client's ability to engage in these steps and to do so competently. Completion of at least the steps that culminate in developing an action plan is recommended for the first practice exercise. During this time, the therapist can provide feedback to the client both about how to use the worksheet properly and the effectiveness, accuracy, and appropriateness of the actual responses.

At this point, assuming that a given client continues to demonstrate only mild problem-solving deficits, feedback to the client about the process can center around the answers to the worksheet. However, if clients display significant problems with applying a particular problem-solving step (e.g., defining the problem), the therapist can use the various information and exercises described throughout this chapter (as well as in the Client Workbook available at http://connect.springerpub.com/content/book/978-0-8261-3523-0) as a means of increasing their competency level. If an action plan is actually developed during the first session devoted to planful problem solving, the therapist should determine whether it is "strong" enough to eventuate in the resolution of the problem at hand. If so, the client should be encouraged to attempt to carry out the plan to determine whether it is, in fact, an *effective* solution. If, however, the therapist determines that this initial solution plan is *not* likely to produce satisfactory results, additional discussions and attempts at using the worksheet need to occur.

In the following section, we provide a case illustration of how clients can use the Problem-Solving Worksheet to help resolve stressful problems based on discussions with and training by their therapists.

THE CASE OF JIM: DIFFICULTIES ADHERING TO A HEALTHY LIFESTYLE REGIMEN

Jim had been diagnosed with type 2 diabetes and was having significant difficulty adhering to a low-carbohydrate/low-sugar diet and an exercise regimen. EC-PST was implemented to help him adhere more consistently. Following are his responses to the worksheet.

Problem Definition

What is the problem (try to be specific)?

> *I knew it was important to start exercising on a regular basis and to reduce my blood-sugar level by reducing the number of carbs and sugars in my diet. At first, I did well. Right after my diagnosis, I educated myself about diets, started taking meds that my doctor prescribed, and signed up for a membership in a local gym. My blood glucose dropped to close to normal range! Over time, however, after my initial weight loss and some success in lowering my blood glucose, I found myself less likely to go the gym because of time constraints and was grabbing fast-food meals when under pressure at work. My glucose readings were starting to be more unpredictable and I was feeling like a failure for not "fixing" the problem correctly. I tried really hard to adjust my attitude to be more realistic. This idea made sense to me and it is what I would say to a good friend who was going through a similar situation. I just had to learn to take my own advice.*

What is your problem-solving goal?

- *To keep my motivation up*
- *To maintain a low-carbohydrate, low-sugar diet*
- *To exercise for at least 30 minutes each day*

What are the major obstacles to achieving your goal at this time?

- I often rush from the house in the morning and have trouble thinking about what to have for breakfast, so I often miss breakfast.
- My work schedule makes it difficult to get to the gym.

- I look forward to my favorite television shows.

- I enjoy the time I spend in the early evening reading to my 3-year-old daughter and I am too tired to work out afterward.

Generating Alternative Solutions

What are some specific things you can do to help you reach your goal (try to think of at least three to five different ways; be creative; be specific)?

This is the part of problem solving that I am good at—coming up with ideas about how to solve a problem. I knew that if I tried to reach all my goals at once, I might be setting myself up for failure. That's probably a good example of how my tendency to try to fix everything worked against me. So, I further separated my goals into both a dietary goal and a workout goal. I decided to work on the dietary goal first. Breakfast was often missed because I did not have the time to make decisions and prepare breakfast before leaving the house before my 30-minute drive to work. I came up with the following list of ideas:

- *Make breakfast the night before.*

- *Buy prepackaged breakfasts.*

- *Eat a breakfast bar on the way to work.*

- *Ask for help from a nutritionist in preparing my meals.*

- *Ask for advice and suggestions from a diabetes support helpline on the Internet.*

- *Ask my wife for help to select a number of different low-carb, low-sugar breakfast alternatives when she shops and to bring home samples for me to test out.*

Decision-Making

I weighed each alternative with a series of plusses and minuses. Many of them had very few positive consequences—for example, most breakfast bars are high in sugar and I don't like the taste of the other ones. Several alternatives were expensive (prepackaged foods) or costly in terms of my time and money (setting up consultation from a professional nutritionist). Some had further health risks (forget the diet, eat whatever I want, and ask my doctor for larger doses of meds). There were two that had the highest ratings—sample food with my wife's help and prepare my breakfast to be eaten on the way to work at the beginning of the week. These two alternatives seemed to go well together and, when combined, offered me the most positive consequences and the least negative ones. Foods I discovered liking were a low-carb cereal, blueberries, and nuts.

Carrying Out the Plan and Determining Whether It Worked

On Sundays, my wife and I made up packets of cereal mixed with nuts and blueberries. I took a packet each day when I left for work, along with a bottle of water. I discovered that I was less hungry for lunch and less likely to gobble down fast food. I actually liked my own special cereal mix and found myself looking forward to my commute and breakfast "on the road." Most of all, this was a great head start for me to realize that there are ways that I can improve my glucose management and tackle the trouble spots as they come up. I used the same principles to work on the exercise problem. The end product? A before-dinner "Gymboree" with my daughter that gave us great exercise and a time to bond each day!

This brief version of the planful problem-solving training would involve continued practice in applying the skills using the worksheet across multiple stressful problems that clients are currently experiencing. This would entail continuous discussions and feedback regarding clients' ability and competence in applying the skills to extant problems. If this process leads to the identification of a deficit regarding a particular planful problem-solving skill (e.g., difficulties in making decisions), more intensive training in that skill, as described in the following section, should occur.

INTENSIVE PLANFUL PROBLEM-SOLVING TRAINING

In the event that EC-PST is being provided to a population presenting with problems that are described in the literature as being associated with ineffective problem-solving ability (e.g., depression, suicide, generalized anxiety, chronic medical illness, substance abuse), the remainder of this chapter provides a more intensive training in each of the four planful problem-solving skills. These tools and exercises are also appropriate for clients found to have significant deficits in one or more of the skill areas. Once again, the degree to which any or all of the tools should be emphasized in EC-PST for a given client is based on prior and continuous assessments. Note that the Client Workbook provides a detailed training experience for this tool kit (see the Preface of this book for information on obtaining the Client Workbook).

"If I Know What I Want, Why Should I Do All These Steps?"

This might be a question asked by clients with regard to the numerous worksheets and forms they may be requested to complete as part of the training in any of the intensive training modules described in this text. It is important to note that it is the therapist's judgment as to which worksheets or activities, if any, are crucial for the client. They are included in the Client Workbook as instructional aids for potential use depending on a given individual's strengths and limitations. We believe that such intense training would be necessary for clients with significant deficits. Therefore, when asked such a question, we have responded—*"In a game of golf, if two people have the same skills, who is more likely to eventually get a hole-in-one: the person who looks for the flag near the hole, estimates the directions of the wind, and carefully selects the correct golf club, or the person who swings hard but aimlessly at the hole?"*

PROBLEM DEFINITION

> *It isn't that they can't see the solution.*
> *It's that they can't see the problem.*
>
> —G. K. Chesterton

There is an old saying by Charles Kettering—"A problem well-defined, is half-solved." A similar adage is "measure twice, cut once." Both sayings suggest the idea that if we take the time to fully understand the nature of the problem we are experiencing, actually solving it will take less time and effort. More important, paraphrasing Chesterton's quote, "seeing the problem" helps to "see the solution." We believe that this activity is the most difficult of the planful problem-solving tasks, because it requires one to be able to adequately identify not only "why" it is a problem but also to do so from multiple perspectives (i.e., oneself, getting others involved).

In describing this process to clients, we often use the analogy of defining a problem as being similar to laying out a course or route for travel. Even if several people have the same destination, they may not all have the same resources, such as time or money, to be able to take the same exact trip. If one has never traveled to a particular destination, it becomes especially difficult because of its unfamiliarity. Simply looking at a map without having a specific destination in mind would be overwhelming. Thus, defining a problem is similar to first identifying a road map that shows where one wishes to go. Another way of saying this is to first identify one's goals. In this way, one can later determine "how to get there" (i.e., the solution plan).

According to our model, correctly defining a problem involves the following five steps:

- Seeking the available facts
- Describing the facts in clear language
- Separating facts from "assumptions"
- Setting realistic goals
- Identifying the obstacles to be overcome in reaching such goals

Seeking the Available Facts

Sometimes people try to solve a problem before they know all the facts, especially if they tend to be impulsive or careless. Having the facts fosters effective problem solving. As an example, it is likely that most people would believe that before they buy a new car, they should obtain a sizable amount of information to make a good decision, for example, how much gas mileage it gets, its safety record, and what other consumers think about it. In this context, we suggest that people do the same with regard to their stressful problems. With any situation that is causing distress, it is important to seek out any facts or information that are not readily available. In addition, if we do not actually know what the problem is, we might wind up working on the wrong one.

For example, Sam, a client we worked with, was getting more and more angry because he felt that since he had been divorced, he experienced his family and friends as being overly worried and treating him very "delicately." This often led him to believe that they were avoiding him. Sam told us that they seemed very careful not to talk about his ex-wife and were starting to avoid telling him about good times they had for fear they would upset him. Sam thought that his friend Bill, in particular, was beginning to think of him as a "fragile person." This made Sam angry, which often led to arguments that left them both feeling sad and frustrated. However, after encouraging Sam to find out more about why his friend acted this way, he learned that Bill was starting to feel like there was nothing he could do to help Sam get past his divorce and his avoidance had more to do with his own feelings of failure as a friend. Thinking of all the times that Sam helped him made Bill feel like he was failing as a friend because he could not be of more help. Ironically, all Sam wanted from Bill was to behave toward him the way he always had and not try to make things better. Thus, it seemed that one thing both Sam and Bill needed to do was to "seek the facts."

We recommend clients think of themselves as detectives, scientists, or newspaper reporters, people whose jobs are to get the facts. They should ask specific questions, such as who, what, when, where, why, and how. Moreover, as would be required for a detective, such questions would have to be answered in a manner that is objective and thorough to allow an uninformed person to understand what actually happened. We also remind clients to remember the "externalization" principle (see Chapter 8)—that is, to record information in their notebooks, journals, computers, smartphones, and so forth. In reading their answers, they can ask further questions, such as "Do I have *enough* facts?" "Do I need to get some more information?" It is suggested that they put on the "detective's hat" and go out and seek more facts if necessary.

Sometimes it is difficult to try to sort out what information is relevant or useful when attempting to answer these types of questions. If so, we recommend that people use visualization as a means of clarification (see Chapter 8), that is, to help identify relevant information to answer the questions such as those given in the preceding paragraph. Following is a sample visualization technique used to help foster this activity.

> *Close your eyes and reconstruct in your imagination a recent experience of a recurring problem or part of a current, ongoing problem. First, imagine that you are in the situation, not viewing it as an observer, and experience it in your mind's eye as it actually happened. As you are experiencing the situation, ask yourself, "What am I thinking and feeling?" Next, repeat the experience, but this time as an observer, as if watching a movie or videotape of the situation. Play it in slow motion and ask yourself, "What is happening? What is the other person(s) saying, doing, and feeling? What am I saying, doing, and feeling?"*

Describing the Facts in Clear Language

People, especially when they feel stressed, tend to use language that may be emotionally laden, and thus, potentially unclear. Getting back to "Sam," for example, who originally stated that he felt Bill was treating him "like he was some kind of psycho" and that Bill was making him feel so frustrated that "his head was going to explode!" Being presented with these problems, imagine Sam's reaction if the therapist told him that, on the basis of such descriptions, she would get him a room on the "psycho ward" and remove the fuse from his head so it wouldn't explode! Of course, Sam's initial description provides a colorful way of explaining his feelings, but for anyone to provide reasonable care to him, it would be very important for Sam to be able to describe his feelings and problems using *clear* language. Note that this is very much in keeping with the third problem-solving "multitasking" principle: *simplification* (see Chapter 8).

Another example involves Juanita, who sought therapy because of feelings of anxiety. She initially stated, *"Riding in elevators is a nightmare. It's like I'm going to die or something!"* A more accurate and factual description might be: *"My anxiety is at its most intense when I ride in elevators. As the doors open and I step inside, my heart beats fast, my skin feels clammy, I think about my family's history of heart disease, and have thoughts about dying. As soon as I step off, I have immediate thoughts of relief and feel my heart rate returning to normal."*

When people do not use clear and unambiguous language, they can exaggerate or have other people misunderstand what is being stated. For example, Sam, when angry, tended to "overstate" the frequency of his friend's avoidant behavior. When he first described the situation, he indicated that his friend "never shared anything with him anymore." In fact, after being encouraged to focus on the "facts" and use clear language, he admitted that the difficulty occurs only about half as often as originally claimed.

Separating Facts From Assumptions

Sometimes people make assumptions, especially when they are emotional, without paying attention to this automatic thought process. Assumptions have a way of becoming a fact before anyone tries to determine whether they are really true. Continuing with the theme of "thinking like a news reporter or a scientist," we recommend that people attempt to seek *facts* and not rely on *assumptions*. A fact is something that most people would collectively agree to be true; an assumption involves a person's *belief, opinion, or interpretation* he or she *thinks* to be true without determining its validity.

When people act on assumptions, they can be unsuccessful in their problem-solving attempts. Therefore, we strongly recommend that clients are vigilant in trying to determine what are facts and what are assumptions before concluding that they have a clear and accurate understanding of the nature of their problem. For example, getting back to Sam, he assumed that his friend, when he avoided telling him about positive things in his life, thought he was no longer any fun to be with and thought Sam was a burden. Note that this was not just false (i.e., an assumption), but Sam tended to blow this idea up even more and began to feel that Bill no longer valued him as a friend. On the basis of these supposed "facts," Sam felt justified in his anger and his arguments. Furthermore, his immediate reactions to these assumptions, and not facts, led to his continued anger, frustration, arguments, and sadness. Thus, in this instance, Sam interpreted his friend Bill's change in behavior as evidence that he no longer wanted Sam for a friend, when the facts later revealed that Bill was fearful that he was not being as helpful as Sam needed him to be.

We have found that a very useful exercise that can help people "separate facts from assumptions" is to show them somewhat ambiguous pictures that can be cut out from a magazine or newspaper. Clients are directed to "look at the picture for a few moments, put it down, and then begin writing everything they can think of to describe the picture." After writing down what they saw or thought was "going on" in the picture, the instructions are to look through the list and to differentiate between those aspects of the picture that are facts versus those that are assumptions. By seeing the picture one more time, along with the therapist's feedback, the client can then become more cognizant of what is a fact compared with something that is really more of an interpretation, which may require one to seek more information to verify its validity. We suggest that pictures involving several people interacting are particularly useful as stimuli for this training activity.

Setting Realistic Goals

In setting goals, it is important to remember to identify ones that are actually *attainable*. This means that they have to be reasonable *and* reachable. Although we recommend not to discourage clients from "following their dreams," unless goals are reachable, it is unlikely they will be able to solve most stressful problems. Expecting oneself to reach unrealistic goals essentially sets one up for failure. Research has repeatedly shown that one major reason why people get depressed is that they set goals for themselves that are unattainable. If a goal initially seems too large to try to accomplish, clients are guided to follow the simplification technique, that is, to break the problem down into smaller pieces, while still keeping their "final destination" in mind. For example, setting the goal of attaining "financial independence by next year" is likely to be out of most people's reach. However, by stating that they wish to "decrease their overall expenses to save an additional 5% of their salary by the end of 1 year" appears more manageable and certainly is moving in the right direction.

Differentiating Between Problem-Focused Versus Emotion-Focused Goals

It is also important for clients to understand the difference between "problem-focused goals" and "emotion-focused goals." *Problem-focused goals* are objectives that involve changing the nature of a situation so that it is no longer a problem. Such goals are more appropriate for situations that *can*, in fact, be changed. Examples include saving more money, improving communication, or losing weight. On the contrary, *emotion-focused goals* are objectives when a situation *cannot* be changed or involve situations in which one's emotional reaction, if unchanged, would create more problems in the long run. For example, fear that one may never be able to get a job that is satisfying, although understandable, is likely to cause more harm if unchecked. Holding onto resentment, anger, or jealousy are other examples.

Therefore, when setting goals, individuals need to determine which types of goals are appropriate for the problems they are trying to resolve. Revisiting Sam, one of the things he *cannot* change is the fact that he was divorced and that some aspects of his social life changed, such as going out as a foursome with Bill and his wife. He cannot be married to his ex-wife again (as per her goals), so that part of the situation is unchangeable. However, decreasing his frustration, embarrassment, and view of himself as a failure as negative emotional reactions he had about being alone are appropriate and important *emotion-focused goals* for him to consider. The goal of *accepting* that his marriage is really over represents another important emotion-focused objective. In addition, his current difficulties with his friend might be possible to change. So, having his friend be more relaxed around him and less avoidant of sharing stories about his own wife and family can be appropriate *problem-focused goals*. This example illustrates the notion that most stressful problems in life usually involve many different types of goals, both emotion-focused *and* problem-focused.

Accepting that certain problems cannot be changed may be especially difficult for some to achieve. From an EC-PST perspective, if a particular client is having difficulty accepting some of "life's negatives" (e.g., loss of a family member, breakup of a relationship, getting older, being diagnosed with a chronic illness), that very goal (i.e., "How can I accept _____") should be identified as a "problem to be solved," and handled using the entire problem-solving process (i.e., applying any of the tools comprising the four tool kits that are relevant). For example, for some, the difficulties in acceptance may be more cognitive (e.g., "I'm not supposed to fail"), emotional (e.g., "I can't deal with my anxiety"), or motivational ("I can never get over losing my spouse—I can never move on") in nature. Thus, the therapist can guide clients to use the appropriate problem-solving tools to foster acceptance that a given problem situation cannot be changed.

Identifying the Obstacles to Overcome

Once one has articulated a goal or set of goals, the next step in problem definition involves identifying obstacles that exist in preventing one from reaching such goals at the present time. Using the analogy of the "problem solver as traveler," goals represent the destination and one identifies obstacles to reaching one's destination (e.g., far distances, time pressure, lack of available resources, conflicts between people regarding where to go to and how to get there) helps greatly to better generate alternative solution ideas (i.e., the means and routes by which to reach the destination).

Identifying these obstacles basically asks the question: *What makes this situation a problem?* This is a key question to answer to help one correctly define the problem. Problems, by definition, involve obstacles to overcome or conflicts to resolve. We may not have sufficient resources or knowledge to reach a goal or there may be too many goals to choose from. As with most of life's more difficult problems, there are usually multiple factors that exist that contribute to the creation of a problem. Identifying such factors also helps us to identify more realistic goals. Sometimes if a problem feels very overwhelming, it is likely that we need to break it down into a set of smaller problems and tackle the various obstacles one at a time (i.e., simplification).

For Sam, one of his obstacles was to overcome his "quick anger trigger" whenever he felt frustrated. He was also experiencing conflicting goals—on one hand, he did want to have Bill's support as well as his friendship; on the other hand, he wanted to feel that he was not becoming a burden and that Bill *wanted* to spend time with him. However, he also wanted to remain honest and be able to tell his friend when he was feeling upset about his divorce.

To correctly define a problem, the client should answer the following questions:

- What present conditions are unacceptable (what is)?
- What changes or additions are demanded or desired (what should be)?
- What obstacle(s) exists that limits my ability to go from *A* to *B* (i.e., what makes it a problem)?

Box 7.1 provides a list of factors that represent why a given situation is a problem for a given individual. By using this list, clients can better identify those dimensions that actually make a situation particularly complex and problematic. Developing a personally relevant list becomes especially important to eventually creating an action plan that truly addresses the most important factors involved in making the situation a problem in the first place.

BOX 7.1 ■ POSSIBLE OBSTACLES TO ONE'S GOALS (WHAT MAKES THIS SITUATION A PROBLEM?)

- *Barriers*—Something or someone blocking your path to a goal
- *Conflicting goals*—Conflicts between yourself and others or regarding two opposing goals you have
- *Conflicting opinions about who "caused" the problem*—Arguments you have with others regarding whose "fault" it is that the problem exists
- *Reduced resources*—Lack of necessary skills or resources that make reaching your goal very difficult
- *The unknown or unfamiliar*—A situation you have not encountered before makes it difficult to know what to do
- *Complexity*—The situation seems very complicated and overwhelming
- *Emotional difficulties*—Your emotional reaction itself is difficult to overcome

Continuing to view oneself as a "problem-solving traveler," the question to specifically ask is: "What is preventing me getting from *A* (where I am now) to *B* (where I want to go)?" Thus, we direct clients to use the list given in Box 7.1 to help complete the part of the Problem-Solving Worksheet that inquires about obstacles. Continuing to invoke the travel analogy: "What kind of roadblocks, long tunnels, expensive tolls, winding roads, or dangerous hills do you need to take into account when planning a trip to get to one's destination by car?" We also remind clients to use clear language and to separate facts from assumptions when completing this task.

Special Considerations When Attempting to Define Problems

The following are important additional issues to consider when training clients in this skill area:

Confusing a solution with a goal. A common mistake that people often make when attempting to define a problem is to think of a "solution as a goal." As an example, consider Jane, a client we worked with who was under stress at her job. Her boss gave her difficult assignments that were rarely given to others. As a result, she felt that he was taking advantage of her and consequently felt overwhelmed with resentment. When Jane first tried to define the problem, she stated,"*How do I let my boss know that I don't appreciate such bad treatment.*" Although she deserved credit for trying to tackle this difficult and stressful problem, criticizing her boss for his way of running the office may be *one* possible alternative solution, but is not a clear description of the problem. When Jane was able to stay focused on *defining* the problem, she took the time to state the facts, separate them out from assumptions, and clarify her goals and obstacles. In her attempt to correctly define the problem, Jane now focused on "the bigger picture problem," rather than how to solve it. She restated her goal as: "*I want to do my job and not constantly have my boss demand more from me; I want my coworkers not to resent me when I can't help them do their work. I want to keep my job secure but also use my spare time to do some things that bring me joy.*" Using this more objective and comprehensive description, there are likely to be many more alternative ways to reach this set of goals beyond the one in which Jane tells her boss that she does not like the way he operates the office.

Another example of confusing a goal with a solution involves a veteran we previously worked with who had recently come back from Afghanistan. During his two deployments, Mario had missed spending time with his preteen son. However, during this same time, Mario's wife functioned essentially as a single mom, by serving as the only parent. Mario's son now tended to avoid him, so Mario originally stated his goal as "I want to spend more time with my son, Mario Jr." However, on delving more deeply into the specifics of the situation, it appeared that Mario and his wife had frequent disagreements about parenting, especially because Mario Jr. tended to listen more to his mom than his dad. This left Mario feeling "impotent" as a father. Given this scenario, Mario's goal was reformulated as "*I want to improve both parenting compatibility with my wife and the quality of my relationship with my son.*" Thus, he was then able to have a much better understanding of the overall problem, identify the relevant obstacles to his newly articulated goals, and to generate multiple alternatives to reach such goals beyond simply spending more time with his son.

> *Whose problem is it anyway?* Most of the time when we describe a problem that we are facing, we tend to think of it solely from our own perspective. Asking this question addresses the notion of whether other people involved in the situation would also consider it to be a problem, as well as whether they would take any responsibility for either having created it or for fixing it (regardless of whether it is justified). In essence, it becomes important for the therapist to ask such questions of clients to broaden their perspective of how other people might react to the situation, especially with regard to identifying additional obstacles. Getting more facts may be an important initial response to this type of question.

> *What is the real problem?* In Chapter 5, one of the EC-PST dos and don'ts we included was the admonition to not focus only on "superficial" problems. It is possible that the problem one enters into therapy with may only represent the "tip of the iceberg." For example, frequent arguments with a spouse or partner about childrearing may be indicative of a deeper set of problems with the basic relationship. Being bored at a job may be more symptomatic of a deeper disillusionment with how one's life is progressing. Thus, it is always important for therapists to keep "their eyes and ears open" to such possibilities. It is frequently the case that going through the entire planful problem-solving process involves circling back to previous steps to reformulate one's problem definition based on more detailed analysis and considerations.

One recent example of this issue involved Marty, an Operation Iraqi Freedom veteran, who came to one of our groups indicating that his major problem was "how to become a better suitcase packer," noting that he was "terrible at packing his clothes properly when taking a trip." On initial further questioning, he continued to be adamant about how important it was for him to learn this skill and that he was hopeful that EC-PST could help him do so. Focusing on a detailed analysis of his "packing problem," plus having him become more comfortable with the group intervention per se, allowed him to later reformulate his problem definition to: *"How can I become less anxious when leaving on a trip away from my family?"* Going through the detailed process of problem definition training, it became apparent that he was very anxious about leaving his family to travel for work because it reminded him of being deployed and being away from them for long periods of time. Having his suitcase packed perfectly somehow came to represent a safe trip, one from which he could return in a timely manner. Although this would appear to be a rather extreme example of this issue, we strongly recommend that the EC-PST therapist be diligent in helping clients to identify and work on the "real problem."

> *When the problem is confusing.* At times, clients may get stuck when trying to accurately define the problem, delineate goals, and/or identify salient obstacles. We have found the following set of questions to be useful in beginning a dialogue that can increase a client's understanding and insight into this process.
>
> - What are your feelings connected with this problem?
> - Is there anything in your past that makes this situation or set of feelings especially challenging for you?
> - Is this situation or problem related to a particular life dream of yours?
> - How is this situation related to your life values?
> - How would your life be different if this problem changed for the better or for the worse?

GENERATION OF ALTERNATIVES

> *Nothing is more dangerous than an idea,*
> *when it's the only one you have.*
>
> —Émile Chartier

The second planful problem-solving skill involves generating alternative ideas to help overcome those obstacles to goal attainment that were previously identified. If we continue to think of problem solving as a journey, reaching one's goals can be thought of as getting from A to B; in other words, reaching one's goals at destination B. As in any journey, even if one is clear about where he or she wants to go, there might be several paths or roads to take to reach B. Often, there are different consequences related to taking different paths—one path might be longer but cost less money, another might be more expensive but is quicker, and yet another might be more scenic yet takes more time. Thus, we recommend that individuals consider "multiple routes to get to their destination."

There are differing consequences associated with differing alternatives; also, believing that there is only one route to take can inhibit one's motivation to actually take the trip (i.e., to solve the problem). To make this point with clients, we would ask them to: "*Think of having only one route to take. Think how you would feel if there was only one cereal to choose from the next time you went to the grocery store, or if there was only one movie listed this coming weekend to see in the entire town where you live.*" When a person is only able to see a very limited number of alternatives to choose from in life, he or she is likely to experience high levels of hopelessness and helplessness. At its most extreme, such tunnel vision can lead to suicidal thoughts and behavior. As noted in the quote from French philosopher Chartier at the beginning of this section, having only one idea can be a dangerous situation. Conversely, when people feel that they have multiple choices, they tend to feel more in control, safe, and full of hope.

Therefore, with real-life stressful problems, we argue that it is generally a good idea for people to think of a *variety* of ways to solve the problem, not only to eventually arrive at the best solution but also to feel more hopeful. The task at hand here is to creatively think about a sizable list of possible ideas. To accomplish this, we recommend applying certain *brainstorming* principles. Brainstorming helps to minimize dichotomous or "black and white" thinking. In addition, it helps to decrease one's tendency to react impulsively—if people are guided to think of a range of ideas, they are forced to be more reflective and planful. Brainstorming also increases one's flexibility and creativity, which can actually improve both quality and quantity of the solutions that are generated.

Using brainstorming principles also helps to discourage judging ideas while thinking about novel solutions. This becomes particularly important when people have strong emotional reactions to problem situations. Emotions can often dominate or influence thinking, such that individuals might rigidly think only of options that maintain their negative thoughts and feelings. When emotions do seem to become overwhelming, brainstorming can help them to get "back on track." Moreover, using brainstorming techniques helps to redirect a person's time and energy to focus on the task of solving a problem. One can concentrate on *productive thinking* rather than on the negative emotions that surround the problem.

Productive thinking involves confronting problems directly by creatively developing a list of possible ways to resolve them. This is in contrast to *nonproductive thinking*, which refers to thoughts *unrelated* to solving a problem, but focused on the consequent emotional distress instead.

In making this point with clients, we offer the following sample rationale:

> *Consider the following differences in the reactions between Rita and Naomi, both of whom missed the last train home from work. Both had dinner engagements scheduled for later in the evening. Rita focuses her attention on her negative thoughts of irresponsibility, carelessness, and unreliability as well as negative emotions of sadness and anger at herself. She also concentrates on her disappointment that the train was gone, which meant that she would arrive home late, causing her to miss her dinner date. She continues to lament and have negative thoughts, which eventually spirals into more negative thoughts and emotions. Several hours later, Rita is still sitting at the station "counting her woes." This is the result of nonproductive thinking.*
>
> *On the contrary, Naomi chooses to stop, slow down, think, and act (SSTA) rationally about her problem ("I have missed the train") as well as her goal ("How can I get home as quickly as possible without ruining my evening, given that I have missed the last train?"). Following this path of productive thinking, Naomi attempts to generate a variety of alternative ways to reach her goal. Her partial list includes calling to delay her dinner date, taking a bus, taking a taxi, asking someone for a ride home, calling home and having someone pick her up, and taking a train to a different station and going straight to the restaurant to meet her dinner date rather than going home first. Several hours later, Naomi is enjoying the evening with a pleasant companion who picked her up at a different train station.*

There are three major brainstorming principles one can to use to foster creativity:

- Quantity principle
- Defer-judgment principle
- Variety principle

Quantity Principle

This principle suggests that it is important to generate a pool of solution options. The concept of generating numerous responses to problems, and to elaborate on these responses, is supported by research findings that show that people can improve the selection of high-quality ideas by increasing the number of alternative solutions proposed. In addition, in keeping with the externalization rule of problem-solving multitasking, drafting a written list of ideas, rather than composing a list of ideas in one's head, can help people to improve both quantity and quality of thinking. Recording ideas on paper (in a computer, smartphone, etc.) keeps the problem solver focused on the task at hand and reduces repetition of ideas or "getting stuck on the same idea." Furthermore, the externalized results of the brainstorming exercise can be maintained for future reference and can serve as a concrete reinforcement of one's problem-solving attempts.

Providing analogies as examples can also aid clients in their attempts to use brainstorming principles. For example, we have often asked our clients the following question: "Which store is more likely to have your size and selection of a sweater, a large store or a smaller store?" Obviously, we all would prefer to go to the larger store to increase our selection choices. Parenthetically, we have come across skeptical clients, who because they may be resistant to learning new techniques, have challenged this analogy. Consider Don, a 46-year-old man who, on hearing the "store" analogy, retorted: "Well, that's not really true because when I went to buy my son's baseball pants, I checked out a few stores and the department store was more expensive than the little shop near our house! I saved 12 bucks!" In response, we pointed out to him, "That's great! Yet, had you not checked out *several* stores, you would have never known what a great deal you got."

Defer-Judgment Principle

To further facilitate brainstorming, we recommend that clients defer judgment. This principle suggests that it is important to first record all ideas that come to mind as a means of increasing the quantity of solutions without judging them. Prematurely rejecting ideas can limit productive and creative thinking that could lead to ultimately identifying the more effective ones. Therefore, we suggest that it is important to refrain from evaluating solutions at this point in the problem-solving process. There is only one criterion to use at this time—that the idea is *relevant* to the problem at hand. Otherwise, we indicate to clients that there is no right or wrong alternative at this juncture—"If you catch yourself (even silently) judging any ideas you have, *STOP* and remind yourself that this will cut down on creativity."

At times, clients may be reluctant to allow themselves to express ideas that they believe are silly, unrealistic, stupid, or could reflect badly upon themselves. We respond to such concerns by emphasizing that deferring judgment actually increases one's effectiveness. For example, even if an idea seems silly or initially impossible, it may spark another related idea that is *not* silly or impossible. Some of the practice exercises that we use when working with people to improve these skills and spark creativity involve having people deliberately offer alternatives that might be regarded as outlandish or impractical if evaluated critically.

Some people may have difficulty adhering to the defer-judgment principle. For example, some clients we have worked with develop the "yeah, but ..." syndrome in response to their own alternatives or ideas offered by another. We have heard the following: "Yeah, *but*, that won't work because ..."; "Yeah, *but*, I would never do that because ..."; "That sounds okay, *but*, what if ..."; "I thought of that, *but*, I didn't write it down because ..." In response to such reactions, we ask clients to consider the following analogy:

> *Think of the list you are putting together as a dinner menu that you need to prepare for your restaurant. On most dinner menus, there are a variety of options to please the tastes of children, adults, senior citizens; people who are very hungry; people who only want a snack; people who want late-night breakfast menus, desserts, or steak dinners. There may be some items on the menu that certain people might not enjoy, or others that they might not have thought of eating at a particular time of day. But, by the very fact that your restaurant offers a variety of choices, you will be more likely to satisfy the vast majority of your patrons. Likewise, deferring judgment about the menu of alternative solutions you create to solve your problems will increase the likelihood that you will have a variety of choices or satisfactory ideas that will meet your goals. You may not like all of the alternatives; however, there is no harm in listing them on the "menu." When you engage in decision making at a later point, you can select the solutions that are best suited for you.*

Variety Principle

According to the variety principle, the greater the range or variety of solution alternatives generated, the more good-quality ideas will be ultimately available. When generating solution ideas, some individuals develop a way of thinking that produces ideas that reflect only *one* strategy or general approach to the problem. This narrow set of ideas can occur even when one applies the quantity and defer-judgment principles. To change such a perspective, we recommend that clients peruse their list of solution alternatives after using the two other brainstorming principles and identify strategies that are different from one another. In essence, this involves identifying different classifications—that is, clients are asked to group solution alternatives according to some common theme.

If any of these general strategies have very few specific "tactics," clients are then guided to think of more specific solution alternatives for that particular strategy. Next, they are asked to think of new strategies that are not yet represented by any of the available solutions and generate additional specific solution ideas or tactics for those strategies.

Learning to differentiate between strategies and tactics can serve to enhance one's brainstorming options. *Strategies* are general courses of action that people can take to try and improve a problem situation. For example, Sophie, a former client, described herself as "angry, sad, and hurt" following several incidents in which her daughter and son-in-law had left her out of holiday plans and special events that involved her grandchildren. She brainstormed multiple ideas about how she might communicate with her grown daughter and son-in-law her hope that their relationship might be improved. Her goal was to communicate how important the relationship was to her and what she believed needed to take place for it to change. She listed a few general *strategies* first, which included the following:

- Ignore their acts of insensitivity.
- Express anger and feelings of hurt.
- Invite them to stay with her for a few days to talk.
- Ask them to be kinder to her and include her in family celebrations.
- Threaten to remove them from her will unless they change.
- Tell them that it is important for her to see her grandchildren.
- Communicate clearly and specifically how she hopes to be treated in the future.

We define *tactics* as specific steps involved in putting a strategy into action. When thinking about different tactics, we encourage people to generate as many options as possible, while continuing to defer judgment. Getting back to Sophie, she also generated tactics in her list of alternatives. For example, under the general strategy of communicating clearly and specifically how she hoped to be treated in the future, she generated the following tactics:

- Speak to her daughter and son-in-law about her concerns the next time she sees them.
- Make specific arrangements to discuss the matter.
- Send an email.
- Write a letter.
- Have another family member communicate her feelings.

- Have someone neutral mediate the discussion.
- Call them on the telephone.

By providing differing ways to think of alternatives, the strategy–tactics principle often provides new viewpoints from which to identify alternative solutions. Overall problem-solving efforts are likely to be less effective or productive if limited by the use of only one strategy. Therefore, we recommend that people think of a variety of both strategies *and* tactics rather than focusing on only one or two narrow tactics or limiting oneself only to general approaches.

For example, returning to Sophie, on the basis of feedback from her therapist, she became aware that all of her strategies were centered on the theme of ways to get her daughter and son-in-law to change. When she realized this, she decided to try to think of other available general strategies. With her therapist's help, she realized that getting herself and her husband to change and accepting their daughter's behavior as out of their control represented a whole series of other options that she had not recognized earlier. There were many new tactics she was then able to list under the category of "ways that I can change to improve the relationship." These included the following:

- Arrange her own family celebrations and events.
- Communicate directly with her grandchildren.
- Change her view of their behavior as less negative.
- Ask her husband's help in arranging special visits.
- Reduce her expectations.

By applying the variety principle for thinking about both strategies *and* tactics, Sophie ultimately was able to choose from a larger pool of ideas about how to handle this problem.

Keeping the Creative Juices Flowing

Sometimes people get "stuck" in being able to generate multiple ideas for solutions. We offer the following ways to help get "unstuck" and become more creative:

- *Combine ideas*—Take two or more ideas, put them together to make a third idea.
- *Slightly modify an idea*—Take one idea and slightly change it (e.g., make it larger, smaller, change its color, add more people).

- *Think of how others might solve the problem*—Think of various people, such as role models (e.g., sports figures, politicians, TV personalities, community or religious leaders) or favored relatives or friends, and think of what they might do to solve the problem.

- *Visualize*—Imagine various obstacles to the problem-solving goal and then imagine oneself (or others) jumping over these hurdles—what did you have to do?

Practice Generating Alternatives

Learning any new skill often requires that people first practice the easier steps or tasks. For example, we often suggest to clients: "*You probably did not go on a major highway the first day you learned to drive; you probably did not enter a tennis tournament the second time you took a tennis lesson.*" If generating multiple ideas proves a bit difficult for certain individuals with regard to the real-life problems that they are currently experiencing, one way to improve their basic creativity skills is to practice with "fun" examples or problems that only may be hypothetical.

For example, we often use the following example when working with groups: How many ideas can we generate about what one can do with a single brick? We suggest that therapists use this exercise consistently with clients. It tends to be a fun exercise, but also generally promotes the insight that a large pool of ideas can actually be produced. More important, clients learn how to use the various tools with regard to a nonemotion-provoking example. For this exercise, clients are directed to write down as many ideas as possible about different things one can do with a single brick within a 5-minute time limit. If they experience creative blocks, guide them to apply the various brainstorming and creativity tools contained in this tool kit.

A second "fun" idea might be to think of as many things as possible one can do with a wire hanger. A more real-life problem, perhaps one that a client is currently experiencing, might be to think of as many ideas as possible regarding how one can meet new people having moved to another neighborhood and feeling somewhat isolated. Note that in addition to providing practice, if one engages in these types of mental exercises (e.g., categorizing alternatives), his or her ability for subsequent creative problem solving becomes enhanced.

Handling Interfering Emotional Reactions

On occasion, one's emotional reactions to discussing a stressful problem can inhibit a person's creativity in generating alternatives. If this occurs, the therapist can briefly introduce some of the strategies given in the "*Stop and Slow Down*"

Tool Kit (Chapter 10) to help such an individual overcome this type of obstacle. In addition, research in the sphere of cognitive problem solving has indicated that distancing oneself from the problem can actually serve to enhance creative problem solving. For example, extrapolating from this research, we suggest that by imagining that the problem is actually situated far away in distance (e.g., miles away) or in time (e.g., 1 year from now), one's ability to solve problems can be greatly enhanced. Additional research also suggests that if a client is stuck with a difficult or complex problem, one effective option is to "take a break" or engage in a different activity, because nonconscious processing has been found to engender effective answers to difficult problems when such problems require an extensive search of stored knowledge.

DECISION-MAKING

Quick decisions are unsafe decisions.

—Sophocles

The third planful problem-solving skill involves decision-making. This set of tools helps individuals to

- Better predict the consequences of their actions.
- Conduct a cost–benefit analysis regarding the previously generated alternatives.
- Develop an action plan that constitutes an overall solution.

Now Is the Time to Judge

In an attempt to increase the number of high-quality solutions available, our recommendations when generating alternative solutions involve applying the brainstorming principle of deferring judgment. Now that several alternatives have been generated, it is time for the problem solver to begin making judgments. This involves evaluating the likely success of the various options and deciding which ones to implement. This initially involves predicting the positive and negative consequences of each alternative idea. People, especially when they are distressed, may initially wish only to consider how effective a solution might be in terms of "taking away the problem ASAP." By being more objective and systematic when evaluating each idea, one stands a better chance of minimizing negative consequences and maximizing positive consequences. However, whether a consequence is positive or negative depends heavily on the situation and can differ greatly depending on *who* is having the problem and who else is involved. The same consequence may be evaluated positively by some, but negatively by others. That is why we strongly recommend, especially for individuals who have particular difficulty with this task, to use a systematic approach when evaluating alternatives and making decisions. As the quote by 19th-century American lawyer, Robert Ingersoll, suggested—*In nature there are neither rewards nor punishments; there are consequences.*

The "Fallout" of Bad Decisions

Often people think of solutions as *any* action taken to solve a problem. What sometimes we forget is that there are many ineffective solutions that may solve a *part* of the problem, but simultaneously also create additional problems, distress, or various other negative consequences. For example, drinking, gambling, avoidance, aggressive statements and behavior, or thinking in ways to try and convince oneself of something that is not accurate are all ways that people try to "solve" problems every day. These solutions often provide some short-term relief or distraction, but can have many lasting negative consequences. Such actions often create additional problems and the individual eventually is left feeling frustrated, hopeless, and ineffective. Thus, it is important for individuals to try to predict both the benefits (as well as the *costs*) of a course of action and its impact on one's overall well-being and that of others.

As indicated in Chapter 1, effective solutions are those that not only help to achieve one's goals but also reduce negative side effects or fallout. Sometimes, effective decisions may be a bit more difficult to implement in the short term, but can ultimately have many positive short-term *and* long-term consequences.

To illustrate this point, consider Bernice, a person who has a history of relationships in which she sacrificed herself for the needs and desires of others. Although she was the only person who had a full-time job in her family, Bernice frequently changed her plans based on the "whims" of her aging parents who lived nearby. When she wanted to move away from them to take a better paying job, for example, she received little support. Her parents complained: "Who would take us to doctors' appointments or family get-togethers?" Bernice had a long pattern of blaming herself and believing that she had to always please others, even though her partner, Lisa, tried hard to convince her to become more independent. However, her parents were always supportive of her same-sex relationship with Lisa. Therefore, in trying to cope with this problem, one of Bernice's initial solution alternatives was "*to convince my partner, Lisa, that the move and the new job aren't so important—I'd rather stay put so I don't have to deal with guilt from my family. After all, they are supportive of us."* However, Lisa often felt frustrated watching others take advantage of Bernice's generous nature and became frequently angry that Bernice's family was not supportive of the move, especially because it meant a significant boost for her career.

Unfortunately, Bernice often fought with Lisa and secretly wished that Lisa would just do what her parents wanted so the problem could be avoided. However, the more that Bernice considered this alternative, the more she realized that there were many long-term consequences for choosing this option. For one, she was missing out on an important and well-earned job. In addition, there were consequences for her relationship with Lisa. Finally, she realized that her family members were unlikely to change, and no matter how much she thought "well, there always will be another job offer," it was likely that she would continually face the same problem. As Bernice became more creative in generating alternatives, she discovered that there were other ways she could objectively be a resource to her parents, without having to sacrifice her career and her own happiness.

Making Decisions Can Help Reduce Worry and Anxiety

Interestingly, neuroscience research suggests that the act of making decisions can be helpful in reducing anxiety in addition to solving problems. According to neuroscientist Alex Korb (2015), making decisions can engage the prefrontal cortex in a positive way, reducing worry and anxiety, which helps to reduce striatum activity (that part of the brain responsible for good and bad habits), which can minimize the likelihood of engaging in negative impulses and can calm the limbic system (the overall part of the brain that is largely responsible for emotions).

Making Effective Decisions

Making decisions about what to do to solve a difficult problem can be hard. As Irish novelist, George Moore, once said—*"The difficulty in life is the choice."* However, even though making decisions can be tough, it can lead to more control over one's life and enhance well-being.

Our model involves the following four steps to making effective decisions:

- Screen out obviously ineffective solutions.
- Predict a range of possible consequences.
- Evaluate the predicted solution outcomes.
- Identify effective solutions and develop a solution plan.

Rough Screening of Solution Alternatives

The overall decision-making task can be made easier if one conducts an initial rough screening of the list of possible alternatives to eliminate any that are clearly inferior. Remember that the only criterion that should have been used during the process of thinking of ideas is one of *relevancy*. Therefore, it is possible that several ineffective ideas were generated "in the spirit of brainstorming." Rather than spending time rating each alternative, it is advisable to conduct such an initial screening. At this point, alternatives can be considered "clearly ineffective" if they have (a) obvious unacceptable risks associated with their implementation and/or (b) low feasibility. *Unacceptable risks* refer to likely serious negative consequences that significantly reduce the effectiveness of the solution. *Low feasibility* refers to the low likelihood that the solution could actually be implemented by the problem solver because of lack of ability, lack of resources, or other major obstacles.

Predicting Consequences

In evaluating the remaining solution options, clients are further taught to think of two major categories when predicting consequences: (a) likelihood estimates and (b) value estimates. *Likelihood* estimates involve two assessments:

- The likelihood that a given solution will actually achieve the stated problem-solving goal(s); that is, *will this solution work?*
- The likelihood that the problem solver will be able to actually implement the solution in an *optimal* manner; that is, *can I carry it out?*

Value estimates involve predicting the total expected positive consequences (i.e., benefits, gains) *and* negative consequences (i.e., costs, losses) of a particular solution alternative, including long-term as well as immediate consequences, and social as well as personal consequences.

Personal consequences that should be considered include the following:

- Effects on emotional well-being
- Time and effort expended
- Effects on physical well-being
- Effects on psychological well-being (e.g., depression, anxiety, self-esteem)
- Effects on economic well-being (e.g., job security)
- Self-enhancement (e.g., achievements, knowledge)
- Effects on other personal goals, values, and commitments

Some of the more important *social consequences* that should be considered include

- Effects on the personal and/or social well-being of significant others
- Effects on the rights of others
- Effects on significant interpersonal relationships
- Effects on personal and/or social performance evaluations (e.g., reputation, status, prestige)

It is clear from the checklists previously mentioned that solutions for real-life problems may have many different consequences. Considering the limited capacity of the conscious mind to handle large amounts of information, it is important to write down (i.e., externalize) the major significant expected consequences (e.g., "I am likely to feel very guilty; my parents will be very hurt; in the long run, I could lose my job"). This will help to facilitate the task of evaluating one's solution alternatives.

Evaluating Solution Outcomes

Considering the consequences listed earlier, we direct clients to ask themselves the following four questions:

- Will this solution solve the problem?
- Can I really carry it out?
- What are the overall effects on me, both short term and long term?
- What are the overall effects on others, both short term and long term?

To foster a systematic approach to decision-making, for each alternative idea remaining after the initial screening, clients can use a simple rating scale in response to these four questions (e.g., −1 = negative; 0 = neutral; +1 = positive). More "complex" rating systems can be developed for high-risk problem solving, in which the consequences of a relatively ineffective solution might be serious (e.g., a scale of 1–5, where 1 = slightly satisfactory and 5 = very satisfactory). Furthermore, if appropriate, clients could place more weight or emphasis on a particular outcome criterion by establishing a minimum rating for a given criterion. For example, if emotional well-being was considered particularly important regarding a given problem, one might decide to eliminate any alternative that is not rated as a "+" for this criterion. Clients can also add new outcome criteria or eliminate criteria, depending on their appraisal of the significance of different outcomes for different problem situations. For example, in some situations, financial cost might be a particularly significant criterion to consider when judging solution alternatives (e.g., "what to do when your washing machine breaks down"). Instead of considering this criterion as part of the overall personal effects criterion, it can be given special emphasis by considering it separately. The point here is to establish a systematic method of conducting the cost–benefit analysis. However, unless the problem is extremely complex, we advocate using a rather simple scale (i.e., −1 to +1) to make the decision-making process more user-friendly. Keeping in mind the externalization rule, the various solution alternatives and ratings should be written down. To simplify the task of comparing alternatives, they can be summarized in a chart.

Difficulties in Anticipating and Evaluating Solution Alternatives

It is not always easy to predict and evaluate specific consequences of solutions before they are experienced, especially subjective consequences such as feelings and emotions. Two visualization procedures that might be helpful in this regard include behavior rehearsal and imaginal rehearsal. *Behavior rehearsal* or role-play (with the EC-PST counselor or other group member if conducting group EC-PST) is particularly useful with regard to solving interpersonal problems (e.g., dealing with the offensive behavior of another person). *Imaginal rehearsal* involves experimenting with different coping options using visualization. Both of these rehearsal procedures may help a person identify and evaluate the various social and emotional consequences of different solution possibilities.

Identifying Effective Solutions and Developing a Solution Plan

On the basis of the systematic evaluation of the available solution alternatives, clients are directed next to ask the following three questions:

- Is the problem solvable? (That is, "Is there a satisfactory solution?")
- Do I need more information before I can select a solution or combination of ideas to carry out?
- What solution or solution combination should I choose to implement?

Is the Problem Solvable?

Answering this question requires that one begins to add up the ratings for each alternative (e.g., how many "plusses," how many "minuses," and how many "zeros"). If one is able to actually identify effective solutions based on these ratings, the answer to the question should be yes. In other words, effective alternatives are those with the least number of negative consequences (i.e., less minuses) and the most number of positive consequences (i.e., more plusses). However, when making this evaluation, clients are reminded that *no* solution is perfect. If one's alternative solutions with the highest ratings would likely produce some negative consequences, people are directed to look over the other listed alternatives and determine whether any other ideas existed would not have the same negative effects. Some people have found that through this process, they are able to think about how to slightly change or adjust the highest rated alternative to further reduce the negative consequences associated with it. However, it is important to remember that it may not be possible to reduce *all* negative consequences.

Do I Need More Information Before I Can Select a Solution or Solution Combination for Implementation?

If the result of the aforementioned scrutiny suggests that one's alternatives appear to be rated as basically negative (i.e., associated with a lot of minuses), it is likely that one should reconsider whether the problem was correctly defined or whether a sufficient pool of alternatives was generated. If so, clients are then directed to circle back and engage in either or both steps once again.

However, another possibility exists if there are very few potentially effective solution ideas—individuals may begin to realize that after contemplating the various options and their consequences, that in fact, this problem is *not* solvable in terms of being able to be "fixed." If so, they then need to reconsider the goals and reformulate them to ones that are more *emotion focused* (e.g., changing one's emotional reaction to the problem; accepting that the situation cannot be changed the way one would like) compared with continuing to try to "solve an unsolvable problem."

What Solution or Solution Combination Should I Choose to Implement?

Clients are next directed to choose those alternatives that have the best ratings to develop an *action plan*. We use the term *action plan* to emphasize the notion that the solution plan needs to be carried out and put in motion, even if it involves "nonaction" (e.g., attempting to accept that a given problem cannot be changed). In keeping with our definition of an *effective solution*, an action plan should be consistent with the general goal of resolving the problem satisfactorily, while maximizing positive consequences and minimizing negative effects.

This "action plan" may be *simple* or *complex*. For a simple plan, based on the evaluation ratings, one can choose a single solution or course of action. When there is one solution that is expected to produce a highly satisfactory outcome, such a simple plan may suffice. There are two types of complex plans—a *solution combination* and a *contingency plan*. For a solution combination, one might choose a combination of solution alternatives to be implemented concurrently. This is done when it appears that the combination is likely to have greater utility than any solution alone, or when several obstacles are targeted for change either sequentially or simultaneously. As noted earlier, many problems in life are complex and require that multiple obstacles be overcome prior to effective problem resolution. Therefore, identifying several specific solution tactics to comprise an overall solution plan at times is highly advisable. Contingency plans involve choosing a combination of solutions to be implemented contingently— that is, implement solution A first; if that does not work, implement solution B; if that does not work, carry out solution C; and so forth.

Another type of contingency plan occurs when one first implements a particular course of action *A* and, then, depending on the outcome of *A*, the problem solver carries out either *B* or *C*. Such a contingency plan is chosen when there is enough uncertainty about any one solution or solution combination that it seems advisable to have a contingency plan to save time in case the initial solution choice(s) is unsuccessful. Once the solution plan has been prepared, the final step before solution implementation is to fill in the details as to exactly how, when, and where the action plan will be implemented.

PRACTICE EXAMPLE

As an example to allow clients to practice these decision-making tools, the following problem can be used:

> *Problem: You and your family are driving to a movie, but running late. You see that you are low on gas. You might be able to make it to the theatre without stopping, and yet, looking at the time, if you do stop, you will probably be late. However, you may not have enough gas to get to the theatre and back home. What do you do?*

> *Goal: To have a nice evening with your family, possibly watching a movie together.*

> *Possible alternatives:*

> - *Do not stop and keep driving to the movie.*
> - *Stop for gas.*
> - *Forget about the movie for tonight.*

- *Stop and call Triple A.*
- *Go to a restaurant closer to where you are now.*
- *Go to a shopping mall instead.*
- *Call a friend to bring gas to you.*
- *Park the car and call for a taxi.*

Predicting consequences (a sample explanation provided to a client is as follows):

> *In predicting the consequences, let's consider the first option, "Do not stop and keep driving to the movie." For now, try practicing how to identify, predict, and evaluate the hypothetical effects that might occur if you were experiencing this problem. Write down the various consequences in your journal, notebook, or computer and then evaluate each one. As an example, note what one person we worked with, Fred, wrote down in terms of possible consequences:*
>
> *Effects on me—I feel very anxious while driving; exhausted from walking if we run out of gas; feel bad for getting family stuck; feel angry with myself for not stopping earlier (an important value I have for myself is being better prepared); we may not get to the movie if car runs out of gas; we may have to walk for gas; I don't know where the nearest station is; I might feel relieved if we make it to the movie in time; gas station may not be open after movie.*
>
> *Effects on others—Family would be scared and upset if we don't make it; family would be happy if we make it to movie on time; I set a bad example for my kids by being unprepared.*

This example obviously has no perfect answer, but it was designed to give clients practice in predicting consequences and rating alternatives and to become aware that most alternatives lead to *some* positive and *some* negative consequences. In part, the actual ratings given by different people may reflect differing values, priorities, or interests. Once again, that is why we underscore the notion that the same problem for different people is likely to lead to differing solutions. For additional practice, we strongly recommend that clients attempt to apply these decision-making tools to their own personal problems in session to receive feedback from the therapist.

SOLUTION IMPLEMENTATION AND VERIFICATION

There are costs and risks to a program of action,
but they are far less than the long-range risks
and costs of comfortable inaction.

—John F. Kennedy

The fourth and last planful problem-solving activity involves both carrying out the action plan (solution implementation) and assessing its outcome (solution verification). Although it is likely that the problem solver might feel satisfied once the action plan is carried out, according to our approach, doing so is not the end of the process. A more careless/impulsive approach is to cease being systematic and planful once a decision is made and the action plan is carried out. To become an effective problem solver, we strongly recommend that there is one more component to this last step—to monitor and evaluate the actual success of the solution plan *after it is carried out.* This is important to:

- Determine whether one needs to continue to work on the problem or whether the problem is actually successfully resolved.
- Understand what areas, if any, of one's problem-solving skills require some additional fine-tuning.

The Problem-Solving Outcome Will Not Always Be Perfect

We emphasize the aforementioned concept with clients because some individuals continue to hold unrealistically high expectations for themselves. We have heard people say, "*But I really tried hard and it still didn't turn out the way I wanted it to.*" Being an effective problem solver is to keep one's expectations realistic. In addition, it is important to focus on the positive consequences, rather than only on the negative effects.

Carrying Out the Action Plan

This step in the problem-solving process involves the following activities:

- Motivate oneself to carry out the action plan.
- Prepare to carry out the action plan.
- Implement the action plan.
- Observe and monitor the effects of the solution.

- Prepare oneself for engaging in the planful problem-solving process.
- Troubleshoot areas of difficulty.

Motivating Oneself to Carry Out the Action Plan

Although many clients are eager to carry out their action plans, especially having gone through all the previous steps of defining the problem, generating alternatives, and making decisions regarding the content of one's action plan, others may remain trepidatious, or even fearful about taking action. This can occur either because of what it means about changes in oneself (e.g., changing the way one has been thinking for such a long time) or changing the nature of the problem situation itself (e.g., trying to change others' behavior or certain situations). For clients who are weary about making changes, and thus tend to avoid implementing an action plan, we recommend that they engage in a motivational exercise to foster their willingness to complete the process. Such an exercise is described in Chapter 9 as the first tool in Tool Kit #3, Enhancing Motivation for Action. Specifically, clients are directed to identify and compare the possible benefits that might occur if the action plan is successful (even partially) versus the consequences if nothing is done to address the problem.

Preparing to Carry Out the Action Plan

The next step is to consider any predicted or perceived obstacles that might have been uncovered during the previous exercise. Obstacles that might impact the problem solver's ability to carry out the solution plan in its optimal form should be assessed. For example, consider Alicia, a client who chose to enroll in a yoga class for relaxation and stress-reduction purposes. In considering the steps by which she would enroll and participate in the class, she subsequently learned that the class time conflicted with her husband's evening work shift. Therefore, a new problem emerged, that of difficulty with transportation (i.e., her husband needed their one car to get to work), one that first needed to be resolved.

To help overcome these newly identified obstacles to *optimal* solution implementation, questions the therapist may ask include, "*Are there ways to modify the solution plan that would overcome the obstacle* (e.g., implement it at a different time of the day, with different supports)?" "*Is there a direct approach by which the obstacle can be handled*?" Depending on the magnitude of the obstacle and the severity of the impact it may have on the problem-solving attempt, clients may need to revisit previous problem-solving activities. The focus of the problem-solving efforts at this point in the process may be to alter the existing plan, develop a new solution plan, or choose to temporarily postpone the implementation of a specific action plan to develop a resolution to the identified obstacle.

If certain skill deficits are identified related to the designated solution plan, the strategies of solving the problem need to be reevaluated. Essentially, in keeping with the problem-solving model, the therapist is faced with deciding among the following options: (a) to incorporate the appropriate skills training into the therapy (or have it obtained outside of the EC-PST intervention), (b) to instruct the client to return to certain previous planful problem-solving activities to develop a new plan, or (c) to work with the client to reformulate the overall definition of the problem situation to include the skill deficits as an obstacle to overcome in the overall solution plan of a particular identified problem. In essence, such a decision requires therapists to engage in problem solving themselves with the overall goal of "helping this particular client with these given limitations and strengths to overcome the short-term problem identified, and the long-term goal of improving certain coping skills in future problematic situations." If the skill deficits identified are likely to interfere with future problem-solving efforts, the client is likely to benefit from addressing these difficulties at some point in therapy.

When individuals are making decisions concerning the options that appeared to be potentially most effective, they need at times also to develop an action plan regarding "how it will be carried out" (e.g., a simple or complex plan, a solution combination or contingency plan). This is particularly important because even with the most creative and useful ideas, it is necessary to have a step-by-step plan of how one will put the plan into action. Once again, we recommend that it is helpful to have the steps of such a plan written down.

To illustrate, let us revisit Jane from earlier in this chapter. She was the individual who was experiencing a problem with her boss at work. Jane's problem-solving goals were to be recognized and compensated for the work she was expected to do that was beyond the requirements of her job as a secretary for a public television news station. More specific, in addition to the secretarial duties that defined her job, she was often planning and managing special events, preparing promotional articles about the station for their public education campaign, and helping the station manager handle the volunteer staff. After generating and rating many alternatives to help reach her goals, Jane selected the alternative of arranging a special meeting with her boss to request a raise as an important first step. Her plan included the following:

- Set up the meeting during the time when budgets were being decided.
- Make this appointment with her boss at the end of the day on a Monday (Mondays, in general, were less hectic and there was less stress in the station).

- Make a list of the work that she completed that was in excess of the requirements of her position.

- Estimate the financial benefits to the station for her additional work (e.g., successfully organizing the volunteers; the amount of donations received after a successful event).

In addition, to help her carry out this plan optimally, Jane asked her cousin Kerry, who worked for a human resources department for a large local company, to role-play this upcoming meeting and provide tips and feedback on the words and behavior that might help get her points across effectively. Jane then made a list of everything she needed to do to optimally carry out her plan to be able to monitor the effects of each step along the way.

Carrying Out the Action Plan

To increase the likelihood that one is able to carry out an action plan in its most optimal fashion, there are some additional tips:

- Rehearse the plan in one's imagination before carrying it out.

- Like Jane, role-play the action plan with someone trustworthy.

- Think the plan "aloud" (e.g., *First I need to state my goals and to think about the positive consequences that will occur when I solve this problem. Now I need to take a deep breath and go ahead and carry out the solution. When I begin talking to my boss, I realize that I might get anxious, so I need to practice what I might say to him right before I see him. Then I will remind myself to speak calmly and deliberately so I don't get more nervous.*").

- Write down the steps in detail, similar to an instruction in a user's manual.

Monitoring the Outcome

For individuals trying to lose weight, it makes sense to be weighed on a weekly basis. If one is trying to save additional money, it makes sense to balance the checkbook and keep sales receipts. If one is trying to lower high blood pressure, it makes sense to go for routine physicals. Such examples, in part, provide for a rationale that we provide to clients to underscore the importance of monitoring one's actual performance in carrying out the solution, as well as the outcome itself. We recommend (what a surprise!) that clients externalize (record) such information. We are amazed by the number and variety of smartphone applications that can help one to accomplish this quite easily.

Evaluating the Outcome

The next step is to evaluate one's actual performance, when relevant, regarding the implementation of the action plan. For example, Jane observed that she experienced significant anxiety and fear thinking that asking for financial recognition would seem too pushy (i.e., she was always hesitant to assert herself). However, she discovered that listing out the actual financial benefits of her work was helpful for her to better realize and accept her own value to the station. Thus, Jane actually found it easier (although still somewhat anxious) to ask for increased compensation for this extra work. In addition, she was able to become aware that until she role-played with her cousin to practice what she would say, she was not feeling very confident. However, the role-play practice and advice from her cousin helped her to develop a flexible "script" with which she felt more comfortable and less anxious.

In addition, clients are further directed to evaluate the overall effects of the solution, at least those that have occurred thus far (i.e., it is unlikely that "long-term" effects have yet occurred). In essence, they are guided to determine how well the actual outcomes match those that were predicted earlier during the decision-making process.

Following is a series of questions that can help this evaluation process in a concrete and focused manner:

- How well did your action plan meet your goals?
- How satisfied are you with its effects on you?
- How well do these results match your original prediction about personal consequences?
- How satisfied are you with the impact on others involved in the problem?
- How well do these results match your original prediction about the consequences concerning others?
- Overall, how satisfied are you with the results of your action plan?

Essentially, clients are directed to answer these questions using a scale of 1 (*not at all*) to 5 (*very much*). On the basis of answers to these questions, they are then asked by the therapist the basic question—"*Was the match between what you predicted or expected to occur and what actually happened a strong match?*"

If the answer to this question is essentially yes, clients are directed to go to the next step in the set of planful problem-solving activities—self-reinforcement.

Giving Self-Reinforcement

If clients are successful in their problem-solving efforts, evaluating the actual resulting consequences allows them to acknowledge their accomplishment and helps them to accept responsibility for their productive and positive actions. To facilitate recognition of effective problem solving, we direct clients to use self-reinforcement as an additional skill in the process of resolving problems. Self-reinforcement helps to underscore the importance of any and all problem-solving attempts. Planning a specific and desired form of self-reinforcement as a reward for successfully overcoming a particular problem can also motivate people to initiate problem-solving attempts in the future. Although the primary motivation for engaging in problem solving should be to reduce distress, overcome difficulties, and increase or decrease a particular behavior, feeling, or thought process, self-reinforcement is intended to be a "bonus" for achieving goals.

Self-reinforcement can take many forms. A reinforcer may consist of a concrete reward such as purchasing a new object, engaging in a pleasurable activity, praising oneself, or relieving oneself of an obligation or chore. In our experience, clients have purchased albums, clothes, sporting equipment, or computer products as rewards. Others have made time for themselves or allotted finances to engage in activities they typically did not have the opportunity to enjoy (e.g., going to the movies, taking a day off from work, sleeping later than usual). The temporary relief from certain obligations or stressors may also serve as a reward for some individuals. A 32-year-old mother, Anna, described her self-reinforcement as hiring a babysitter while she spent 1 day doing pleasurable activities for herself without having to take care of her 4-year-old daughter. Clients should be encouraged to begin brainstorming a potential list of reinforcers prior to implementing a given action plan. Problem-solving attempts are initiated for different problems, so the list of reinforcers may change to reflect a reward that is more closely related to overcoming the difficulty at hand (e.g., purchasing new clothes as a cancer patient improves her body-image concerns after breast surgery).

The practice of self-reinforcement is particularly important for individuals who think of themselves as poor problem-solvers and who have poor self-efficacy beliefs with regard to their ability to cope with difficult problems. Recognizing their ability to successfully resolve a problem will increase their belief that they will be able to handle difficult problems in the future. Furthermore, if people increase their awareness of how the application of problem-solving skills aided them in resolving problems, they will also be more likely to rely on these skills when problems arise.

Troubleshooting When Problem-Solving Efforts Are Not Successful

Clients should be prepared during the training sessions to expect that everyone encounters situations in which their problems are not solved by the *first* solution plan attempted. The importance for the therapist to discuss this likelihood cannot be overstated. However, clients should also be reassured that after troubleshooting and recycling through other problem-solving operations, most problems are likely to eventually get resolved. Therefore, having implemented an action plan that results in less than optimal consequences is not a reason for giving up. Those whose solution plans were not found to be effective should follow the course of troubleshooting.

Troubleshooting for the client represents reviewing each step of the problem-solving process to identify where the complications surfaced. Specific to solution implementation, *troubleshooting* refers to identifying the areas where the actual consequences do not match the predicted consequences and subsequently attempting to understand why the discrepancy occurred. On the basis of information accrued when people monitor and evaluate the solution outcome, they will be able to determine where the changes are necessary. For example, did the solution plan fail to achieve the desired personal effects, social effects, or goal attainment? Evaluating the difficulties that arose will lead to a quicker optimal resolution than immediately dismissing the entire problem-solving effort as a failure. By choosing not to review the problem-solving steps and overall solution plan, people risk repeating ineffective methods for coping with their problems. If clients do need to find new approaches to solve their problems, it is recommended that the entire set of tools (where relevant) across the four tool kits be reviewed and used to increase the structure of renewed attempts.

CLINICAL EXAMPLES OF EC-PST WORKSHEETS: REVISITING MEGAN, MARK, AND DAVID

The following section includes examples of various Problem-Solving Worksheets completed by the three clients presented earlier in Chapter 6. Note that each had completed numerous worksheets throughout the treatment as a means of practicing various planful problem-solving skills. What follows is a selection of worksheets that represented areas of unique challenge for each person.

Revisiting Megan: Challenges With Problem Definition

We offer an example of a client's difficulties in defining a problem. As Megan tried to complete this worksheet, she had the benefit of six previous sessions in which the other tool kits were introduced and practiced separately. In the current session, the therapist made the decision to incorporate tools that were introduced earlier to help her "bring it all together" and use the planful problem-solving tools to begin developing an action plan. When Megan tried to use the worksheet to define a problem, it became apparent that she was stuck and had difficulty "seeing" a successful outcome. Her therapist decided to use the visualization exercise to help her overcome feelings of hopelessness to increase her efforts to manage her anxiety, as well as to use visualization to help her better clarify her problems.

Megan had revealed an exaggerated fear of being alone if she were to disappoint or be the source of any discomfort to any of her friends or family members in even the smallest way. Thus, it was important for her to identify this as a possible obstacle that often prevented her from brainstorming alternative solutions without judgment. As the clinical dialogue that follows illustrates, Megan had difficulty generating any alternatives that might involve even a gentle and kind interpersonal confrontation.

This clinical dialogue occurred after Megan stated that an important goal for her was to "face the problems that I have with my roommate so we can connect again." When considering several of the obstacles that stood in the way of her achieving this goal, Megan listed three barriers that she had come to recognize that were in her way: anxiety, sad feelings, and low motivation. These barriers appeared chronic and significant and she was becoming hopeless about any successful resolution. These became evident as she attempted to define her problem.

Megan's therapist suggested that to increase her motivation (one of her barriers), they should practice the visualization exercise together. Following is a brief dialogue between Megan (M) and her therapist (T) discussing the worksheet that she was attempting to complete. This captures the results of the visualization and continued work on the worksheet (see Chapter 9 for a description of the visualization exercise).

M: So, the goal I wrote down is to get my roommate to abstain from drinking completely, because I used visualization for motivation to help me picture where I wanted to go with my problem. In this visualization, I was relaxed, happy, and saw my roommate as sober. But I know that she doesn't see herself as an "alcoholic" like me.

T: And it's really tough if you focus your goal on trying to change someone else. That is what we call an unrealistic goal. Let's discuss for a moment the visualization you just described to me with regard to a future point in time when the problem is largely resolved.

M: You mean the part where I was happy and relaxed?

T: Yes. What was going on in this image that you had of a future point in time? Describe the scene for me. Let's see whether we can also use this visualization to better clarify your goals and identify some obstacles.

M: In the scene, my roommate and I are having coffee and planning a garden at our place and I was thinking "we can actually do this!"

T: Is it necessary for your roommate to fully embrace abstinence and label herself as *alcoholic* for you to do this project together?

M: No, but I would need to do it with someone reliable, who I could count on, who wouldn't go on a weekend binge and leave me with the whole project unfinished.

T: Okay. Have you asked your roommate whether this is something she would want to do with you and commit to it?

M: Oh, gosh … [starts crying]. Here I go, starting to cry.

T: This might be a good time to use the "Stop and Slow Down" tool kit (see Chapter 10) to give you some balance so we can continue to complete the worksheet together.

M: Okay … okay [makes a yoga mudra with her hands over her head and takes several long breaths with her eyes closed].

T: What are these important feelings telling you?

M: I'm scared she won't follow through and I'm afraid to tell her that because she may think I don't trust her and feel bad … that's why it would be an easier solution if she committed to total sobriety, like me.

T: Great … good insight. Of course, though, that's just one solution. After we define the problem, list your goals and barriers, we can also think of many others and list them on your worksheet.

After working together to complete Megan's worksheet, the end result was a realistic goal that Megan believed was possible for her to implement. Following are parts of her worksheet.

PROBLEM DEFINITION

What is your problem-solving goal?

> *To invite Chelsea to work on planning and executing a weekend gardening project in our backyard and not drinking when we actively work on the project together.*

What are the major obstacles to achieving your goal at this time?

1. *Fear that my roommate (Chelsea) will be hurt or get angry that I don't trust her*
2. *Fear that Chelsea will decline and I have no help in completing this project*
3. *Concerned that I will start crying when I attempt to speak with Chelsea*
4. *Low motivation and problem believing that the goal is possible because of my strong emotional barriers*

GENERATION OF ALTERNATIVES

What are some specific things you can do to help you reach your goal?

1. *Ask Chelsea to commit to sobriety along with me.*
2. *Ask someone else to do the garden project.*
3. *Talk to Chelsea and ask her whether she would be willing to limit drinking when we are working on the project, so that we can get it done.*
4. *Make a schedule for completion with required time to dedicate to the garden project.*
5. *Write a letter or an email to Chelsea rather than talk to her.*
6. *Involve other people to talk to Chelsea.*
7. *Do all the work on the garden project on my own.*
8. *Ask for time off from work to do the project.*

DECISION-MAKING

What are some of the pros and cons of these alternatives?

1. *Ask Chelsea to commit to sobriety along with me—this would likely get the project done, but Chelsea is likely to reject the idea, possibly making the relationship between us worse.*
2. *Ask someone else to do the garden—my sister Katie and her friend Rob have an interest in gardening but neither may have the time.*
3. *Talk to Chelsea and ask her whether she would be willing to commit to the project and limit drinking while we are working on it—this would help to assert what I need from her in the project, but I will likely start crying and back out of my request.*

4. *Make a schedule for completion with required time involved for both—this would help us both know what is involved and help Chelsea to give me an answer, and I can't really think of negatives; that's like using externalization and simplification, right?*

5. *Write a letter or email to Chelsea rather than talk to her—this may give me the time to think carefully about what I have to say and to say it without crying or backing out. On the contrary, Chelsea may see this as not personal, sort of like a work memo.*

6. *Involve other people to talk to Chelsea—I would like to have other people do this for me, but I think that's copping out of me learning to do this myself and Chelsea might feel like I was going behind her back.*

7. *Do all the work on the gardening project on my own—it would eventually get done, but it wouldn't be as much fun and it wouldn't meet the goal of connecting with my roommate or others.*

8. *Ask for time off from work to do the project—I would enjoy doing that, but I only have very limited time off from work, other than weekends.*

After reviewing the pros and cons, Megan chose to combine alternatives 2, 4, and 5 because they collectively appeared to have the most likely result of attaining her goal while addressing important obstacles. She decided that she could write a personal note to Chelsea, so that she could think about what to say without tears, and make it as personal as possible (versus an email or text).

Ultimately, Megan developed the following action plan that took into account the emotion-focused and problem-focused aspects of her problem.

1. *Construct a letter to Chelsea with the support of my friend Rob, my sister Katie, and my therapist, that communicates how much I enjoyed the times that we worked on projects together in the past. Also, tell her that I miss these times and let her know that if she chooses to drink as much as she does, it makes me sad that we may not be able to do some things together that I know we both enjoy.*

2. *Tell her that I would like to start a gardening project next weekend and that I am hopeful that she will join me. Also, make it clear that I would like a no-drinking rule when actually working on the project. If she chooses not to do it with me, I will understand but will miss her company.*

3. *Agree to have Rob and my sister Katie as part of the gardening team, so if Chelsea decides not to buy in, or keep up her end, we will still get it done. If Chelsea buys into the plan, the additional help would be very nice to have, and make the whole project more social.*

Megan was able to implement her plan, and, to her surprise, Chelsea indicated that she welcomed the chance to not get "smashed" every weekend and do something more productive. This increased Megan's use of EC-PST strategies in general and motivated her to continue to apply these new skills to other problem areas as well.

Revisiting Mark: Struggling to Think in a More Structured and Planful Way

Mark was introduced earlier as an artist who experienced emotion dysregulation and expressed significant concerns that his work was not "distinctive" (in other words, "bourgeois, conventional, boring, and middle class"). His challenges with emotion regulation while trying to complete the worksheet seemed to mirror attempts to identify and accept his own identity. For this reason, he had been taught to apply the "Stop and Slow Down" tool kit, as well as the Enhancing Motivation for Action tool kit prior to learning the Planful Problem-Solving tools, with the prediction that he would need these other skills to help him manage his emotions, gain insight from them, and get through the somewhat mundane structure of a worksheet. Following is a clinical dialogue that occurred during its completion. At that time in his life, Mark (M) was experiencing panic and self-condemnation for his failure to complete several paintings on time for a gallery opening. This showing had been arranged by a former professor with whom he has continued to have contact.

M: The thing I need to deal with is stopping work every time I try to finish these pieces for the gallery show. I start working and when I stand back to look at it, I think it looks like crap and it's not distinctive enough. I get mad when I feel so pressured and blame John (his former professor) for getting me involved in this thing to begin with ... it pisses me off, makes me panic, and I want to give up.

T: As we follow the structure of this worksheet, let's try to define your goal and describe more clearly what "distinctive" means to you.

M: *Distinctive* means, well, that it's my work, has my identity.

T: Sounds like you want it to express who you are. I can understand how difficult this is, as you have struggled with your actual identity.

M: I know—I go back and forth.

T: But you seem to know that you want to continue to work as an artist. Isn't it true that artists' identities change over time and that's reflected in their work? I'm no expert, but I'm thinking of people who go through different periods in their lives.

M: Yeah, but at any given time you want to reflect who you are at the time.

T: Okay. What do your feelings tell you about your identity now? You don't have to accept this identify forever—just for now.

M: I feel like I'm real ... like not phony, but truthful, dark, cynical, yet I do have some hope.

T: Great use of simplification in breaking this down. Do you believe that this is reflected in the pieces you are working on now?

M: I haven't thought about it but yes ... here's a sketch of one I'm working on [shows therapist a charcoal sketch]. I keep thinking that this part here looks too commonplace and "cheesy," but I do want to give it an element ... maybe just a flash of beauty and hope.

T: It's difficult to work without feedback. But I have noticed that even if you get feedback, you often don't believe it. So, if I say this looks very interesting and seems to me to have depth, you might assume that I was just trying to be nice and encouraging?

M: Yeah ... so don't say anything—it doesn't matter. I think it's more that I get self-critical and angry and then can't hear anything except the voice in my head that says, "this sucks."

T: Let's check some facts—what is your opinion of this preliminary drawing?

M: Well, its truthful and dark, but this part here looks like I'm trying to make a happy ending [points to a part of the abstract painting that is lighter and suggests a spiritual quality]. I don't want to force a trite happy ending, just show that there may be some kind of positive transformation, if possible.

T: Would your former professor John give you false praise or would he be honest in giving feedback regarding what you are trying to say with this piece?

M: He would be pretty direct.

T: Can you receive his constructive criticism without, to use your words, losing it, freaking out, or experience panic to the point where your emotions control your thoughts and actions?

M: I could try ... but probably not without help. Having some guidance would be nice, but I think I just couldn't take his disapproval with the work. Then I would start to see my whole career as worthless.

T: Whoa ... that's a lot of pressure. Is it possible for John to provide some constructive criticism yet respect your work?

M: Yes, of course. But I avoid getting his opinion because if he doesn't like it, I'll be devastated.

T: How likely is that? Isn't it John who nominated you for your award and scholarship when you were in the program? Why would John recommend your work for the gallery?

M: Okay ... good point.

T: Let's think about possible barriers to asking his feedback during the process of preparing your pieces.

Following is the list of barriers Mark developed concerning seeking feedback from his former art professor:

- When I'm mad I can't take in or hear what he is saying.
- I can't control my feelings and I'll look like a mental case.
- He may tell me to change something that I don't want to change.

T: So, if your goal is to complete the pieces to show in the gallery, I can well understand how important this is for you. However, you have some significant barriers to such a challenging goal. I would like to pause for a moment now and introduce another type of worksheet, one that asks you to list out the predictable results if you continue to work on the Problem-Solving Worksheet with me and come up with an action plan, but also what is likely to happen if you don't work on this goal.

After working on this activity (see Chapter 9 for information on the Motivational Worksheet), Mark agreed that although his barriers were significant, it did made sense to at least try to continue to work toward the goal of getting the pieces in on time. Working with his therapist, here is the final Problem-Solving Worksheet that Mark completed, which includes an action plan.

PROBLEM DEFINITION

What is your problem-solving goal?

> *To complete the paintings that the gallery owner agreed to show for the opening. I want them to show who I am right now—truthful, dark, cynical, but hoping for transformation.*

What are the major obstacles to achieving your goal at this time?

1. *I stop and think the painting is not distinctive and just want to avoid the whole thing.*

2. *I go back and forth between feeling like "don't you dare say anything negative about my work" and "this sucks ... everyone will hate it ... I hate it."*

3. *I don't know how others see the painting. I want feedback that I respect, but I'm terrified to hear it.*

GENERATION OF ALTERNATIVES

What are some specific things you can do to help you reach your goal?

1. *Just keep working on it and hope for the best.*

2. *Work through until the project is finished, then ask for feedback from John (professor) before submitting.*

3. *Use the "Stop and Slow Down" tools when my anger or feelings of panic are triggered.*

4. *Just complete it and show to friends at the coffee shop before submitting; submit the ones they like.*

5. *Ask John to show a piece to some of his best students or other art professors and ask their opinion of what it says to them.*

6. *Accept that "hopeful" is not equal to "corporate," "middle class," or "boring."*

7. *Specifically ask whether the piece reveals truth, darkness, and hope for positive transformation.*

8. *Take only suggestions for change that I want to make.*

9. *Show the work in stages to my former professor John.*

10. *Use visualization and externalization for ideas of how to show real, dark, but hopeful.*

DECISION-MAKING

What are some of the pros and cons of these alternatives?

1. *Just keep working on it and hope for the best—this would take the least amount of effort, but I would probably not be able to finish based on what's been going on for the past few months.*

2. *Work through until the project is finished, then ask for feedback from my former professor before submitting—it's not likely that I'm going to keep up motivation if I think the work sucks, and I may get more depressed if John hates it.*

3. *Use the "Stop and Slow Down" tools when my anger or feelings of panic are triggered—this will help me not to freak out. I can't think of any negatives, if I can keep my sanity.*

4. *Just complete it and show to friends at the coffee shop before submitting. Submit the ones they like—I would be turning in the pieces as promised, but my coworkers are clueless about art. I would feel humiliated and self-critical.*

5. *Ask John to show a piece to some of his best students or other art professors and ask their opinion of what it says to them—that would give me more information, but I would be setting myself up to be embarrassed and angry hearing criticism from someone whom I don't respect.*

6. *Accept that "hopeful" does not equal "corporate," "middle class," or "boring"—this is probably useful, because it's almost like I want to fight that part of myself; like I'm afraid to believe in good things. I'm afraid people might see me as "normal." Pretty messed up, and probably means I have multiple personalities.*

Note that in response to these types of responses, Mark's therapist would often reframe his exaggerations as "assumptions" and remind him that completing a Problem-Solving Worksheet requires "facts."

7. *Specifically ask whether the piece reveals truth, darkness, and hope—this would help because I could know if it says what I want it to say. On the contrary, I can feel the panic creeping in because of possible criticism—that's when my pride kicks in and I get angry. The one good thing about this is that I'm not asking for the opinion of "good" or "bad" but does it say these three things? I could also choose the next idea and take only suggestions that I want.*

8. *Take only suggestions for change that I want to make—I can't think of a negative, except that John may be disappointed if he makes a suggestion*

that I don't take. I will need to remind myself that the choice is mine. But it scares me.

9. *Show the work in stages to my former professor John—although it would be helpful to have an opinion from someone I respect, I don't like the idea of showing my work at all during the process because I think it would cut down on my creativity.*

10. *Use visualization and externalization for ideas of how to show real, dark, and hopeful—I already use some of the visualization and externalization tools as part of my artistic process (I just didn't use those words). I could do that more intentionally and it may increase my creativity a little.*

After continued discussions, Mark selected to combine several alternatives. He was continually reminded to stay with the facts when engaging in planful problem solving (vs. assumptions that were fueled by his fears of criticism and his own harsh self-criticism). The following is Mark's action plan:

1. *Ask former professor John to view a completed piece and provide specific feedback regarding what identity the piece conveys with specific focus on "truth," "darkness," and "hope for transformation."*

2. *Use "Stop and Slow Down" tools for at least 5 minutes before, during, and after the feedback, and before responding or making any further choices about the piece (tools would be yawning and breathing and visualizing his relaxed muscles).*

3. *Make decisions about any changes to the piece that he wants to incorporate based on John's feedback.*

4. *Complete piece.*

5. *Follow this process for the completion of the current three pieces he is working on to submit to the gallery.*

6. *Set a deadline for submission and commit to it.*

Mark set a deadline for himself of 2 months to complete the projects to submit to the gallery. He agreed that he would submit at least one if he had not completed all three that were promised. Mark submitted two pieces at the end of the 2 months, determining that the third piece was not as "distinctive" (defined as uniquely capturing his identity to his satisfaction) as he had hoped. For those that he submitted, his professor did provide feedback suggesting certain choices of color tone that better captured the paintings' multiple themes of truth, darkness, and hope for transformation. Mark did take his advice.

Of the two pieces that he submitted, there was interest in both the paintings at the gallery opening. One sold at the event and the other sold about 3 weeks later. Mark was pleased with the outcome and agreed to stay in treatment to continue to work on increasing his confidence in his problem-solving abilities, and apply these skills to other interpersonal problems regarding dating and his relationship with each of his parents.

Revisiting David: A Discovery That Planful Problem Solving Buffers Hopelessness

In this last section, we revisit the example of David, the client who had experienced multiple major stressors in his life: the early trauma of witnessing his father's failed attempt at suicide by drowning, the chronic stress of his father's hostility and depression, and the successful suicide attempt by his father 1 year ago. When the suicide actually occurred, David was distraught and blamed himself for not having stopped it, stating that he "knew" this was going to happen one day. The anniversary of his father's death presented a particular challenge for David—he was experiencing an increase in his own suicidal thoughts as the day approached. Furthermore, he anticipated that being with his family would be unbearably painful. After engaging in the motivational exercise in which he was able to visualize a positive scene with his family, he was able to begin completing a Problem-Solving Worksheet.

We provide the clinical dialogue that occurred as David (D) began his efforts to work on the Problem-Solving Worksheet:

D:	I know that I have to be with my family on the anniversary of my father's death, but I am dreading it. I didn't think I could see any positive scenes until we did this visualization. It was nice, but it's just in my head … I have no idea how to get there.
T:	So, I think we have a goal for this worksheet that we can use to practice using the planful problem-solving tools. It sounds like your goal is to be with your mother and other family members on the anniversary of your father's death, to be able to help each other through this very painful time, and to find the positive strengths you have as a family.
D:	I actually would never have thought of phrasing it that way.
T:	Understandably, David, I think that's because your goal was one of avoiding emotional pain and guilt and thus, stating a goal in the negative and trying to figure how NOT to have something happen—this isn't realistic or even very effective. Your visualization

> allowed you to state a goal as something achievable, rather than something to avoid, that is, be with your family, encourage and strengthen each other, support each other, and manage the pain.

D: I never thought that a positive experience could happen at the same time when there's so much pain. This actually is sort of amazing to me.

T: There is research that shows that having a positive goal can actually have an impact that creates brain changes in various brain pathways and neurochemical levels.

David's therapist at this time shared research that supported the importance of making decisions about positive goals, even in very stressful circumstances. He appeared much freer to work on the problem of the family reunion and less angry at his wife for wanting to help and support him. He was now able to understand that all of his negative emotions and guilt did not need to be "fixed" or removed before he and his family could help and support each other. David's worksheet is as follows.

PROBLEM DEFINITION

What is your problem-solving goal?

> *To be together as a family to support and enjoy each other and share some good memories DESPITE the horrible tragedy of losing Dad.*

What are the major obstacles to achieving your goal at this time?

1. *I will see my family and lose it [breaks down sobbing] and then the family will lose it.*
2. *My wife wants to go, but she has always been critical of my family.*
3. *I have no idea what my mother wants to do that day.*
4. *My one sister may try to take over and control all the activities.*
5. *My other sister will constantly break into tears and get my mom going.*
6. *My brother is messed up and may do something stupid such as hang out with his friends and smoke weed.*

GENERATION OF ALTERNATIVES

What are some specific things you can do to help you reach your goal?

1. *Don't go.*
2. *Just go and hope for the best.*

3. *Leave my wife and son home.*

4. *Talk to my wife about what will help me.*

5. *Ask my mother what she wants on that day.*

6. *Talk to my brother.*

7. *Don't talk about feelings; keep conversation superficial.*

8. *Write family an email or letter, telling them how I feel.*

9. *Write only mother a letter so she knows how I feel.*

10. *Plan the activities for the day.*

11. *Ask my bossy sister's help in planning the activities.*

12. *Ask my mother's priest to stop by.*

13. *Ask my mother's friends to stop by.*

DECISION-MAKING

What are some of the pros and cons of these alternatives?

1. *Don't go—The only positive consequence is short-term relief from dread for me. Lots of negative consequences on me for long term (guilt), and long-term consequences on family.*

2. *Just go and hope for the best—That's what my family always did. It would be easier for all of us to do that, but hoping for the best that my dad may not need treatment and would not kill himself did not work.*

3. *Leave my wife and son home—I would not have to worry that my wife would put down my mother or sisters, but on the contrary, this would make more problems with my wife, who already says I keep way too much inside. I do, and then I get enraged because she doesn't understand. My mother would not get to see her grandchild and that might hurt her.*

4. *Talk to my wife about what will help me—She may lecture me and remind me that her family is much more open and freer than mine is. I may feel criticized and angry if that happens. On the contrary, she may understand and support me. I may not get so angry with her.*

5. *Ask my mother what she wants on that day—This would help because I could probably make sure we do what she wants, but the negative is that it may upset her to think about it.*

6. *Talk to my brother—If I tell him that I need him to help me with Mom and give him something specific to do, he may help. On the contrary, he may be too messed up and want to avoid the whole thing.*

7. *Don't talk about feelings; keep conversation superficial—It sounds crazy, but that might be what my mother wants to do. There is this sort of old Catholic philosophy my mom has about not crying over what has happened, but pick up and go forward.*

8. *Write family an email or letter, telling family how I feel—My brother and sisters have their own problems. Even though they may know how I feel, they have their own grief and take it out on me. If I open up to them, and that happened, I would be hurt.*

9. *Write only mother a letter so she knows how I feel—My mother might try to tell me that it's not my fault. I need to work on that myself. I probably wouldn't believe her anyway.*

10. *Plan the activities for the day—That may actually provide a distraction. It would also give us something to do together, so we could support each other without so much talking.*

11. *Ask my bossy sister's help in planning the activities—She may try to take over, tell me what to do, and I may get angry. On the contrary, if I ask for her help, maybe she would take over and plan, but not try so hard to be the boss. That actually really would be a help.*

12. *Ask my mother's priest to stop by—My mom has already spiritually accepted what happened. But maybe he could be helpful for the rest of the family.*

13. *Ask my mother's friends to stop by—My family is very private and my mother would be really uncomfortable involving someone outside the family. One exception is John, who worked with my dad. He actually was the last person to speak to my dad before he killed himself. I didn't know this until recently, but when he told my mom that my father seemed at peace that morning and told him how proud he was of his family, she was very relieved.*

David decided to combine several alternatives that served to maximize the positive consequences of each and to minimize the negative consequences. Specifically, he selected alternatives 4, 5, and 11, and came up with the following plan:

1. *Talk to his wife and tell her that despite any of their shortcomings, he wants the day with his family to reflect their love for each other even though they are in pain.*

2. *Ask his mother what she wants to have happen on that day.*

3. *Ask his (bossy) sister to plan activities to provide his mother with what she wants to have happen.*

David's wife was helpful and supportive of his request. She agreed to focus only on the positive aspects of the family for that day. David's mother predictably said that she did not want to spend time talking about their father's depression or death, or try to figure out what happened. She stated that she preferred to do something pleasant as a family and focus on good things. David's sister planned for them to stop at the church, light a candle, then to go for a walk in a nearby park, and then come home, make something to eat, and play cards.

The outcome of these efforts included the following: The presence of his wife and son provided some pleasant distraction and the various family members seemed relieved that they had come. The family carried out the sister's plans, and for the most part, David's mother appeared relaxed and glad to have the whole family together. David's younger brother did leave to see his friends after the family returned home from the park but ate dinner with them. David was able to accept that was what his brother needed to do. After dinner, as David and his sisters were cleaning up, his mother came to the doorway and told them that his father was so proud of them all—David and his sisters cried and hugged each other. The family remained focused on the card game, but allowed for small moments of good memories and even a few jokes. Through the activity of completing the worksheet, David learned that perfect solutions may not be possible, but realistic solutions that best match the problem solver, the situational context, and other people can create a significant buffer to hopelessness.

SUMMARY

This chapter focused on *planful problem solving*. This tool kit is composed of four major activities: (a) defining the problem (i.e., clarifying the nature of a problem, delineating a realistic problem-solving goal, and identifying those obstacles that prevent one from reaching such goals), (b) generating alternative solution ideas (i.e., thinking of a range of possible solution strategies geared toward overcoming the identified obstacles), (c) making decisions as to which alternatives to include in an action plan (i.e., predicting the likely consequences of these various alternatives, conducting a cost–benefit analysis based on these identified outcomes, and developing a solution plan that is geared to achieve the problem-solving goal), and (d) carrying out the action plan and verifying its outcome (i.e., carrying out the solution plan, monitoring and evaluating the consequences of the plan, and determining whether one's problem-solving efforts have been successful or need to continue). Two versions for training in these tools were provided: (a) "Brief" Planful Problem-Solving Training and (b) "Intensive" Planful Problem-Solving Training. Which one to engage in with a given client or population depends on both findings from the literature and individualized assessment data.

The briefer form of training in this tool kit involved providing clients with an overview of the four planful problem-solving steps, as well as guided practice applying the Problem-Solving Worksheet, which provides a specific structure to help clients better handle stressful problems. The more intensive training program allows for additional extensive training in any or all of these four tasks. Training in *problem definition* involved teaching clients to engage in five specific activities: (a) seek available facts, (b) describe facts in clear language, (c) separate facts from assumptions, (d) set realistic goals, and (e) identify obstacles to overcome to reach such goals. As an instructional aid, we advocated thinking of the process of problem solving as analogous to mapping a travel plan to reach a particular destination. The importance of differentiating between problem-focused goals and emotion-focused goals was underscored. Additional problematic issues involved in accurately defining a problem were highlighted, including confusing a solution with a goal, not looking at the problem from other people's perspectives, focusing only on "superficial problems," and being confused if the problem is complex.

Training in the *Generation-of-Alternatives* tool focused on applying three brainstorming principles when attempting to think creatively of possible solution options. They include the quantity principle, the defer-judgment principle, and the variety principle. Ways to overcome "feeling stuck" when generating ideas were also presented. Practicing this tool with "silly" examples, such as thinking of differing uses of a single brick, was strongly recommended as a standard practice task to engage clients to foster creativity.

The *Decision-Making* tool teaches clients to engage in the following steps: (a) Screen out obviously ineffective solution ideas, (b) predict a range of possible consequences of the various alternatives, (c) conduct a cost–benefit analysis of these consequences, and (d) identify effective solutions and develop an action plan. In helping clients to be successful in their predictions of the likely effects of a given action plan, we strongly recommended that they consider personal consequences, social consequences, short-term effects, and long-term effects. On the basis of such predictions, clients are then guided to evaluate each alternative according to (a) the likelihood that the action plan will, in fact, help reach their goals (i.e., overcome the identified obstacles), (b) the likelihood that they are able to carry out the action plan optimally, (c) the short- and long-term personal consequences, and (d) the short- and long-term social (i.e., effects on others) consequences.

The fourth and last planful problem-solving task involves carrying out the action plan (i.e., solution implementation) and evaluating the outcome (i.e., solution verification). Training in this set of tools included helping clients to (a) motivate themselves to carry out the action plan, (b) undergo certain preparations to ensure the plan can be carried out optimally, (c) implement the solution, (d) monitor the actual effects of the plan, (e) self-reinforce for attempting to solve a problem, and (f) troubleshoot if the solution was not successful.

Last, we revisited the three clients described in detail earlier (Megan, Mark, David) as a means of illustrating how to use these problem-solving tools. It is important to note the complexities involved in applying these tools as exemplified by the challenges and difficulties these three clients faced during this process.

REFERENCE

Korb, A. (2015). *The upward spiral: Using neuroscience to reverse the course of depression, one small change at a time*. Oakland, CA: New Harbinger Publications.

8

TOOL KIT #2—PROBLEM-SOLVING MULTITASKING: OVERCOMING "BRAIN OVERLOAD"

A brain is a lot like a computer. It will only take so many facts, and then it will go on overload and blow up.

—Erma Bombeck

A hunter who tries to chase two rabbits at the same time will catch neither.

—Ancient Buddhist saying

This chapter focuses on the second of the four emotion-centered problem-solving therapy (EC-PST) tool kits. Remember that all tool kits are presented to clients as strategies geared to help them overcome a variety of common major obstacles to effective problem solving, especially under stress. This particular tool kit addresses the challenges posed by the limited capacity of the human mind.

RATIONALE

Although the first quote given at the beginning of the chapter is attributed to a famous humorist and the second emanates from a religious philosophical perspective, actual research by cognitive psychologists consistently demonstrates that doing more than one task at a time, particularly if the tasks are complex, negatively affects accuracy and productivity (Rogers & Monsell, 1995). In essence, the conscious mind engages in three important activities during problem solving: (a) receiving information from the environment (i.e., information or stimuli is received and input from both external and internal sources), (b) displaying this information when needed (e.g., the mind attempts to remember information needed to address the problem), and (c) manipulating the various pieces of information that are remembered in an attempt to comprehend how the data fit together (e.g., combining different pieces of information, adding and subtracting information, and placing the different pieces of information in a logical sequence).

However, the capacity of the conscious mind is quite limited in that it cannot perform all three of these activities efficiently at the same time, especially when the quantity and/or complexity of the stimuli is significant. Trying to do two of the aforementioned activities at the same time without aid is very difficult. Often, one activity interferes with another. For example, attempting to remember all the important information about a problem can interfere with the manipulation of information that is involved in trying to comprehend or understand how they fit together.

In addition, the processing of information becomes increasingly difficult when a person is under stress. For example, in Chapter 2, we described LeDoux's concept of the high-road versus the low-road processing of emotional stimuli. In this context, consider the difference between the situations in which the brain is attempting to process or interpret the differential danger of a given sound associated with either a snake or a twig being broken. Now consider how the brain likely reacts when a person is engaged in a very heated argument with a spouse or partner for *several minutes*, or the situation in which individuals are being told that they are being laid off after recently purchasing a new home, or the circumstance of persons who are told that they have cancer (i.e., continuous stimulation of the amygdala). When attempting to handle such complex situations, because the brain is not a "super computer" with unlimited memory and processing capabilities, productivity and accuracy can be severely compromised. In essence, the human brain is not designed to perform heavy-duty multitasking—people are not machines or computers. Unfortunately, we are not able to go to the computer store and purchase a hard drive with more memory for our brains. If we require computers with low amounts of memory (i.e., our brains) to simultaneously process many requests involving many pieces of data, we can easily experience a "computer crash."

In addition, research has also shown that attempts to engage in *normal* multitasking (i.e., attempts to attend and respond to several sources of stimuli simultaneously) can actually produce negative effects on the immune system (i.e., increase in secretory immunoglobulin A), suggesting that attempts to cope with stress in such a manner can ultimately have negative biological effects as well (Wetherell, Hyland, & Harris, 2004).

More specifically, according to neuroscientist and cognitive psychologist Daniel Levitin, multitasking has been found to increase the production of the stress hormone cortisol as well as the fight-or-flight hormone adrenaline, which can overstimulate your brain and cause mental fog or scrambled thinking. Multitasking creates a dopamine-addiction feedback loop, effectively rewarding the brain for losing focus and for constantly searching for external stimulation. To make matters worse, the prefrontal cortex has a novelty bias, meaning that its attention can be easily hijacked by something new—the proverbial shiny objects (Levitin, 2014, p. 96).

Given these limitations of the brain, additional tools become necessary to help people cope with problems, particularly if such problems are stressful and engender high levels of negative emotions. EC-PST focuses on teaching individuals the following three multitasking strategies to address this concern:

- Externalization
- Visualization
- Simplification

Note that we characterize these three strategies as fundamental tools necessary to engage in effective problem solving even under low amounts of stress. Many people may already engage in one or all of these techniques for a variety of reasons. But we suggest that it becomes important for individuals to use these tools as often as possible, so that they become more habitual. The importance of these tools can be explained by using the analogy of teaching people who are interested in beginning to jog or run for exercise that correct stretching and breathing are fundamental activities required to run properly without negative consequences.

Externalization

Externalization involves the display of information externally as often as possible (e.g., writing information on paper; drawing diagrams or maps to show relationships; recording information in one's computer, smartphone, or tablet; using an audiotape recorder). This procedure relieves the conscious mind from having to actively display information being remembered, which allows one to concentrate more on other activities, such as better understanding the nature of a problem, creatively thinking and then writing down solutions on paper, and making decisions based on visually examining and comparing a list of pros versus cons.

In describing this strategy to clients, the therapist should ask for examples of how they use this tool (e.g., smartphones, to-do lists, post-it reminders, calendars, computers, or tablets) and how that helps their lives. Useful analogies include the notion that in building houses, blueprints are necessary, as are manuals when learning how to use a new camera, and the major reason we provide handouts and guidebooks—that is, externalization works! As mentioned earlier in Chapter 7, we strongly encourage clients to purchase a small notebook or journal to use as aids while undergoing EC-PST (or to use any electronic device they already have that has the capability to record information).

Note that this tool, in principle, is consistent with the effective intervention known as *expressive writing*. James Pennebaker, a psychologist, pioneered this strategy in the 1980s. Specifically, this approach asks clients to write about a traumatic experience that they have not shared with others and to "dig deep inside oneself" and put such information down on paper. The intervention recommends that one does this intensely three or four times over a 1-week period. Research has demonstrated that such expressive writing has positive effects on one's immune functioning and overall well-being (Pennebaker, 2004). For certain clients, therapists may consider using this intervention as an adjunct to EC-PST when and where appropriate.

Visualization

This tool emphasizes the use of visual imagery for a variety of purposes that can positively impact the problem-solving process. These include the following:

Problem clarification: People can visualize the problem in their mind's eye to separate differing parts of the problem to "look" at them one at a time, creatively generate new ideas for solutions, "map out" new pathways to get from *A* to *B*, and/or draw imaginal diagrams or pictures to help describe the problem in a graphic format. Chapter 7 includes a brief "visualization induction" to help the process of more accurately defining a problem.

Imaginal rehearsal: Sports figures frequently imagine engaging in various activities to enhance their success in a more time-efficient manner (e.g., a skier can visualize how one needs to bend his or her knees while going down a new slope; a basketball player can visualize how to throw the ball into the hoop when being chased down the court). Relevant to problem solving, this form of visualization can be useful when a client is soon to carry out a solution plan but needs extra practice in how to carry it out.

Stress management: "Guided imagery" is a form of stress management that helps clients reduce their stress and anxiety levels by "taking a vacation in their mind." A therapist can provide detailed instructions that help a client to better visualize taking a trip to a "safe place." Essentially, the client is requested to use his or her mind's eye to vividly imagine a scene, one that represents a safe place, such as a favorite vacation spot.

This activity can be taught to clients as a general stress-management strategy, and also as a tool to help them to "slow down," a crucial EC-PST concept that is part of Tool Kit #4. A sample script and description of visualizing a safe place is given in Client Workbook (see the Preface of this book for information on obtaining the Client Workbook).

One additional form of visualization is included in Tool Kit #3 (Chapter 9) specifically to help clients overcome feelings of hopelessness and to increase their motivation to continue "working" in treatment. Essentially, this approach asks clients to visualize how they feel *after* a problem is solved but not to think about *how* they got to that point. It is similar to having a runner visualize "crossing the finish line" as a motivational tool.

Simplification

Simplification involves attempting to break down or simplify a large or complex problem to make it more manageable. To apply this strategy, clients are instructed to focus on the most relevant information; break down complex problems into more manageable subproblems; and translate complex, vague, and abstract concepts into more simple, specific, and concrete terms. It also refers to the process of identifying smaller steps to reach one's goals, as well as to specify these goals concretely. For example, rather than perceive graduating from high school (or college) as encompassing 4 long years, one can conceptualize completing 1 year (or one semester) at a time, which can make it appear less formidable (i.e., "What do I need to do to complete this semester?" vs. "What do I need to do to graduate college?").

REVISITING "MEGAN": OVERCOMING "BRAIN OVERLOAD"

To illustrate the use of this tool kit, we revisit Megan. Her initial treatment sessions introduced the concepts of the multitasking tool kit to provide her with a set of strategies that she would be able to apply throughout her treatment and thus improve her management of stimulus overload. This was extremely important for Megan's treatment in that her symptoms of detachment seemed to occur when she was overwhelmed with worry and ruminations. More specifically, training in this tool kit provided her the opportunity to work on effectively managing the experience of being overwhelmed that frequently fueled her rumination about how much her past behavior may have harmed her brain and body and resulted in avoidance of problems. The strategic use of externalization and simplification principles ultimately resulted in a significant decrease in her experience of interpersonal and emotional detachment.

After teaching her the various multitasking tools, Megan was directed to put them into practice by writing in a journal those experiences that occur during the week when she experienced thoughts and/or feelings that led to feeling overwhelmed. She shared these notes with the therapist, as discussed in an early treatment session. Following is an example of how her therapist (T) demonstrated the process of simplification to help Megan (M) begin to clarify her feelings and set reasonable and approachable targets for life change:

M: I decided to start writing when I was at work. I felt consumed with a sense of dread and worry that I had messed myself up and kept hearing the label "alcoholic" in my head. I started to shake, so I went to the bathroom and sat in a stall, but tried to write this stuff down in my journal.

T: Can you share it with me here?

M: Okay. [Begins reading her notes] "For some reason my mother comes to mind—she has no idea of what problems I have and I don't want to tell her. I'm going to visit my family in 2 weeks. It will be the first time that I'm not drinking. I can't imagine telling my mother that I stopped drinking. My aunt told her that she doesn't want her (my mother) to drink when she and her children are in my mother's company, and my mother gets real nasty and sarcastic about it. She always plans to go out for drinks when we're together and has wine and beer in the house. I'm crying here [starts crying while reading] because I'm not there yet—I can't even think about telling her."

T: What do you expect will happen?

M: I don't know ... I don't know [sobbing]. She'll be disappointed, upset, and maybe be distant ... [now laughing and crying] ... I'm the favorite in the family. Wow. This is hard.

T: Stay with it Megan, lets break down your rush of feelings and worries here and see whether we can use the simplification tool to break down the goals a bit.

M: Okay.

T: You started to cry as you read about telling your mother that you had stopped drinking. I notice that you are less focused on the specific challenges of not drinking, but more focused on actually telling your mother about your decision.

M: Yeah ... that's true. That's what my parents do. Our family drinks ... a lot. I'm afraid that if I tell them, they will be disappointed. Worse, they may blame themselves.

T: Why would that be so terrible?

M: Because I'm supposed to make everyone feel better! [Catches herself and laughs.] The weird thing is, my dad would probably be supportive, and my mother would eventually get over it. It's more me, that's the problem.

T: Megan, I know this is hard for you. But let's see whether we can make some sense of these big complicated issues. Looking at what you wrote, it seems that one problem is accepting and acknowledging your alcohol problem and developing new ways to cope with stress. Another part of your stimulus overload involves the worry and sadness you experience when you imagine sharing anything with someone you care about that you believe may disappoint them.

M: That's so true. It's like poison to me. I hate it. It makes me feel sick and queasy. But I think that these are two things I absolutely need to work on.

T: What you have done over this past week with your journal writing is an excellent example of how using the externalization and simplification tools can help move you forward with your goals for improving your life. Let's review. You were experiencing symptoms of detachment, worry, and a vague sense of dread. Pretty overwhelming, I'd say. By writing down these experiences on paper and allowing yourself to get the thoughts and feelings "out of your head," you were able to identify three important areas that we can work on in treatment—acceptance of your alcohol vulnerability, the need for new skills, and changing your overmagnified fear of disappointing others. This is a very good start.

M: Sounds really hard, but not so impossible. I like these tools.

T: I'm glad you found these helpful. Remember that they are important basic tools to apply throughout the problem-solving process.

Through the use of both externalization and simplification, Megan came to realize that the intensity of her fears of disappointing others were strong barriers that thwarted her other goals for learning new skills and moving forward with her life.

SUMMARY

This chapter described the second tool kit, Problem-Solving Multitasking: Overcoming "Brain Overload." As with the other tool kits, this one is included in EC-PST to help clients overcome ubiquitous barriers to effective problem solving, particularly when under stress. This set of tools addresses the concern of the brain's inability to multitask efficiently, especially when addressing complex and/or emotionally laden problems. We suggested that to overcome this barrier, an individual should use three specific strategies: externalization, visualization, and simplification. Externalization involves placing information in an external format, such as notes, lists, diagrams, maps, and audiotapes. Visualization, or the use of one's mind's eye, is recommended for three important purposes: problem clarification, imaginal rehearsal, and stress management. Simplification involves breaking down complex problems into smaller ones; delineating a series of steps to goal achievement rather than one singular overall goal; and using simple, user-friendly language when describing problems and goals. We ended this chapter by revisiting the case of Megan to illustrate certain points about problem-solving multitasking.

REFERENCES

Levitin, D. J. (2014). *The organized mind: Thinking straight in the age of information overload.* New York, NY: Plume.

Pennebaker, J. W. (2004). Theories, therapies, and taxpayers: On the complexities of the expressive writing paradigm. *Clinical Psychology: Science and Practice, 11,* 138–142. doi:10.1093/clipsy.bph063

Rogers, R., & Monsell, S. (1995). The costs of a predictable switch between simple cognitive tasks. *Journal of Experimental Psychology: General, 124,* 207–231. doi:10.1037/0096-3445.124.2.207

Wetherell, M. A., Hyland, M. E., & Harris, J. E. (2004). Secretory immunoglobulin A reactivity to acute and cumulative acute multi-tasking stress: Relationships between reactivity and perceived workload. *Biological Psychology, 66,* 257–270. doi:10.1016/j.biopsycho.2003.10.008

TOOL KIT #3—ENHANCING MOTIVATION FOR ACTION: OVERCOMING LOW MOTIVATION AND FEELINGS OF HOPELESSNESS

Visualize this thing that you want; see it, feel it, believe in it. Make your mental blueprint, and begin to build.

—Robert Collier

To accomplish great things, we must first dream, then visualize, then plan... believe... act!

—Alfred A. Montapert

This third tool kit is included in emotion-centered problem-solving therapy (EC-PST) to specifically address certain problem orientation issues if relevant to a particular client, that is, reduced motivation and/or feelings of hopelessness. Not being motivated to learn and/or practice the various EC-PST tools can severely curtail the likelihood that meaningful change can occur.

This tool kit comprises two activities geared to enhance one's motivation for action. The first tool in this skill set, creating a motivational worksheet, would be used at any point in time in treatment in which a client is hesitant to continue with any learning or practice activity. This may especially occur if individuals are trepidatious about carrying out an action plan to solve an extant problem. This could occur because they are afraid that the solution may not work, they have concerns about what might occur if the problem was solved (e.g., fear of change per se), or are unwilling to engage in extensive efforts to implement an action plan (e.g., avoidant problem-solving style).

A second activity in this tool kit involves the use of visualization to further enhance motivation and to reduce feelings of hopelessness. The application of visualization in this context, which is different than that described within

© Springer Publishing Company DOI: 10/1891/9780826143167.0009

Tool Kit #2: Problem-Solving Multitasking (Chapter 8), is to help clients to sensorially experience what it "feels" like to successfully solve a difficult problem; in other words, "to see and experience the light at the end of the tunnel."

COMPARING PROS AND CONS OF MOVING FORWARD

When clients are hesitant to continue in any part of the problem-solving process, they are directed to create a motivational worksheet. In essence, they are asked first to make two columns in their notebook or journal and then to first list those potential benefits and costs associated with *not* continuing (e.g., not willing to implement their solution plan) in the left-hand column. Next, they are directed to list, in the right-hand column, possible benefits and costs associated with moving forward (e.g., problem being solved). In doing so, they are guided to compare these overall consequences and apply the cost–benefit analysis learned earlier to reappraise the problem with regard to their well-being. We remind clients to consider possible *immediate* benefits and costs, possible *long-term* benefits and costs, as well as benefits and costs to *themselves* and to *significant others*. Such a worksheet can be posted on the refrigerator at home or any other appropriate place to continually remind themselves of why they chose to focus on this problem and worked so hard to discover a solution. Furthermore, we suggest individuals remember what Leonardo da Vinci once stated—*"Iron rusts from disuse; water loses its purity from stagnation … even so does inaction sap the vigor of the mind."*

At times, it is possible that this subsequent analysis leads to the conclusion that the benefits of not doing anything at the present time outweigh the costs compared with actually carrying out the proposed action plan. If so, it is probable that this is valid because of one of the following reasons: (a) the situation has changed for the better on its own, (b) the individual may have reappraised the problem as less of a priority than originally stated, or (c) the proposed action plan itself appears to be weak. If the latter, rather than carrying out this plan, it is suggested that the client circle back through the previous planful problem-solving steps to produce a stronger plan.

VISUALIZATION TO OVERCOME FEELINGS OF HOPELESSNESS

Another major barrier to coping effectively with stressful problems are feelings of hopelessness and poor motivation characteristic of a negative problem orientation. A phrase that we often hear when a client feels overwhelmed and hopeless is "*I just can't see the light at the end of the tunnel.*" In other words, some clients feel that they "*just can't see themselves successfully resolving a problem or achieving a particular goal.*"

With regard to the power of visualization to overcome hopelessness, a story that we often share with clients as an example of a profound use of this technique involves Viktor Frankl, psychiatrist, author, and Holocaust survivor. In his book, *Man's Search for Meaning* (1946/1984), Dr. Frankl describes a person's ability to visualize the future as "salvation in the most difficult moments of … existence." He recalled the poignant and powerful memories of his experience of pain and humiliation in a Nazi concentration camp during World War II and the endless problems that continually consumed him. However, he also described experiencing a type of personal epiphany when, during some of his darkest moments, he was able to force his mind and thoughts to a future time and place. For example, on a forced march during the winter, suffering from malnutrition, a severe cough, and lack of warm clothing, he dropped to his knees, overcome with exhaustion. As was typical when a prisoner stopped marching, a Nazi guard began to beat him, yelling that if he did not get up, he would be left to die. At this point, Frankl simply said to himself, "*This is it for me*" and thought he was going to perish.

However, he managed to actually get up by visualizing himself in the future, standing at a podium in a warm and well-designed lecture room, with a full and attentive audience, giving a lecture on "the psychology of the death camps." He later stated in his book, "by this method I succeeded somehow on rising above the situation, above the sufferings of the moment, and I observed them as if they were already past … emotion which is suffering, ceases to be suffering as soon as we form a clear picture of it" (p. 95). Those familiar with Frankl's biography know that after he survived the atrocities of this experience, he did go on to become an internationally known psychiatrist and author who actually lived out his visualization to the extent that no one would have believed possible.

Obviously, we are not advocating that simply visualizing a solution to difficult and complex problems alone will solve them. However, we are confident that people who can successfully visualize an improved future or a "problem solved" are more likely to be motivated to persevere in their problem-solving efforts. Therefore, in this tool kit, we offer a specific visualization tool to help individuals overcome feelings of hopelessness and continue to move toward goal attainment.

This EC-PST activity is useful when it is apparent that clients feel particularly hopeless and have significant difficulty moving forward within treatment. In other words, they do not feel that success in coping with problems is likely. This visualization exercise asks clients to use their imagination or mind's eye to "travel to the future" *after* they successfully solved a difficult problem. They are instructed *not* to think about how one got there—just that they did reach a problem-solving goal. Feelings of hopelessness are usually accompanied by depressive affect and feelings of fatigue and sluggishness, so the emphasis, similar to other visualization exercises, is to attempt to *experience* as much as possible a variety of positive physical sensations, including sight, sound, touch, taste, and smell, to really *feel* different in the moment than just simply thinking about it.

At times, when people feel overwhelmed, they pay more attention to all the negative feelings associated with the problem, rather than the potential positive consequences associated with the problem being solved. This exercise is used to help individuals *experience* something positive so as to feel somewhat more motivated to try to do something different. This is similar to the situation in which runners, on seeing the finish line or ribbon, actually become more motivated to run faster to reach their goal (i.e., to complete the race).

Such an exercise can easily be used in the very beginning of treatment if the therapist perceives the client to feel particularly hopeless. It can also be applied throughout treatment whenever clients indicate difficulty in applying the various other EC-PST tools as a means of coping with stressful situations. Note that this activity is directed by the therapist, who should be competent in creating strong imaginal pictures for clients.

Following is a sample script that describes a visualization induction that the therapist can use.

> *Close your eyes and take a deep breath—filling all the spaces in your abdomen, just under your rib cage and hold it for a count of three ... [wait for 3 seconds] ... now release it and let all the air flow out. Do this one more time and notice that when you hold your breath, your abdomen is full and deflated as you let it out. Now, just allow your breathing to be normal, calm, and regular, no special rhythm, just whatever comes natural, and just focus on your breath. Notice where you experience the breath, maybe your nostrils or abdomen ... keep your focus on your breath for a moment [wait 3 seconds].*
>
> *Now use your imagination to visualize yourself at a future point in time—it could be a few months from now or a year from now when the problem that you are facing is largely past, largely resolved, such that it is no longer a major problem for you. It doesn't matter how you got there, just that you are on the other side of the obstacles between you and your goals. Use all your senses to fully put yourself there in this visualized scene where your problem is largely improved. Picture your surroundings ... where are you? Do you see yourself as inside or outside?*

Picture what you see close by and picture what you see at more of a distance. Think to yourself, if I was describing this to someone, how would I describe what this looks like? See if you can imagine the smells or the sounds of this scene in the future ... using all of your senses. How does it feel in your body? Imagine what you would be touching or what your body would feel like. What would you be doing? If you are with other people, how do they appear? How are they relating to you? If you are alone, what are you thinking?

Now fully experience this future point in time, thinking, "How would my life be different in this scene from how it is now before my visualization?" Try to imagine all of the positive thoughts and feelings associated with this moment.

Now take a deep breath and open your eyes. Write down the visualization you just experienced in as much detail as possible. Write down how you felt believing that the problem was solved—that you actually finished the race!

REVISITING DAVID: USING VISUALIZATION TO OVERCOME HOPELESSNESS

We now provide a clinical example of how the specific use of creative visualization was used to increase hope and motivation for David, a client introduced earlier. When we introduced him in an earlier chapter, David came to his initial session significantly depressed and hopeless. Despite his apparent success, he disclosed a history of hiding a painful inner life with periods of intense anxiety and significant depression. David had described an unrelenting self-blame for his father's suicide, which occurred approximately 1 year earlier.

Early in David's treatment, his therapist was aware that the upcoming anniversary of his father's death would be a particularly challenging time for him emotionally. It was predictable that this time might provoke his sense of hopelessness, disconnection from others, and ultimately his own suicide risk. The following transcript is from the session focused on the use of visualization to decrease hopelessness and increase his motivation to continue in treatment. Note that for clients such as David, who are experiencing significant difficulty seeing *any* possible positive outcome, it may be useful to convey the Frankl story. Such a description can provide a very compelling rationale to continue trying and helps show how using creative visualization can help an individual choose to stay alive for 1 more hour, 1 more day, or longer while working to achieve a goal or resolve a stressful life problem.

D: I appreciate your help and I think this is one of the first times that I can talk to someone who understands what I've been going through, but I just don't see how anything will help. I am supposed to see my family (mother, brother, and sisters) in about a month and be with them because it will be 1 year since my father died. I can't face them. I can't do anything to make it better for them, and I know they blame me.

T: Have they said that?

D: Of course not, nobody says anything in my family—that's just the problem, but I know they will be looking to me to make things better and I can't. When I have said that it was all my fault for not saving him, they would try to convince me that it's not my fault, but I always knew he would do this someday. How could they not blame me?

T: I realize that right now it's difficult to see a way through your pain, and despite the fact that you are doing the best that you can here, there doesn't seem to be a light at the end of this tunnel. The irony is that when people don't see a light at the end of the tunnel, why would they even try? This ends up ensuring that they don't get to their goal. You have a goal here that is complicated because it involves your own self-blame, your relationships with your deceased father and surviving family members, and your relationship with your wife and new baby. It feels overwhelming and hopeless.

D: Yes. There's no way out.

T: Let's pause for a moment and think about any other time in your life when things were really hard … like maybe when you were in medical school, trying to get through your training, making visits home when your dad would become so depressed, and trying to help your younger brother who was going through a tough adolescence—what positive images or types of things did you visualize for your future to help keep you going?

D: I saw myself getting my degree so I could be in a world-class children's hospital one day, where I could save kids' lives. I pictured my dad and mom together and proud at the graduation.

T: After all the struggles, hard work, and so many problems to solve, did that eventually occur?

R: It did. My dad wrote me these private letters about how he was proud to be my father and I was one of the good things in his life [begins crying]. It turned out that it wasn't enough … I'd give it up if I could have him back and convince him not to do it.

T: I understand. I'm sorry that this is so painful for you. I do need to make the point here that even though at various important times during your training, when you were trying to manage so many stressors at both medical school and home, so much so that you didn't have immediate answers to all of your concerns, you did maintain a positive image that helped you to get through it all and continue the hard work toward your goals.

D: Yeah. I had to have something to work toward, that's for sure.

T: Exactly! We all need that motivating image. Another example that comes to mind might be an individual who is training for a marathon. During the painful hours of their training, they don't visualize the muscle cramps, feeling ill, or falling down. They visualize crossing the finish line, relieved and victorious in completing the marathon, as a way to keep going. To help you, I would like to engage you in a technique we call *visualization to enhance your motivation*. This exercise is geared to help you overcome your feelings of hopelessness. Unlike when you were in medical school, you have been focused only on the obstacles in your way, rather than visualizing the goal—yet, this is exactly what you need to give yourself a reason to even try to take the next step. Are you willing to do this exercise with me?

D: Okay [sighs], I'll try.

At this point in the session, the therapist engaged David in the creative visualization exercise, guiding him through a visualization in which David was directed to close his eyes and systematically use all of his senses to create a positive image of the future in which the current problem he was experiencing was largely resolved and the obstacles overcome. It is important to note that in cases in which someone has died, the client may begin to image that the deceased is alive again or other losses recovered. In such a situation, the client will need to be gently guided to create an image that is *in the future*.

The following is the dialogue that occurred after the 15-minute visualization exercise:

T: Okay, David. Please slowly open your eyes now and remember that you are in my office. Can you describe the scene you visualized to me?

D: Whoa … that was pretty intense [slowly recovering, he begins to reveal his image]. I imagined being at my mother's house in the kitchen next month. It's a big kitchen with a center isle and a fire in the fireplace in an open dining area. My sister and mother are sad, but okay, and we are hugging each other.

T: Is there anyone else there?

D: My wife. She's usually so critical of my family … calls them repressed … but you said make it the way I would want it to be, so she's actually smiling here and saying nice things to my family. My sisters are playing with my son and laughing at him.

T: Anything else?

R: My mom tells me she knows that I did all I could for my dad and that she knows how proud he was [starts crying]. She tells me it's going to be okay for all of us.

T: What are your tears saying to you?

D: I actually believe it [pauses for a few moments].

T: How did you physically feel in this image?

D: Hard to describe. Maybe lighter, looser, not as tight, much warmer and more affectionate toward my wife. I also felt less pressure.

T: These are the feelings worth working toward.

D: Yes, they are.

The reader is referred back to Chapter 7 to view David's attempts to complete a Problem-Solving Worksheet soon after this visualization exercise.

SUMMARY

The focus of this chapter involved helping clients overcome low motivation and feelings of hopelessness and included two different tools. The first tool involved directing people to construct a motivational worksheet on which they would externalize (write down) both pros and cons for "not moving forward" versus having a problem solved. This tool would be useful for clients at any point in treatment when they are hesitant to continue, particularly with regard to implementing an action plan.

The second tool involved yet a fourth application of visualization, the first three being parts of Tool Kit #2: Problem-Solving Multitasking. The present tool is geared to help clients who display significant feelings of hopelessness and directs them to engage in a future visualization. The story of Viktor Frankl was described as an example of how visualization can be helpful and a useful vehicle to inspire individuals to tackle difficult barriers. This tool attempts to foster motivation to continue treatment (i.e., engage in the problem-solving process) by guiding clients to visualize seeing "the light at the end of the tunnel"; in other words, to experience having solved the problem, in contrast to attempting to visualize "how to get there." The rationale behind this approach involves enhancing individuals' ability to actually experience the feelings of achievement to enhance their motivation, similar to how one might feel more motivated to run faster on seeing the finish line. Last, we revisited the client David to illustrate how this visualization tool can be helpful.

REFERENCE

Frankl, V. E. (1984). *Man's search for meaning.* New York, NY: Pocket Books. (Original work published 1946)

TOOL KIT #4—"STOP AND SLOW DOWN": OVERCOMING EMOTIONAL DYSREGULATION

10

> *Stress and worry, they solve nothing. What they do is block creativity. You are not even able to think about the solutions. Every problem has a solution.*
>
> —Susan L. Taylor

> *It's not stress that kills us, it is our reaction to it.*
>
> —Hans Selye

As noted earlier, another potential barrier to effective problem solving involves difficulties in emotional regulation when attempting to cope with stressful problems. Thus, this fourth emotion-centered problem-solving therapy (EC-PST) tool kit focuses on helping individuals to better modulate their emotional reactions to stressful stimuli to prevent one's immediate negative emotional responses from becoming more intense and long-lasting. In essence, we describe this to clients as helping them to prevent the "train from leaving the station at an accelerating speed." Doing so is important for individuals to:

- Become more aware and mindful of the actual nature of their emotional reactions (as compared to attempting to suppress or avoid such experiences).

- Allow such emotions to better inform the problem-solving process (i.e., to better understand why they reacted to a given stimulus with a given emotion to eventually better understand why a given situation is actually a problem).

- To ultimately process the stressful situation in a more thoughtful and "calm" manner via planful problem solving (e.g., *"Can I do something about this situation? Should I do something about this problem? Can this problem be changed? Is this my best solution to accept that this problem cannot be changed?"*)

If asked the question, "Is it usually a good time to make an important decision when you are upset?" it is likely most people would quickly answer "no." Even though individuals frequently do make decisions or react to problems when upset, most persons (if calm) would agree with such an answer, suggesting that being angry, sad, disappointed, or tense can direct one's choices in ways that ultimately may be detrimental. Thus, when we do have strong initial immediate reactions to problem situations, it is in our best interests to attempt to "regulate" such emotions so they no longer inadvertently take over, dictate, or heavily influence our problem-solving efforts.

However, the thesis of EC-PST suggests that although there are ways in which our emotions can potentially *hurt* us, they can also *help* us, even the negative ones, such as sadness, tension, and anger. Emotions in general are important to (a) alert us to act a certain way, (b) fine-tune decision making, (c) enhance our ability to remember certain events, and (d) foster interpersonal interactions (Gross & Thompson, 2007). Therefore, it becomes important to become more aware of our emotions and to actually experience them, rather than to engage in avoidant or impulsive problem-solving strategies that are geared to suppress, deny, or minimize our feelings. By becoming more mindful of our emotional lives, we become more insightful about ourselves and our problem-solving orientations. These are important goals of EC-PST.

Moreover, we suggest that it is important to convey to clients that we do not wish to *eradicate* negative emotions, rather to minimize the negative impact that they may have on their overall well-being and functioning. In addition, negative emotions represent information that something in one's life is "not right," in other words, that a problem exists. As discussed in detail in Chapter 5, to better explain this concept to clients, we use the analogy posed by the rare genetic disease of congenital analgesia.

RATIONALE

As explained in detail in our problem-solving stress–diathesis model of psychopathology described in Chapter 2, encountering emotional stimuli triggers a multitude of neurobiological reactions in the body as well as cognitive interpretations of the source and nature of such stimuli. For example, stressful stimuli (e.g., getting stuck in a traffic jam, having a boss yell at you, being criticized, receiving a failing grade on a test, being rejected for a date, feeling someone behind you in a movie theatre continuously kicking the back of your seat) are initially perceived by the brain's switchboard (i.e., the thalamus), which then sends the message to both the amygdala (the low road) and the cortex (the high road), within milliseconds. This information is then passed onto the parts of the brain representing working memory (i.e., frontal cortex, parietal cortex, anterior cingulate, and parts of the basal ganglia), which is the system that stores the information for the mind to engage in reasoning and comprehension (similar to a computer's hard drive). How this information is interpreted is a function of past experience and learning, the situational context, and one's appraisal of the current situation (similar to one's unique software programs).

However, the amygdala is triggered within milliseconds, so the body is likely to react more automatically based on past learning as compared to an attempt at reasoned understanding. If we do not have the time and ability to stop this process, and if the emotional stimuli are continuous (e.g., the traffic jam gets *worse*; your boss *continues* to yell at you) and/or we acknowledge that we are indeed being threatened, particularly if in a ruminative manner (*"I'm always getting yelled at by my boss; I'm probably going to get fired, I'm not going to be able to get another job; I'm going to default on my mortgage and become homeless; I'm such a failure"*), the amygdala also gets "bombarded" continuously and our emotional reactions are likely to become more intense. Experiencing such chronic stress can have significant negative effects on one's working memory, including actual architectural changes in the prefrontal cortex, such as dendrite atrophy and spine loss (Radley et al., 2006). These notable negative effects on both structure (e.g., brain cell connectivity) and functioning (e.g., weakened ability to engage in the integration, processing, disposal, and retrieval of information) of the prefrontal cortex can significantly impact problem-solving effectiveness and are likely to be partially responsible for how stress leads to psychological disorders. In other words, stress sensitivity can lead to poor coping, which can then engender more stress and more distress (i.e., stress generation), and ultimately lead to poor adaptation and health outcomes.

Given the quickness by which a negative emotion can be triggered by a given stimulus, it becomes important to help an individual learn skills that can "stop and slow down" this process. In other words, our goal is *not* to eradicate one's emotions (which would be analogous to cutting off individuals' fingers to prevent them from ever getting burned by a hot cooking pot), so we believe it is important to teach individuals to "stop and slow down" their immediate emotional reactions to allow their executive functioning processes to handle the problem situation using a calmer, more thoughtful approach. In this manner, the negative effects of stress can be minimized and the likelihood that one's initial negative emotional reaction becomes more intense and long-lasting is attenuated. As suggested in the quote by Childre and Martin at the beginning of this chapter, it does not make a difference if the reason why someone is upset, angry, hurt, or disappointed is justified or correct (e.g., the boss made a mistake in yelling at you; you do not deserve to be in a traffic jam because you woke up early this morning to avoid such a jam, but an accident caused it anyhow)—the negative effects will emerge nonetheless. This is why we believe that lowering one's stress reaction is important regardless of its source and potentially arbitrary nature and causality.

To help prevent intense and long-lasting emotional responses, EC-PST provides individuals with a set of tools geared to help them "stop the train from leaving the station," or at least to help them decelerate its speed. In other words, the present tool kit is geared to help improve people's resilience to stress by helping them to "return to their emotional baseline" (e.g., their emotional state prior to the amygdala being triggered) to more thoughtfully attempt to cope with the stressful problem that initially triggered the emotional reaction. However, before we describe this tool kit, titled "Stop and Slow Down," in detail, we wish to place the concept of emotional regulation within a larger problem-solving context.

EC-PST AND EMOTIONAL REGULATION

According to Gross and Thompson (2007), five different sets or categories of emotional regulation processes or strategies can be identified:

- Situation selection
- Situation modification
- Attention deployment
- Cognitive change
- Response modulation

Scrutiny of EC-PST suggests that it actually includes treatment goals and specific strategies in *each* of these five categories, potentially enhancing its breadth, and ultimately, its robustness as an intervention. Thus, therapists should highlight to clients each of these five processes as frameworks within which they can learn how to better manage their emotional lives, especially within the context of solving real-life problems and attempting to adapt to stressful circumstances. In other words, an important tenet of EC-PST is the notion of flexibility and choice. Providing a menu of various means to conceptualize and identify ways to better manage strong negative emotional reactions is in keeping with such a philosophy. Note that these five categories can also serve as a framework of potential strategies when one is attempting to generate multiple solution alternatives using the variety (i.e., to think of both strategies and tactics) principle.

Situation Selection

These activities involve approaches to emotion regulation whereby people engage in actions that make it more or less probable that they will ultimately be involved in situations that engender desirable or undesirable emotions. One goal of EC-PST is to help individuals better understand the consequences of their behavior, particularly with regard to understanding the potential outcomes of a given solution or action plan in response to solving real-life problems (see Tool Kit #1: Planful Problem Solving). More specifically, in addition to analyzing whether a given solution is likely to be effective, individuals are also taught to predict the consequences of that solution using the following additional criteria as guides: *personal* effects (e.g., emotional cost or gain, physical well-being, time and effort involved, consistency with one's values), *social* consequences (e.g., effects on one's spouse/partner, family, friends, coworkers, community), *short-term* effects, and *long-term* consequences.

EC-PST teaches people to become more aware of their personal stress triggers, as well as their emotional responses to such triggers, so in addition to becoming more adept at predicting the consequences of their action plans (Tool Kit #1: Planful Problem Solving training), the combination of these strategies can also be conceptualized and applied as an emotion regulation strategy. An example of this type of process might involve individuals who are very unhappy with their current job. Considering the goal of becoming less unhappy (and possibly even fulfilled and satisfied), an emotion regulation strategy in this category might include changing jobs (within or outside of the present company or business), but doing so with a comprehensive self-understanding of what it is about various jobs and positions that make one happy as well as unhappy, and seeking employment in those specific contexts that are consistent with such criteria.

Situation Modification

The overarching goal regarding these types of emotional regulation strategies is to modify or change the nature of the situation such that it no longer engenders the type of emotional reactions one wishes to change. This is one of the major goals of EC-PST, that is, to help individuals identify the means by which to change a situation so that it is "no longer a problem" (i.e., resolving the problem). Getting back to our unhappy employees, one strategy in this family of emotion regulation approaches might involve identifying those aspects of their current job that are associated with negative emotions (e.g., low pay, too much or not enough responsibilities, physical work environment, and lack of opportunities for growth and/or promotion) and developing an overall action plan that is geared to change some or all of these negative job dimensions.

Attentional Deployment

Attentional deployment includes strategies that help individuals direct their attention in certain ways within a given situation as a means of influencing their emotions. One form of attentional deployment is *distraction*, in which individuals focus their attention away from certain aspects of the situation or from the situation altogether. In the "Stop and Slow Down" tool kit described in this chapter, several techniques are offered for individuals to help them "slow down" (i.e., attenuate the arousal) by directing their focus to other activities (e.g., counting down slowly from 20 to one). Remember from Chapter 8 that the brain is incapable of successfully multitasking (i.e., engaging in two activities at the same time without losing productivity); thus, teaching individuals to engage in distracting techniques can help them to refocus their attention on another task and not on the emotional stimuli. With regard to the unhappy employees described, when various aspects of their current jobs trigger negative emotional reactions of hopelessness, frustration, or "burnout," focusing their attention on one of several "slowing down" activities can serve to attenuate the negative arousal and allow them to "use" these emotions to better inform the problem-solving process.

Cognitive Change

This fourth class of emotion regulation processes involves cognitive change strategies, including potentially changing how one thinks about the situation (e.g., appraisal of threat vs. challenge) and/or about one's ability to meet the demands of the threat (e.g., "*Can I adequately solve this problem?*"). In Chapter 7, we focused on the difficulties inherent in accurately defining a problem and suggested the importance of being able to separate facts from assumptions, to set realistic goals, and to differentiate between problem-focused and emotion-focused goals. Doing so can enable individuals to cognitively "reframe" or redefine the problem (i.e., view it from multiple perspectives) to (a) better understand the nature of the problem and (b) use such information to ultimately develop an effective solution plan. Revisiting our unhappy employees, possible cognitive-change strategies may involve redefining their current positions and focusing on the more positive aspects of the job to minimize negative arousal while they remain in this situation, as well as attempting to solve the problem using planful problem solving.

Response Modulation

This family of regulation strategies includes attempts to directly impact the physiological, experiential, and/or behavioral responses comprising the emotional reaction itself. Examples might include relaxation, physical exercise, and guided imagery to attenuate a person's physiological arousal. As described in the following section, many of the activities included in this tool kit are specifically geared to helping individuals decrease the intensity of their emotional reactions (as compared to suppressing or eradicating such reactions) to provide the opportunity to engage in planful problem solving within a less emotionally volatile context.

THE SSTA METHOD OF EMOTIONAL REGULATION AND PROBLEM SOLVING UNDER STRESS

The acronym *SSTA* represents

S = Stop; be aware

S = Slow down and only then

T = Think

A = Act

This tool kit encompasses the following components: (a) becoming more emotionally mindful, (b) identifying unique triggers, and (c) "slowing down." Although this tool kit focuses primarily on the "Stop and Slow Down" components, we suggest introducing this acronym early in treatment to provide clients with the overarching guide of:

- *Stopping* when becoming aware of experiencing an emotional reaction that has the potential to "grow into a full-blown negative response"
- *Slowing down* one's emotional response to be able to engage in the next step
- *Thinking* more planfully about what to do within the context of a reduced level of interference from the triggered negative emotionality
- *Acting*, subsequently, by carrying out a solution plan geared toward effectively coping with the stressful situation

This acronym can serve as a mnemonic that can guide coping efforts, particularly under stress. Readers familiar with prior problem-solving therapy (PST) treatment manuals (e.g., D'Zurilla & Nezu, 2007; Nezu, Nezu, Friedman, Faddis, & Houts, 1998; Nezu, Nezu, Felgoise, McClure, & Houts, 2003) will note that the mnemonic recommended earlier was the phrase *Stop and Think*. However, on the basis of our clinical experience with a wide variety of patient populations, including those with more severe levels of distress, in combination with identifying a neurobiological explanation for why it may be so difficult to do so (i.e., to stop and then think in the face of continuous amygdala stimulation), we decided to add the component of "slowing down" to provide individuals with effective ways to do so. Adding the final "act" helps to underscore the notion that "ideas without actions are worthless" (Mackay, 2011, p. 2) in terms of ultimate coping effectiveness.

As in previous manuals, EC-PST continues to emphasize the notion that to effectively be able to "stop," one needs to be aware of the types of affective, cognitive, physical, and behavioral reactions that uniquely constitute one's responses to stressful stimuli. By being aware, one can then identify the circumstances under which one needs to *stop*. Some individuals may be very aware of the types of reactions they have in response to stressful stimuli, whereas others may not. However, in addition to using such emotional reactions as "cues that a problem exists," becoming more aware of the nature of the emotions themselves and what they mean uniquely to a given individual becomes especially important later when attempting to define the problem accurately. Therefore, if relevant for a given individual, EC-PST recommends training individuals to become more mindful of their emotions.

BECOMING MORE EMOTIONALLY MINDFUL

Training in this strategy is geared toward

- Helping individuals to become more aware of their unique reactions to stressful stimuli to be able to identify when to *stop*
- Helping them to become more attuned to the meaning and nature of such emotional reactions (e.g., *"Why am I so upset about this situation?"*)

This activity also helps clients to better recognize and label their emotions accurately when they occur. According to neuroscientist Korb (2015), becoming aware of one's emotional states activates the prefrontal cortex and allows it to actually suppress the amygdala. In support, he cites a study by Lieberman et al. (2007) in which participants were presented with pictures of people with emotional facial expressions. As would be predicted, each subject's amygdala was activated. However, when they were asked to name the emotion, the ventrolateral prefrontal cortex (the part of the cortex that is more involved in motivation and impulse control) was then activated leading to a reduction in amygdala reactivity. As Korb concludes "consciously recognizing the emotions reduced their impact" (p. 44).

In addition, by being more aware of such reactions, one can become better able to identify unique "triggers"; that is, those situations, events, people, internal thoughts, external stimuli (e.g., a song, visual image reminding one of a lost loved one) that stimulate the amygdala to produce potentially strong negative emotional reactions. In becoming better able to identify personal triggers, people can improve their ability to engage in "situation selection" types of emotional regulation (see the Situation Selection section).

Following is an example of describing this activity to a client (remember to think of this script as one of *many* possible ways of presenting this material):

> *In this exercise, I want to talk about feelings. People experience upsetting feelings every day. However, emotions can be very tricky. Sometimes, our feelings are a reaction to just one situation and they simply pass. At other times, we are bothered by upsetting feelings for longer periods of time. Problems such as occur with depression, anxiety, anger, and bereavement, all involve distressful feelings. It is important for you to use this tool if you find that such feelings serve as an obstacle or barrier for you to adopt a positive orientation or if a strong emotional reaction hinders your ability to effectively resolve a particular problem.*
>
> *It is very common for most people to need some help managing their negative feelings. Emotional problems are often the reason why people seek help from counselors. The following guidelines are designed to give a step-by-step approach so you can use the power of feelings adaptively and to your advantage. By practicing these steps, you will be more aware of your negative feelings and be able to use them as signals or cues that a problem exists, rather than simply dwell on them, only to feel worse. In addition, this approach can help you deal better with such feelings, as well as with the problem that is causing your distress.*
>
> *Consider the idea that negative emotions are one of nature's gifts to you. It is a mistake to view negative feelings as being all bad. Actually, negative emotions can*

be thought of as nature's way of telling you that something is wrong and that a problem exists. In this manner, they are helpful to our ultimate well-being, even though they may be unpleasant at the time. (The therapist may wish to discuss the example of congenital analgesia at this point.)

Furthermore, research has shown that trying to suppress negative feelings makes the situation worse—in fact, suppressing feelings actually increases their intensity! So, follow these steps to learn how to use your feelings as cues.

Step 1. Throughout the day, any time you begin to feel distressed or physically uncomfortable, stop to notice what you are feeling and how intense these feelings are. Try to put into words what emotion or feeling you notice first. Is it sadness? Boredom? Anger? Tension? Guilt? Recognizing your feelings can actually reduce their negative impact. It really helps to write them down in your notebook, journal, laptop, or tablet. Remember to externalize. Externalizing can help you to remember, as well as to clarify what you are feeling.

Step 2. Now notice how you experience this feeling. Do you have any physical sensations such as your heart pounding, a lump appears in your throat, or your face flushing? Do you say things to yourself such as "I can't take this," "I don't need this," "I hate to feel this way," "I'll show him what it feels like," or "I give up"? What are you feeling? Sadness? Tension? Anger? What is your affect? Are you acting differently? Do you feel an urge to run away, fight someone, or shut down? As you begin to get familiar with how you experience your own emotions, consider all of these signs, that is, the physical sensations, the things you say to yourself, your affect or mood, and any changes in your behavior, such as cues, signals, or clues that "something is going on." In other words, "I'm upset about something—there's a problem that's occurring that I need to attend to!" Now go to Step 3.

Step 3. "Stop, be aware, and Slow Down!" Imagine a stop sign or a flashing red traffic light as a way to help you stop. This step means stopping all action, almost like you would when you press the "pause" button on your smartphone or computer. You are going to stop all actions (even talking) for a few seconds to become more aware of your emotions. In this frozen moment in time, allow yourself first to experience the emotion and then identify what you are feeling. Become more mindful of your experience. Inhibit the tendency to try to feel better before realizing what is truly going on or to deny the feeling to "make it go away."

Step 4. This step is geared to help you "learn to be wise"—in other words, to be able to better understand what your emotions are trying to tell you. When you react only with your feelings, it is difficult to listen to the logical or reasoned part of your mind. In such a case, you are likely to act impulsively, which is followed by more feelings. For example, in reaction to something that has happened, you might get angry. However, for some people, getting angry leads to embarrassment, then embarrassment leads to fear, then fear leads to more anger. In this manner, one might never get away from these bad feelings and the original reason why you became angry (which may be natural and predictable) is lost!

On the contrary, if you think only with logic (e.g., like "Dr. Spock" of Star Trek *fame), you may disregard the important information that your emotions are telling you. For instance, suppose that you are feeling sad because you are lonely. Your logical thinking may lead you to discount or discredit your feelings ("I shouldn't be feeling this way; I'm okay!"), which may lead you to be unaware of the importance of seeking more support or friendship from others. What happens when we bring emotions and thinking together? In general, it takes both types of thinking to be wise—in other words, to be able to use your emotions to let you know what is "really going on." This can be hard work, because it means taking the time and effort to figure out what important information your feelings are providing you. With this new wisdom, however, you will be able to answer the question of what your emotions are telling you. Having this information allows you to decide what to do next.*

Step 5. This next step helps you to answer the question, "What are my emotions telling me?" Remember that one reason why you have emotions is to give you information. Your body is set up to react with certain feelings for very good reasons. Look at this table of emotions [Table 10.1]. *It contains the type of information you should be looking for when you are trying to identify what your feelings are "telling you." We have also provided a few common examples of what the information may reveal.*

Some of the information that a feeling "tells you" may point to an actual situation that you need to do something about. It may also involve something that you are telling yourself or a situation that you are having difficulty accepting. Therefore, the information you receive from feelings can let you know what situations you may need to focus on changing; self-statements that are irrational, exaggerated, or incorrect; or new situations or change that you must realistically confront.

Step 6. To achieve emotional balance in your life, it is important to work toward changing things that you can

TABLE 10.1 ■ EMOTIONS AND WHAT THEY MAY BE "TELLING YOU"

What You Are Feeling	What Your Feelings Might Be Telling You	What This Information Might Reveal About You
Fear/anxiety	You feel that threat or danger is nearby.	What are you afraid of—physical harm, being laughed at, feeling inferior, being rejected, getting fired?
Anger	You are being blocked from getting something you want.	What do you want—to be successful, have a relationship, an accomplishment, to be loved?
Sadness	You have lost something significant.	What have you lost—a friend, lover, or partner; your power, status, or role; losing what you like to do; your importance?
Embarrassment	You believe that others can see your imperfections, mistakes, or problems.	What do they see—your intellectual weaknesses, your emotions, your faults?
Guilt	You are focusing on something you regret.	What do you regret—that you hurt others? Is someone else telling you that you hurt them?

change, and becoming more realistic and accepting of things that you cannot. This is where true wisdom comes from—learning to actually "listen" to your emotions and then apply your logical thinking to decide what you need to do. In other words—Stop, be aware, and Slow Down! Stopping and slowing down allow you to put the brakes on a potentially fast-moving train that is carrying negative emotions as baggage and so determine your next move.

When you are in a calmer state, you can then attempt to go on to the next steps of SSTA—"think, and then act." As Ernest Hemingway once said, "before you react, think." In other words, if we don't stop and slow down, we might allow our negative arousal to direct our actions. By slowing down, you can give yourself the chance to really think about what's the best course of action. "Slowing down" is easier said than done, but it is important to emphasize that this tool kit contains a variety of specific techniques and tools that can teach you to do exactly that: "Stop, be more aware, and slow down."

IDENTIFYING UNIQUE TRIGGERS

By becoming more mindful and aware of their specific emotional reactions (i.e., affect, thoughts, physical sensations, behavioral changes), individuals can also become more aware of those types of situations, events, or stimuli that uniquely serve as triggers of such arousal. To accomplish this, clients are asked to record the reactions that occur immediately prior to experiencing a negative emotion. By having such information available, the therapist can then engage patients in a discussion to better identify their unique triggers. We have also used the phrases "red switches" or "hot buttons" to denote the idea that certain stimuli can be responsible for engendering a negative emotional reaction (i.e., *pictures of your ex-wife, or women who physically resemble her, serve as switches to turn on your feelings of sadness, regret, and remorse; because of your previous experiences, hearing your neighbor's dog barking actually pushes your anger button and makes you obsess whether the dog is actually on your lawn eating your beautiful flowers*).

Box 10.1 provides a list of categories of both personal and environmental stimuli that can serve as triggers. Note that reactions to stress (e.g., affect, thoughts, physical sensations, and behavioral changes) can also serve as triggers for other reactions as well as increasing their own intensity (e.g., having a negative thought can lead to additional negative thoughts). From a

---

BOX 10.1 ■ CATEGORIES OF POTENTIAL UNIQUE TRIGGERS

Personal
Affect: Sadness, anxiety, anger, guilt, embarrassment, concern, anger, etc.
Conflict: Occurs between emotions, thoughts, goals, values, beliefs, ideas, etc.
Thoughts: Good and bad thoughts, flashbacks, memories, internal images, "hunches," etc.
Physical sensations: Headache, pain, dizziness, stomachache, fatigue, sweating, etc.
Urge to act differently: Run away, fight, drink alcohol, sleep, overeat, take drugs, etc.

Environmental/Social
Interpersonal: Being criticized, yelled at, intimidated/bullied, rejected, ignored, etc.
Physical: Noise, hot/cold weather, crowds, music, pictures, smell, etc.

---

behavioral chaining perspective, these internal (or personal) stimuli are all part of a network of responses that comprise a larger (often implicit) emotional reaction that is likely to have been engendered by stimulating the thalamus → amygdala → cortex pathway. In other words, for example, individuals may become aware that they are experiencing anxiety only seconds or minutes after encountering an external stimulus (e.g., being criticized) that likely triggered such a response. Thus, the affect itself may be experienced by the individual as the immediate trigger. Other internal stimuli can also serve as triggers, such as memories of a previous painful experience or thoughts about an upcoming anxiety-provoking meeting with one's boss.

External stimuli that are possible triggers are also important to identify emanating both from the social and physical environments. For example, a variety of interpersonal events can serve to trigger negative emotional arousal, such as being the recipient of criticism, rejection, or aggression from another person. Possible physical environment triggers can include music, noise, bad weather, traffic, crowding, and so forth. Note how movies tend to be able to manipulate our emotional responses simply by varying the type of music presented (e.g., think of your reaction to a horror movie that contained music usually associated with a comedy or romantic drama).

It is not so important to be able to have individuals identify the actual initial stimulus within the behavioral chain that ultimately led to increased negative arousal (i.e., "What started me feeling this way in the first place?"). Rather, it is more important that they understand that a multitude of stimuli can serve as triggers within a network of factors and that they are ultimately better able to identify such triggers. Identifying one's unique buttons helps individuals to obtain increased clarity about their emotional experiences as well as ultimately to better identify *why* such stimuli tend to reliably trigger such reactions; that is, *why is this situation a problem for me?* Thus, it can provide a fuller understanding and appreciation of how one can engage in a multitude of emotional-regulation strategies across the five categories described earlier as a means of attenuating or preventing high levels of negative arousal. For example, knowing what types of situations typically have engendered certain types of negative emotional reactions in the past can allow people to decide whether to avoid such situations, become better prepared to deal with such events in a different coping manner (e.g., engage in various stress-management strategies to enter the situation with a lowered level of stress), to practice focusing on the more positive aspects of the situation as compared to ruminating about the negative features, or attempt to change their thinking about such situations (e.g., try to be more accepting that such negative events are a part of life that is unavoidable).

In addition, such discussions can help the client to identify particular patterns whereby various triggers appear to represent possible themes, such as fear of committing to relationships, sadness about being continuously rejected by people, anxiety about never "advancing in life," becoming angry when confronted with criticism, and perceiving any disagreement as a threat to one's self-esteem. Identifying patterns can be very helpful to later clarify the nature of one's problem-solving styles in relation to specific types of situations. Furthermore, it can provide a mechanism of enhanced self-awareness of what types of problems particularly are troublesome for a given individual.

STRATEGIES TO HELP "SLOW DOWN"

In teaching individuals to slow down, we suggest that a menu of several possible slowing-down strategies be available that can be taught to clients, some of which may be relevant and effective for a given individual, whereas others may not. The point here is to demonstrate that multiple choices are available and that it may be important for clients to try several of them to have a number of tools at their disposal to address differing circumstances and situations. In describing the various strategies, we strongly recommend that the therapist actually demonstrate how to apply those that appear "strange" (e.g., yawning) or novel (e.g., deep breathing) and have the client practice them in session. Many of the approaches listed are effective major stress-management strategies in and of themselves. Note that we provide instructions for several of the listed approaches in the Client Workbook. In addition to those presented here, we urge the clinician to engage in a discussion with patients regarding additional ways they, themselves, may have used in the past to help "slow down" and "prevent the train from leaving the station."

Note that some of these approaches require more time than others, as well as more practical private space (e.g., we would not recommend that a client engage in a closed-eye guided-imagery exercise in response to becoming very angry in a traffic jam while driving). In discussing these techniques, the clinician should ultimately help clients to determine which may be specifically effective and appropriate and under what circumstances.

The following are recommended strategies to use to slow down:

- Counting (up from one to 20 or down from 20 to one)
- Guided imagery/visualization
- Deep breathing
- "Fake" yawning
- Mindful meditation
- Deep-muscle–relaxation exercises
- Exercise/mindful walking
- Talking to someone
- Prayer

Counting. Slowly counting up from one to 20 or down from 20 to one and attempting to visualize the numbers changing is a brief and simple method of "slowing down." It can be considered one form of an attentional deployment strategy of emotion regulation in that it helps distract the individual by focusing away from both the emotional stimulus and one's reaction to the stimulus.

Guided imagery. Using one's mind's eye to go to a safe place or to take a vacation in one's mind is another highly effective stress-management tool. This was initially presented in Chapter 8; detailed instructions on using guided imagery are included in the Client Workbook (for availability, see the Preface of this book). This strategy would be most useful when individuals have the time and privacy to engage in the visualization.

Deep breathing. Diaphragmatic breathing, or deep breathing, is a common stress-management tool that helps individuals lower their arousal. This tool requires an individual to engage in slow, deep, and rhythmic breathing to counteract symptoms of tension and negative arousal (e.g., irregular, rapid, and shallow breathing). Practicing this strategy when one is in a calm state ultimately fosters skill acquisition and proficiency in applying it under stress. When able to engage in deep breathing, it can be a very powerful means to "slow down," especially because it requires little time to apply. Specific instructions on learning this technique are given in the Client Workbook.

"Fake" yawning. Yawning is a human reflex that involves simultaneously taking in air and stretching the eardrums, followed by exhalation of

breath. It is socially contagious (i.e., seeing someone yawn can elicit a yawn) in humans as well as chimpanzees and dogs. The major reason why it is included as a "slow-down" technique is because of its highly positive effects on the brain and body. More specifically, neuroscience research indicates that yawning simultaneously both relaxes and energizes the body; influences brain chemistry in a positive manner; decreases the temperature of the brain; improves focus; and enhances awareness, compassion, and communication (e.g., Newberg & Waldman, 2009). Suggesting this strategy to individuals can be easily met with skepticism. However, in addition to telling them about the neuroscience research that has identified yawning's powerful positive effects, the therapist can also inform them that this is a common strategy used in voice therapy to relax the throat and reduce anxiety and to enhance focus and improve relaxation among sharpshooters and paratroopers in the military and among high-level athletes. A prime example is Apolo Ohno, a speed skater who won eight Olympic medals during the course of his career, who was frequently seen yawning right before the beginning of a race.

Real yawning is usually not possible "on demand," so we recommend that individuals engage in "fake yawning"; that is, to fake a yawn and stretch their arms widely if possible (the combination of simultaneously yawning and stretching is known as *pandiculation*) about six to eight times in a row. For most people, doing so will actually begin to elicit real yawns. The therapist should demonstrate this strategy and possibly underscore the notion that although it may seem "silly" at first, practicing this activity and applying it in appropriate contexts can be very effective as a means of "slowing down."

Mindful meditation. The concept of *mindfulness* refers to a centuries-old meditative practice that has been an integral aspect of spiritual training in various Eastern religious faiths such as Buddhism. It can be described as a conscious state of nonjudgmental awareness; that is, the ability to be fully aware of a situation (or emotion reaction), without judging what one is experiencing. Practicing this strategy allows one to more fully experience what is happening in the present moment (e.g., awareness of one's breathing, physical sensations, movements) without getting caught up in thoughts or emotional reactions. Thus, mindfulness meditation can help individuals slow down by approaching a situation "mindfully," that is, to simply experience the situation rather than allowing one's emotional reactions to escalate. Mindful meditation has been scientifically found to be highly effective for a variety of psychological difficulties.

An important aspect of mindfulness meditation is the notion of "distancing" oneself from one's experience. More specifically, as independent observers, people are directed to pay close attention to their thoughts and feelings as they occur in the present moment, but simultaneously attempt to separate their thoughts and feelings from themselves. In other words, to eventually be able to realize that such thoughts and feelings are just that—thoughts and feelings—and as such, they do not need to direct one's actions—"*the thought doesn't own you, nor does it define you—it's just a thought*" (Nezu, Nezu, & Jain, 2005, p. 172). Although it does take practice to be able to quickly distance oneself from a negative emotional response, for some people, mindfulness mediation can be a powerful means of decelerating such reactions to better understand why the situation is a problem and what to eventually do about it. Detailed instructions are included in the Client Workbook.

Deep-muscle relaxation. Muscle relaxation (also known as *progressive muscle relaxation*) helps to relieve muscle tension and provides a feeling of warmth and well-being to the body. This exercise helps individuals to focus on various muscle groups (e.g., right hand) and to tense and then release such tension in that muscle area, which results in a feeling of relaxation. One progresses through all the various muscle groups in the body to the point where the entire body feels relaxed. Extensive research shows this to be a very effective means for overall stress management, as well as improving emotional and physical well-being among individuals who recently experienced a myocardial infarction (i.e., heart attack; Löwe et al., 2002). Becoming proficient in this strategy does take significant practice. However, again, it can be a powerful tool, not just for general stress management but as a slow-down technique as well. We include detailed instructions in the Client Workbook.

Exercise/mindful walking. Another slow-down strategy involves exercise activities. These can include walking, jogging, bicycling, hiking, and so forth and are recommended according to the patient's abilities and physical stamina and strength. Although exercise is a robust stress-management tool overall, in this context, brief exercise activities can serve as an effective slow-down approach.

One specific way to combine exercise and another type of slow-down strategy is to go on a "mindful walk." In doing so, individuals can benefit from exercise, decelerate their negative-emotion arousal, and consciously capture the full experience of their day-to-day activities as being important and valuable. In practicing this activity, one can become more proficient at distancing oneself from one's negative arousal as a means of preventing such arousal from escalating. Instructions for this strategy are included in the Client Workbook (for availability, see the Preface of this book).

Talking to someone. Talking to a family member, friend, or colleague can be one method of slowing down. We would highly recommend, however, that one does not attempt to engage the other person in a dialogue geared toward helping justify or support one's emotional arousal. Rather, this should be discussed earlier with a given person and mutually agreed upon that a conversation subsequent to a strong emotional reaction will serve to slow the client down. For example, on the basis of a previous plan, the support person can remind the client to engage in various stress-management techniques (e.g., deep breathing and mindful meditation), provide guidance and help in applying these strategies, or engage in a conversation that allows the person to be distracted from the situation that triggered the initial reaction to prevent the "train from going out of the station." For some individuals, catharsis (i.e., talking about how one feels in a strong emotionally demonstrative manner) can be helpful (e.g., allows people to externalize their feelings; engenders fatigue); for others, it can serve the opposite function, that is, exacerbate one's arousal. Thus, it is important for the therapist to assess the likelihood of positive versus negative consequences of systematically applying this strategy with a given client or client/support person pair.

Prayer. Prayer can be a very powerful slow-down strategy for those individuals who consider themselves religious or spiritual in nature. Recommending this strategy requires being sensitive to a client's values and belief systems.

Other techniques. In addition to providing the preceding menu of strategies as potentially effective and relevant ways of "slowing down," it is also important for the clinician to inquire about other techniques that may have worked for a particular client in the past. These can be added to the overall list.

REVISITING MARK: OVERCOMING EMOTIONAL DYSREGULATION

As described in the clinical introduction to his treatment in Chapter 6, Mark displayed an inability to self-regulate his strong emotions. He had a tendency to fluctuate between extreme responses of surrendering to his self-doubt or overcompensating and exaggerating his superior artistic talent. These conflicting extremes were additionally observed as repeating responses to negative emotions that occurred in his relationships with others. The following dialogue demonstrates the use of this tool kit by the therapist (T) with Mark (M), who described his emotional turmoil as triggered by not being able to balance "self-criticism and pride," especially when it involved his artwork.

M: I didn't like writing my emotional reactions down on paper, but I did it and maybe this will show you how I can't find balance, and why everyone expects me to freak out at any moment.

T: If we can use the information you provided here to begin to understand why you often experience this sense of extremes in which you are challenged at finding, to use your words, "balance," then I think you are really onto some important self-discovery. Okay. Let's look at what you wrote down.

M: It probably won't give us any great insight but whatever ...

T: Sorry to interrupt, but did you notice what just happened? As I indicated that you might have some insights, you downplayed it—showed some "self-criticalness" to use your words, before we even began.

M: Well, what do you want me to say? That I had these great insights and now I'm all fine?

T: Wow ... you just went from 0 to 60 mph in the opposite direction from "self-criticalness" to "pride" (as you refer to it). How about something in the middle, like "Well, I'm not sure if this is what you are looking for but I tried to write down what I agreed to." Just wanted to make a point with you here in the moment about how subtle our reactions can be. Now let's see what you wrote down.

M: I worked all week to finish this piece for a former instructor from my program who said he would display it in this downtown gallery where he knows the owner. It was nice of him to offer, but I kept restarting the piece because everything I did looked like crap. He asked me when it would be ready and inside I thought: "You've gotten so corporate ... more concerned about pleasing the gallery owner and making money than what I am doing" ... my physical sensations ... I was just pissed off. I'm not sure what exactly you wanted me to write here.

T: Let's see if I can help. Remember last week we talked about how feelings can arise very quickly because we have made some nonconscious connections that are so well learned and occur so rapidly that we don't actually remember a conscious experience until after the fact?

M: [Nods head]

T: That sounds like what happened here. In such a case, our bodies may provide us with some "expert information" so that we can recognize a negative feeling before it's too intense that our brain is unable to process what's going on. So, where do you remember feeling the anger physically?

M: I was hot in my face and I felt almost panicky. When he first asked me how the piece was going, he had no idea how tortured I was to create something meaningful. It really pissed me off—that's when I felt the physical stuff—my heart beating out of my chest—I started to sweat like crazy—the thoughts came after that because he saw my reaction and tried to say that I'm overly critical of my work and that if he could see what I'm working on, maybe he could help. He said that he only wanted to support my work and I was acting like a jerk, accusing him of seeing me as crazy and trying to convince me to display work that was not good. When he saw that I was upset, he started talking very softly and trying to calm me down. I can't take this anymore ... I'm always the one who is "crazy" or "nuts" and everyone is expecting that I will just freak out and not deliver.

T: Do you see any pattern with situations like this, where the trigger for you is when someone indicates that they view you as overreacting and disagrees with the way you handle things?

M: Of course. My mother always put me down, blamed me for everything, and acted like she was the one who knew everything. My father abused me to teach me a lesson.

T: So, when anyone disagrees with you, or gives you even constructive feedback, you hear it as a put-down, criticism, or fear that you will lose control, before you even realize it?

M: Okay ... so, what if that's true? The gallery owner said I could take an extra few weeks before his next big show is booked, but I'm thinking now that I'll probably go nuts before I'm able to finish a piece. It would probably suck anyway.

T: How about recording your reactions again this week when you experience that trigger? Each time you start out to work on the piece this week, knowing your unique triggers, you can use the "Stop and Slow Down" tool kit. It appears that your triggers include the following: Your heart starts to beat faster, you start to sweat, you have angry thoughts toward your former professor, you think that your work will suck, or you have other thoughts about being too fragile for this career. These triggers can serve as a cue to stop, be more aware of what you are feeling and thinking, apply a slow-down technique to stop any action, and turn down the volume on your arousal. This will help your brain to be able to process what is happening. Please jot down a note when this happens for us to discuss next session. Okay, which slow-down technique do you want to use? [These were previously described.]

M: The counting is stupid … the yawning thing intrigues me, and I've used breathing before.

T: Great. Now let's try to visualize or imagine when you are likely to experience one of these triggers and let's walk step-by-step through the imagery of when you will use the slow-down strategy, what you will specifically do, and predict how things will go after you use it.

It was important to end this therapeutic exchange with Mark by having him go through the following steps:

- Use visualization to go through a situation that he was likely to encounter during the week.

- Visualize what he might say to himself when he notices and "listens" to his physical cues, as well as his thoughts and feelings to *STOP*.

- Be aware and use slow-down technique to "buy time" for his brain to process what he was experiencing, and only then decide what to do next.

Mark imagined himself working on his artwork, stepping back to look at what he had just done and hearing a voice inside his head saying, "*this sucks … it's not distinctive … people will ignore it.*" Together with his therapist, Mark imagined applying the yawning technique to help him stop and slow down, and when he was less aroused, he began to define his goal of having his piece achieve "distinction." This led to training in the Planful Problem-Solving tool kit at the next session (as described in Chapter 7).

SUMMARY

This chapter focused on the fourth EC-PST tool kit—the "Stop and Slow Down" method of overcoming emotional dysregulation and maladaptive problem solving under stress. We introduced the acronym SSTA, which represents the phrase "Stop, be aware, and Slow down, Think, and Act." The importance of this tool kit is to help individuals prevent strong emotional arousal from escalating and impacting their ability to engage in effective problem solving. Emotional stimuli can trigger reactions almost instantaneously, so clients are taught to initially become better aware of their overall reactions to stress, including affective, cognitive, physical, and behavioral responses. Such knowledge can also help people to become more aware of what their feelings are, especially within the context of what situations, events, people (etc.) appear to engender such reactions, as well as what these emotional reactions "tell" people about themselves and their goals. This tool kit also helps individuals become more aware of such triggers to provide a more complete picture of one's unique stress–distress sets of associations, as well as helping to choose the various ways by which to better manage and regulate strong emotional reactions. To provide a greater context within which to understand emotional regulation, we described five classes or categories of such approaches: situation selection, situation modification, attention deployment, cognitive change, and response modulation. In describing each of these types of processes, we also highlighted how EC-PST actually incorporates each of these five sets of emotion regulation strategies in the various tool kits.

Although the present tool kit focused primarily on helping individuals to "Stop and Slow Down," which are only the first two aspects of this acronym, we suggested that the acronym and associated phrase ("Stop, Slow down, Think, and Act") provides a useful mnemonic for individuals to use to approach the overall process of solving real-life stressful problems. In helping clients to "slow down," we described a wide variety of possible techniques, some of which are logical choices, whereas others may appear novel or even "strange." Those that are novel were included because of the associated neuroscience research supporting their potential efficacy as a stress-management and "slow-down" strategy. We ended this chapter by revisiting the case of Mark to illustrate aspects of training in the "Stop and Slow Down" approach to emotion regulation.

REFERENCES

D'Zurilla, T. J., & Nezu, A. M. (2007). *Problem-solving therapy: A positive approach to clinical intervention* (3rd ed.). New York, NY: Springer Publishing.

Gross, J. J., & Thompson, R. A. (2007). Emotion regulation: Conceptual foundations. In J. J. Gross (Ed.), *Handbook of emotional regulation* (pp. 3–24). New York, NY: Guilford Press.

Korb, A. (2015). *The upward spiral: Using neuroscience to reverse the course of depression, one small change at a time.* Oakland, CA: New Harbinger Publications.

Lieberman, M. D., Eisenberger, N. I., Crockett, M. J., Tom, S. M., Pfeifer, J. H., & Way, B. M. (2007). Putting feelings into words. *Psychological Science, 18,* 421–428, doi:10.1111/j.1467-9280.2007.01916.x

Löwe, B., Breining, K., Wilke, S., Wellmann, R., Zipfel, S., & Eich, W. (2002). Quantitative and qualitative effects of Feldenkrais, progressive muscle relaxation, and standard medical treatment in patients after acute myocardial infarction. *Psychotherapy Research, 12,* 179–191. doi:10.1093 /ptr/12.2.179

Mackay, H. (2011). *The Mackay MBA of selling in the real world.* New York, NY: Penguin.

Newberg, A., & Waldman, M. R. (2009). *How God changes your brain.* New York, NY: Ballantine Books.

Nezu, A. M., Nezu, C. M., Felgoise, S. H., McClure, K. S., & Houts, P. S. (2003). Project Genesis: Assessing the efficacy of problem-solving therapy for distressed adult cancer patients. *Journal of Consulting and Clinical Psychology, 71,* 1036–1048. doi:10.1037/0022-006X.71.6.1036

Nezu, A. M., Nezu, C. M., Friedman, S. H., Faddis, S., & Houts, P. S. (1998). *Helping cancer patients cope: A problem-solving approach.* Washington, DC: American Psychological Association.

Nezu, A. M., Nezu, C. M., & Jain, D. (2005). *The emotional wellness way to cardiac health: How letting go of depression, anxiety, and anger can heal your heart.* Oakland, CA: New Harbinger.

Radley, J. J., Rocher, A. B., Miller, M., Janssen, W. G., Liston, C., Hof, P. R., ... Morrison, J. H. (2006). Repeated stress induces dendritic spine loss in the rat medial prefrontal cortex. *Cerebral Cortex, 16,* 313–320. doi:10.1093/cercor/bhi104

11

GUIDED PRACTICE, FUTURE FORECASTING, AND ENDING TREATMENT

Practice is the best of all instructors.

—Publilius Syrus

An ounce of practice is worth more than tons of preaching.

—Gandhi

After the major emotion-centered problem-solving therapy (EC-PST) training has taken place, the remainder of treatment is devoted to practicing the skills learned. The importance of such practice is conveyed in the two quotes given at the beginning of the chapter by Syrus and Gandhi. Simply put, as with any new skill, the more one practices, the better one gets. Beyond actually solving stressful problems, continuous practice in this context serves three additional purposes:

- Applying the entire problem-solving model (i.e., *SSTA*) under the guidance of a therapist allows for helpful professional feedback.
- Increased facility with the model through practice can decrease the amount of time and effort necessary to apply the model with each new problem.
- Practice facilitates maintenance and generalization of the skills.

GUIDED PRACTICE

The therapist's goals for these practice sessions are to

- Help clients fine-tune the problem-solving skills they have acquired.
- Monitor their application of these principles.
- Help clients to meaningfully integrate the various tools.
- Reinforce client progress as a means of further increasing patients' sense of self-efficacy

The number of practice sessions required after formal training ends is dependent on the competency level that a client achieves as well as actual improvements in the areas related to the initial reasons for seeking treatment (e.g., decreased depression, anxiety, anger; improved self-confidence and self-esteem; improved adjustment to a chronic medical illness; enhanced overall quality of life). However, regardless, we do strongly encourage that several sessions be devoted specifically to practice. A useful approach to guide practice sessions is to use the SSTA process to continue to inform clients on how to approach various stressful situations to instill and reinforce the basic procedures (i.e., to *Stop and be aware, Slow down, Think, and Act*).

A typical practice session begins and ends in a manner similar to previous skills-training sessions. Clients are asked to review how they applied the various EC-PST tools to assigned or new problems since the past session, as well as to discuss areas that have been difficult for them. Extensive feedback should be provided as appropriate. If some individuals find they could not complete any of the Problem-Solving Worksheets because of confusion or feeling stuck, it is important for the therapist to provide guidance and additional practice. At times, the therapist may need to circle back to various training exercises or activities to enhance a client's understanding or skill acquisition regarding a particular area.

Therapists are advised to continue evaluating and monitoring clients' motivation to apply and practice the various problem-solving tools. The importance of practice cannot be overemphasized. Yet, some clients may value practice sessions less than skills-training sessions because they misperceive the bulk of the effort necessary. Other clients may believe that the skills-training sessions adequately addressed the problems that brought them in for therapy, and therefore no longer believe additional sessions are necessary. For these reasons, it is imperative that the purpose of the practice sessions be underscored at the end of formal training.

INTEGRATING VARIOUS PROBLEM-SOLVING TOOLS: THE CASE OF "JOHN"

As noted in the preceding section, these practice sessions, in part, can be helpful in teaching clients how to "put it all together" (i.e., to integrate various tools). The following example illustrates how multiple tools were applied together to help reduce a client's feelings of hopelessness. John was a 36-year-old national guardsman who recently returned from deployment in the Middle East and was wrestling with significant issues of readjustment; he was feeling overwhelmed and confused. John was attending an EC-PST group at the counseling center at his local university, where he had recently returned to school. John was experiencing significant difficulty defining his problem. We include this example as a demonstration of how to help clients handle the challenging task of defining complex problems by using certain "Stop and Slow Down" tools in concert with planful problem solving.

Therapist (T): Okay, John. I see that when you indicated you were wrestling with the worksheet for homework that your problem had to do with trying to clean up your house and that you were feeling pretty upset with your difficulty organizing things. You listed your goal as "clean house" and your obstacles as "motivation" and "playing video games."

John (J): Yeah … and there's only one alternative I can think of to reach my goal—just get off my butt, stop whining, and do it! But I end up getting out of bed late, playing video games, and living like a slug—if I could do that, don't you think I would? Not sure if I buy this problem-solving stuff.

T: I can see how frustrating this is for you and that you're feeling pretty hopeless about ever being able to accomplish what you want to get done. I also hear a lot of self-criticism.

J: You got that right, Doc—I'm so mad at myself.

T: I'm wondering, though, if we can try to define your problem differently by using the visualization and simplification tools you've already learned. Let's do this to see whether we can look at the problem, your feelings about it, and the goal you have set in a different light. Is that okay?

J: Can't hurt.

T: Please tell me a little more about how you feel about this problem. Does it represent some block to any important value or life goal you have for yourself?

J: It really gets me angry. I always wanted to be sort of a hero, you know? Really do something meaningful to make life better for other people and [he starts to hold back tears at this point] ... now I can't even clean a room ... see this ... these feelings? Whenever I think about doing anything, I realize that my feelings are so close to the surface ... dealing with all the crap I saw ... and I don't feel like I can do anything ... so I just veg out and tell myself I'll deal with all that when I'm feeling better.

T: Thanks for trusting me, John, and letting me help with this problem. So now I see that cleaning and organizing the house is more than just about making things tidy. It's one strategy you can think of that may lead you to feel like you can do anything, something meaningful. But when each day goes by that you don't do it, you feel worse and get angry at yourself, on top of feeling hopeless. I think it may make sense to hold off on strategies for now and to look at the real problem here ... becoming more hopeful that you can make a meaningful contribution here, back at home, in your postdeployment life. Does this sound right?

J: Yeah ... when you taught me that visualization stuff, I started to think that I really could get myself going ... but now I'm not so sure.

T: Let's start by having you write down your "real" goal—the one that your feelings signal you into and that is aligned with your values: making a contribution. What obstacles come to mind that prevent you from reaching your goal?

J: Well, I start thinking that if I can't clean my apartment, how can I do anything else?

T: Okay, your negative orientation ... remember how this is one of the barriers to planful problem solving?

J: Oh, yeah, and some of the others included were negative feelings and hopelessness. I guess I have all the barriers operating here.

T: Excellent, yes, you have identified them correctly, and particularly when you become very angry at yourself, your arousal combines with these other barriers and you will need to use the "SS" part of SSTA to calm your brain and body so that you can begin to generate alternative ideas about what you can do ... to start coming up with creative ideas that are ways to reach your goal of making a contribution. I'm going to give you a hint here and ask you to consider also using the simplification tool to break down your ideas into smaller steps that you could take toward this goal.

J: [Starts to get aroused] ... but if I can't even clean my apartment ...

T: Stop ... Slow down ...

J: Okay ... give me a second, I'm going to stand up and breathe a few times.

T: Great ... I'll do it with you ... remember ... no active thinking while we're breathing ... just allow any thoughts or feelings to occur and pass. [A minute of breathing has passed.]

J: [Smiling] I guess using SSTA is one alternative.

T: It sure is! Now what else can you do?

J: Okay ... I can check the Internet to learn more about different opportunities to help people.

T: Wow, when your brain is calm you can really think creatively!

J: Or volunteer at the vet center or my church.

T: Any others?

J: I could help my nephew with his baseball game.

T: Another creative idea that could start a whole series of ideas about helping family and friends as well as charities. Now, what about your apartment? Remember my hint to simplify.

J: Well, I could do just one thing each day, that way I wouldn't get as overwhelmed and I would at least be able to say I did something.

T: Great, John! Now, what about those negative thoughts that you can't do anything useful if you have difficulty cleaning your apartment?

J: So, I would be able to get something done in my apartment if I don't try to do everything at once. That would make me feel more helpful ... and I suppose I could still do something like the volunteer work.

T: Right! If you develop this as an action plan that you can carry out, you could learn that you can do just a small part of the apartment cleaning, while at the same time, begin doing something helpful to others. I think we're on our way to overcoming some of these obstacles. Let's look at what tools you used to overcome your hopelessness about feeling useful. You used "Stop and Slow Down" to be able to listen to your feelings, with the volume turned down a bit so they were not screaming at you, and without becoming overwhelmed by them. Paying attention to your sad and angry feelings put you in touch with how much you wanted to feel useful again and contribute something to the lives of other people. It's your negative feelings put to better use. Thus, you were able to think of some creative ways to do what matters to you. You were able to think this through with a calm and reasonable mind, so you can now develop an action plan to carry out— this will give you an opportunity to learn new information: Specifically, that you can commit yourself to helping others while you slowly work on organizing your apartment. You don't have to complete the apartment organization all in one step before you can get started making a meaningful peacetime contribution to the lives of others.

J: I could also help other vets with computer skills ... that's something that I'm good at. Thanks, Doc. This has been helpful.

FUTURE FORECASTING

As a means of enhancing maintenance and generalization, potential problems that may occur in the future should also be discussed to help individuals plan accordingly and begin to associate the possibility of managing these difficulties by using the newly learned tools. More specifically, they can be given various problem checklists, such as those completed earlier (see Chapter 4), to identify any changes in their lives that might occur in the near future, both positive and negative, as a means of developing effective action plans to address them effectively. We suggest that even positive events should be addressed, such as moving to a new house, getting married, having a baby, or getting a promotion, because all such events, however positive, basically represent stress. Thus, there are likely to be differences in one's "fantasies" about the future versus the reality of change. This is not to suggest to clients that all life is filled with negativity; rather, a positive problem orientation recognizes that problems *do* exist. A quote by Theodore Rubin is apropos here—"The problem is not that there are problems. The problem is expecting otherwise and thinking that having problems is a problem."

ENDING TREATMENT

When the therapist and client agree that ending treatment is appropriate, the therapist may wish to provide additional worksheets for duplication and future use. During these final sessions, the therapist should discuss various termination issues, especially within the context of the therapeutic relationship. The therapist should also review the goals of EC-PST as discussed during the initial sessions. Clients should be asked for examples of how these goals have been met. Feedback regarding the therapist's perspective of treatment progress is also important. Areas of limitations and strengths may be addressed and discussed, and recommendations of how to maintain gains (i.e., practice, monitor self-improvement) should be provided to clients. Reinforcement is especially important during these final sessions, because clients often experience some trepidation about "losing" their support. Furthermore, people often recall the most recent message given by therapists and words of encouragement may be internalized as positive self-statements in future stressful situations.

In general, clients should be encouraged to practice the EC-PST tools in as many day-to-day situations as possible to facilitate a true incorporation of the philosophy and skills underlying this approach into their daily thoughts, feelings, and actions. They are especially encouraged to maintain all of the handouts and worksheets given to them during treatment, and to continue to refer to the Client Workbook (for availability, see the links provided in the Preface of this book).

Termination as a Problem to Be Solved

For some individuals, ending treatment itself may represent a "problem-to-be-solved." In addressing these issues, therapeutic tactics for termination are built upon the general strategy of helping patients to use those skills they learned earlier and apply them to any problems concomitant with ending treatment. For example, SSTA tools can be used when encountering feelings such as sadness, fear, anger, guilt, or abandonment. Such emotions are often mixed and represent a *powerful* signal that can help a client better understand what is happening and that a problem exists. Individuals should be encouraged to use problem definition tools to help them become more aware of what is going on and to acknowledge the loss of the therapy relationship. They should define problems to address any difficulties they are experiencing regarding leaving therapy. Each patient's goals for and personal obstacles to an optimal end of therapy can then be specified. After they are clearly defined, various strategies can be generated to meet these goals. In this manner, the last session(s) can serve as the time to self-monitor and evaluate the effectiveness of the strategies mutually chosen by the therapist and client to ease termination difficulties.

REVISITING MEGAN, DAVID, AND MARK

The three client cases that we have referred to throughout the book to illustrate the use of various EC-PST tool kits were based upon people we have worked with during the course of our practice. Although all identifying information, descriptions, and distinctive characteristics have been carefully changed to ensure their confidentiality, each case was chosen to provide examples of how EC-PST is translated to real-life settings and contexts. A summary of the outcome of treatment, including the treatment length and other relevant intervention details, are given for Megan, Mark, and David in the following section.

Summary for Megan

Megan had a long history of emotional suppression and fears of disappointing other people. During her adolescence, she discovered the anesthetic and calming effects of alcohol and this remained her primary means of coping until the time she referred herself for treatment. In one of her journal entries, she made the observation that her ability to mature and learn how to cope with life had been stunted for the past 10 years, which resulted in a type of emotional adolescence. This was a metaphor that was often useful as she continued to practice using the tools that she learned in EC-PST treatment. One particular challenge confronted by Megan and her therapist concerned was the habituated styles of avoidance and dependency that would be triggered during times of increased stress, particularly when an interpersonal confrontation or conflict was present. In addition to various emotion regulation tools she learned in EC-PST, Megan sought additional help in this regard through a mindful yoga class, which provided her with additional methods to *stop, be aware, and slow down.*

Over the course of her 15-session treatment, Megan experienced improvement in several problem areas using the Problem-Solving Worksheet format. For example, she completed a garden project in her yard with her roommate and sister and started to ride a bicycle to work to improve her fitness routine. At this point in time, Megan indicated that she had significantly improved with regard to her symptoms, and by mutual agreement, ended her treatment approximately 5 months after her initial session.

However, as Megan began to improve her skills at work and demonstrated both an increased energy and sense of competency at work, she began to encounter a competitive situation with several of her fellow workers. When this initially occurred, she was pulled to return to well-worn and largely nonconscious patterns of interpersonal avoidance and hopeless crying episodes. In addition, Megan was experiencing increased anxiety and desire for avoidance, as she faced the idea of dating and choices regarding other social activities. Megan had learned to be sensitive and follow her feelings and identify her triggers through her EC-PST treatment. As a result, she requested to reengage in treatment as a means of collaborating with the therapist to problem solve these areas as well. Megan referred to her return, which lasted about 3 months, as her "graduate course in problem solving." Megan communicated with her therapist for several years during the holidays, providing her with accounts of the positive changes in her life.

Summary of David

The case of David was selected for inclusion in this therapy manual because his treatment began with a need to focus on depressed and hopeless symptoms that were both intense and severe, which included active suicidal thoughts. However, David's treatment was actually the briefest intervention of the three cases presented. Initially, he had been almost exclusively focused on how he failed to save his father's life. His related symptoms of anger, irritability, and avoidance appeared to reflect his feelings of shame that resulted from this event. His self-punishment easily triggered anger and withdrawal from those who sought to support him, such as his wife. When he relented and agreed to attend treatment, despite a keen intelligence and high degree of education as a physician, his lack of psychological and emotional intelligence was striking. For example, he had suffered since childhood with worry and sadness regarding his admired father's lifelong struggle with depression. When he learned that his own perspectives had been shaped by his early life stress and he let go of the pressure to solve what was essentially impossible (prevent his father's suicide), he was better able to discover real effective solutions to the challenges of his own life. For example, when one of his repeated marital challenges was framed in the "language" of EC-PST ("*Your goal is to maintain the respect and love you have for your father, yet accept and acknowledge your wife's awareness of how your dad's choices did have a negative impact on your family*"), he was relieved to learn that his father's strengths could coexist with emotional vulnerabilities and self-destructive choices. This insight led to a rapid decrease in his symptoms.

David's brief treatment of 10 sessions (including the initial clinical assessment sessions) provides an example of a phenomenon that we have repeatedly observed when conducting treatment. Specifically, that deep insight is possible through the combined experience of a nonjudgmental awareness of emotional information and the planful problem-solving process. Initially, David lacked an insight regarding the intensity of his avoidance and refusal to acknowledge his father's responsibility for his suicide, which resulted in anger toward others who did and self-blame for his father's ultimate death. Previous attempts of his wife or close colleagues to "cognitively reason" with him to see a different perspective were met with David "digging in his heels" and maintaining a stronger stance. However, when engaged in asking "how" to get himself and his family closer to their goals, rather than "why" his father made the choices he did, he was able to see his love and admiration for his father as ironically the very obstacles to accepting his suicide. The insight that he could simultaneously acknowledge his father's stressful impact on his family, yet preserve the loving aspects of his legacy, allowed him to choose to live and create a more positive future for his family.

Summary of Mark

Mark was presented as a 25-year-old single Latino American artist with symptoms of self-doubt, depressed mood, anxiety, inattentiveness, past suicidal thoughts, and experiences of depersonalization. A combination of possible genetic influences and a stressful childhood with significant family difficulties resulted in a very low threshold for stress, particularly with regard to his self-concept. For example, Mark wanted to develop a more positive self-concept, but his instability was often seen in fluctuations of overconfidence or "pride" and intense self-criticism. At the initial session with his EC-PST therapist, Mark appeared to have chosen a dark, brooding, cynical, and idiosyncratic identity, which rejected other people and anticipated being continuously disappointed or abandoned.

The initial focus of his therapy provided him with a structure he lacked earlier to achieve several artistic goals. When he experienced some initial success with his artwork, he received a grant scholarship for further study in a major city and was able to eventually leave his job as a barista. During the period of time in which Mark prepared for his next move, he continued in treatment, which focused on how his early learning experiences of abandonment and mistrust often kept him anticipating that he would lose everything he had worked for. This particular emphasis was framed by Mark and his therapist as reducing the impact of chronic barriers to his problem solving. As he improved and developed greater excitement for his fellowship, Mark began to visibly change as well, cutting his hair, dressing differently, starting to date, and "daring to be normal." Mark's treatment occurred over the course of approximately 1 year and at times the frequency of sessions was prescriptively increased to twice weekly.

SUMMARY

After formal training in the four problem-solving tool kits is concluded, multiple sessions should be devoted to guided practice, during which clients address various problems they are currently experiencing across various life areas (e.g., family, health, career/job, finances, social relationships, and leisure time) using the overall SSTA approach. Such sessions can provide basic practice in the various tools, as well as the opportunity to identify possible new problem areas or any remaining problem-solving skill deficits or limitations. Clients are also directed to engage in future forecasting by predicting any changes in one's life circumstances, positive or negative, that might occur in the near future as a means of adequately addressing them via problem solving. Any problems with termination (e.g., a client feeling a loss of support) should be addressed by the therapist and client as a problem to be solved. Individuals should be encouraged to keep all handouts and worksheets for future reference and encouraged to apply them more formally if appropriate and necessary. We ended the chapter by revisiting the three patients, Megan, David, and Mark, providing brief summaries of their overall EC-PST treatment.

12

SPECIAL APPLICATIONS: SUICIDE PREVENTION AND TREATMENT, FOSTERING POSITIVE FUNCTIONING, MILITARY/VETERAN POPULATIONS

All the world is full of suffering,
it is also full of overcoming it.

—Helen Keller

This chapter provides specific suggestions and considerations regarding the relevance of emotion-centered problem-solving therapy (EC-PST) in three areas of focus:

- Reducing suicidal ideation and behaviors
- Fostering positive functioning
- Treating military service members and veterans

SUICIDALITY

Suicide continues to be a major public health concern, both nationally and internationally. According to the National Center for Health Statistics (Curtin, Warner, & Hedegaard, 2016), suicide is the 10th leading cause of death in the United States; each year, approximately 45,000 Americans die by suicide. The relationship between problem solving and suicidal ideation and behaviors has been the focus of conceptual and empirical inquiries for decades. Consider the common saying (often attributed to the television talk show host Phil Donahue)—"suicide is a permanent solution to a temporary problem." A more academic source invoking the concept of problem solving is by Edwin Shneidman, the cofounder of the

American Association of Suicidality—"the common purpose of suicide is to seek a solution; a suicidal person is seeking a solution to a problem that is generating intense suffering within him or her" (Shneidman, 1996, p. 130).

Research continues to document an important relationship between social problem-solving (SPS) deficits and suicidality (e.g., Chang, 2002; Chang & Hirsch, 2015; Grover et al., 2009; Hirsch, Chang, & Jeglic, 2012; Nezu et al., 2017; Pollock & Williams, 2004; Stern et al., 2015). Although only a small number of investigations have been conducted to date that have evaluated the efficacy of problem-solving therapy (PST)-based protocols to reduce suicidality, the extant literature basically supports its effectiveness (e.g., Choi, Marti, & Conwell, 2016; Fitzpatrick, Witte, & Schmidt, 2005; Gustavson et al., 2016; Hatcher, Sharon, Parag, & Collins, 2011; Hopko et al., 2013; Stewart, Quinn, Plever, & Emmerson, 2009).

Recently, we presented an SPS model of suicidality that focused on interplay among three major variables: chronic stress, heightened emotion reactivity, and impaired SPS (Nezu & Nezu, 2015). Specifically, we posited that the probability of a suicide attempt is increased when individuals experience high levels of chronic stress, have a heightened emotional reaction to such stress (characterized by it intensity and persistence), and are unable to, or have substantial difficulties in effectively identifying goals and pathways to such goals that are nonsuicidal in nature.

Although no study to date has evaluated this model in its entirety, we have found that SPS does serve to moderate the relationship between emotion reactivity and suicide ideation among a population of U.S. military veterans (Nezu et al., 2017) and among a sample of college students (Stern et al., 2015). Previous research has further demonstrated that SPS is a moderator of stress and suicidality (see Clum & Febbraro, 1994). Collectively, such research is in keeping with our model.

The value of this model is that it provides for a meaningful heuristic for future research to confirm or disconfirm. In addition, it offers certain clinical recommendations. More specifically, although research has shown that SPS deficits are associated with suicidal ideation and behaviors, one major thesis of this book was to emphasize the importance of identifying strong negative emotions as a crucial clinical target. Within the context of the research documenting the strong influence that stress has on people's neurobiological and psychological states, it would be important to focus on treating emotion dysregulation as a means of reducing suicide risk. Thus, we would strongly recommend that EC-PST for suicidality include all four tool kits in the following order:

- "Stop and Slow Down"
- Overcoming "Brain Overload"

- Planful Problem Solving
- Enhancing Motivation for Action (interspersed throughout treatment when appropriate)

We would argue that the intensity of self-perceived stress and suffering is so great when someone contemplates suicide such that one's ability to engage in planful decision making is extremely taxed. In the absence of concrete and specific tools to help better manage the impact of intense stress on one's brain, body, mind, spirit, and coping ability, it would be very difficult to initially learn and apply various problem-solving activities, such as defining a problem, generating alternatives, and making decisions. We are currently conducting a program evaluating such an approach to reduce suicide risk of U.S. military veterans.

FOSTERING POSITIVE FUNCTIONING

As noted earlier, ineffective SPS is related to psychopathology and behavior disturbance, but effective SPS is associated with more positive functioning. For example, recent studies indicate that SPS is associated with social self-efficacy, self-confidence, and persistence among teachers (Erözkan, 2014), self-esteem and coping among adolescents attending school (Srivastava & Kiran, 2015), extraversion, openness, conscientiousness, agreeableness, and self-esteem among college students (Koruklu, 2015), and emotional intelligence among prospective teachers (Deniz, 2013).

Thus, it makes logical sense that training in EC-PST skills can foster positive functioning among nonclinical populations. For example, a recent study found that training in rational problem-solving skills enhanced the decision-making and critical thinking skills of emergency medical personnel (Heidari & Shahbazi, 2016). Problem-solving skills training also leads to enhanced interpersonal communication among midwives working in hospitals (Modarres, Mohseni, & Shiran-Noogi, 2017).

One positive psychology variable involves hope. Snyder (2002) has defined *hope* as "the perceived capability to drive pathways to desired goals, and motivate oneself via agency thinking to use those pathways" (p. 249). Given this definition, it would appear that hope should be associated with SPS. Studies by Snyder et al. (1991) and Chang (1998) provide support for this relationship. More specifically, Chang found students characterized as "high-hope" persons reported a greater positive problem orientation and rational problem-solving style compared with "low-hope" subjects. Low-hope participants were further found to have a greater negative problem orientation and avoidant problem-solving style.

Given the aforementioned context, we offer the following series of visualization exercises to provide individuals a means of fostering hope, and, in combination with the planful problem-solving tools, it can significantly enhance goal attainment.

Lesson 1: Develop a Specific Visual Picture of the Future

Many times our personal goals are too vague and cloudy. For example, if your goal is to improve your health, what is your *visual* picture of this goal? Do you see yourself eating three well-balanced meals a day? Do you picture yourself completing 10 push-ups and running 2 miles? Do you picture yourself with a blood pressure of 120/75 mmHg, smoke-free, or meditating in the park? Do you picture playing catch with your grandchildren in the park? Likewise, a goal for more financial security may include increasing your savings to a certain amount, starting a retirement plan, or picturing yourself in your own home or apartment.

It is very important that you develop your visualization of the future in very *specific and concrete mental pictures*. Try it out right now. Describe the mental picture of what you wish to accomplish and write down a description of that picture. For example, individuals who want to learn how to scuba dive might picture themselves in warm, clear water, wearing a wet suit and scuba gear, slowly following the path of a beautiful fish. They approach the surface with a sense of enjoyment and satisfaction. Later, they picture themselves sitting in the warm sun on the deck of the boat, sharing the experience with friends.

Lesson 2: Break Down Your Visual Picture of the Future Into Small Steps

It is important to have both *short-* and *long-*term goals to visualize (remember to simplify!). For example, if your long-range visualization is seeing yourself smoke-free and walking 1 mile each day, make a series of visual images that are steps to this goal. For example, in this situation, a person may have a short-range goal of initially cutting-out smoking while on the telephone and walking at least two blocks each day. The next step might include no smoking after meals and walking five blocks a day, and so on—practice visualizing your goals by creating both short- and long-term goals in your visual images.

Lesson 3: Develop Different Types of Goals

Remember to visualize your goals in terms of things that you can accomplish. You can only make changes in yourself. For example, if your overall goal is to improve your marriage, goals, such as "my husband will not complain so much," "my wife will not drink too much," or "my husband will find me attractive," may not be reachable because they are not in your control. However, "I will be more patient," "I will communicate my concerns and disagreement with her behavior more effectively," or "I will feel more confident about the way I look" are goals that can be achieved because they involve things that *you* have control over. In the same way, goals involving physical or athletic accomplishments should be focused on improving your performance, not simply on winning a game or an event. Winning involves other players' performances—something over which you have no control. In this way, your goals are actually reachable.

Lesson 4: Remove the Barriers to Your Goals Through Visualization

In this lesson, you will travel, in your imagination, to the future, and visit yourself 5 years from now. In this image, remember that anything goes—so picture it just the way that you want it to be. You will look around at your possessions, notice your accomplishments, see who you are with, be aware of how you spend your leisure time, and so on. Remember, it is a good idea to have a friend or family member with a "calming" voice record the "script" given in the next section.

Before you begin, find a comfortable location to practice visualization, such as a recliner, couch, bed, or soft floor covering. Remember to loosen your clothing, remove glasses or contact lenses, and lower the lights to create a more calming effect in the room. Practice once every day for at least 1 week. Practicing this tool is important—trying this strategy only once or twice will not produce the kind of results that you hope for. Therefore, practice is essential. A single session will take about 10 to 15 minutes to complete. Use positive statements or affirmations when you begin the visualization. These should be short, positive statements that state your intention to yourself, for example:

- "I will experience success in my mind."
- "I can have peace within myself."
- "A goal is a possible future."
- "If I can dream it, I can do it!"
- "I can put distractions aside for now."

    (Think of some new ones yourself!)

VISUALIZATION INSTRUCTIONS

> [Reader: Read softly and slowly; pause between sentences throughout.] *Close your eyes and relax—let go of any tension in your body. Now go to a safe and tranquil place in your mind—a special, outdoor place. Look around, take note*

of what you see nearby as well as in the distance. Describe the scene silently to yourself. Now look for a path—this is your path toward the future. Notice a tree stump or log across the path. Imagine that this piece of wood in front of the path is getting in the way of your ability to walk down the path. This piece of wood is your own hesitation or fear of changing and walking toward your goals. Step over it; step over this log and visualize overcoming your hesitation, overcoming your fears.

Now, as you walk along the path, you come across a steep hill. This hill is your doubt about yourself. Slowly keep walking up the hill, even though you are not absolutely sure of what you will find at the top of the hill. With each step, begin to let yourself become more self-confident that you will reach your goals. When you reach the top, you walk through a dark forest of trees that blocks out the sunlight. This forest has all the obstacles that block you from seeing your final goals—interference from others, day-to-day problems that keep you from working on your goals, or your own fears that you don't deserve what you want. However, you push past the trees to a clearing and you are now in a sunny field. You can see your home in the distance. This is your home 5 or 10 years in the future. Go into your home and look around. What do you see? How many rooms are there? How are they decorated? What things do you own? What pictures or photographs do you see? Look at yourself in the mirror. What do you look like? What are you wearing? Look at your family come in. How do they act toward each other? Listen to yourself as you picture yourself in 5 years. Listen to yourself as you talk to people or make phone calls—what do you say? Follow yourself to work or school. What are your achievements? What are your activities? Watch yourself at leisure. What are you doing? For example, maybe you're watching TV, race-car driving, sailing, fishing, listening to classical music?

Now ask yourself how you feel. In other words, look back over your life of the last 5 years—what are you especially glad that you had the chance to experience? What are you most proud of? Maybe you gave a successful speech, ran a marathon, had several good friends, raised self-confident children, or people knew that they could count on you. Anything is possible. Remember—visualize what you hope and wish to be in the future—not what is going on now!

When you have finished exploring, let your images fade away and come back to the present the here and now. Open your eyes and make a brief list of the images while they are still fresh in your mind. Pick one or two major goals for your future and write down the details and the specific visual images that come to mind for them.

Lesson 5: Write Down Your 5-Year Goal

Choose just one image that you had from the previous visualization exercise and write down your 5-year goal. It could be a personal, physical, career, family, or social goal. Remember to be very specific and concrete, as explained in the first lesson.

Lesson 6: Break Your Goal Into 1-Year Goals

Look at the goal again, and break it down into smaller 1-year goals—one goal for each year. These would be smaller steps leading to your larger goal. Write these down—externalize!

Lesson 7: Break Your First-Year Goal Into Smaller Steps

Now look at your first 1-year goal and break it down one more time into several steps to achieve over the course of a year. Write these down. Once again, remember to be very concrete and specific.

Lesson 8: Create a Daily Visualization

Create a visualization for each day to accomplish the steps toward these goals. In your imagination, picture yourself clearly carrying out the steps needed to achieve your immediate goals. For example, you might be picturing yourself exercising 2 days per week for the next 4 months. If so, visualize yourself in workout clothes; imagine that you will experience a sense of pride in arranging for enough time to spend at the gym. Imagine your favorite music playing on a personal smartphone; visualize your body feeling strong and the perspiration dripping off your skin as you are working hard.

As you reach each goal that you have visualized, begin daily visualizations of the next step in your series of goals, finally leading up to your 1-year goal. After that, develop a series of visualization steps toward the next year's goal.

In general, use the basic strategy of visualizing future goals to develop a "road map" of steps that you need to take to achieve such goals, whether this involves solving a particularly stressful problem at present, reaching toward a goal that involves only a week, or going for something that involves a much longer time. In developing such road maps, write down both overall goals and smaller steps or objectives leading to these goals.

Visualize Reaching Each Step and Then "Go for It!"

Remember though—sometimes we set unrealistic initial goals or set goals that depend on other people. If either of these situations occurs, maybe you need to redesign your smaller goals to those that are reachable in a smaller period of time and involve situations that you have control over and do not necessarily require others for change to occur.

MILITARY SERVICE MEMBERS AND VETERANS

Applying EC-PST with veterans and military personnel does not necessarily require changes in the inherent structure of the protocol. Rather, it is our experience that it is important to understand how to adapt EC-PST within the context of understanding and appreciating the military culture. The following are helpful sources for clinicians unfamiliar with working with active service members or veterans:

- Center for Deployment Psychology, Uniformed Services University of the Health Sciences: https://deploymentpsych.org/military-culture
- Department of Veterans Affairs: www.mentalhealth.va.gov/community providers/military_culture.asp
- Substance Abuse and Mental Health Services Administration: www.samhsa.gov/sites/default/files/military_white_paper_final.pdf

As noted earlier, we have worked with the Department of Veterans Affairs (VA) and the Department of Defense to help develop *Moving Forward*, a four-session group program based on EC-PST principles, that is currently being implemented across multiple VA medical centers in the United States. Initial program evaluation data underscore the efficacy of the program. Specifically, results from 479 veterans who completed the entire program (of an initial 621) indicated significant improvements in SPS, resilience, and overall distress levels (Tenhula et al., 2014). Moreover, data demonstrated that the *Moving Forward* program was feasible and well received by veterans.

The following is an excerpt from the face-to-face program that adapted the basic treatment rationale to this population:

> *Your military training has taught you to react automatically under stressful situations, which has enabled you to survive, and possibly thrive or excel, in many situations. When we do something frequently, it often becomes a "habit." We call this "overlearning"—in other words, we engage in certain behaviors in a certain way because it's a habit, rather than because we had to think about it. Take driving, for example. We all drive without thinking "how do I stop the car? how do I make a left turn? how do I signal that I am making a right turn?" Instead, we just drive. Now imagine, however, that you wake up one day and all the cars have steering wheels on the right side and everyone drives on the left side. Of course your basic driving skills would help you to learn more quickly to adjust to this change. BUT … given all the years of driving that you have already done, overcoming some of those "overlearned" driving habits can interfere with how easy or difficult this adjustment can be. To drive well, it is likely that you would need to be more thoughtful and planful in this new environment. In other words, you need to do something differently to "solve this new problem," that is, the problem of driving well and not causing an accident. In a similar way, our ability to "move forward" often requires us to be more thoughtful and planful to solve many of life's problems.*
>
> *As a veteran, some of the "overlearned" ways of handling stressful situations that helped you to survive during your military service or in a combat zone can now actually interfere with your daily functioning. For example, scanning the roads in Afghanistan helped you survive by locating improvised explosive devices (IEDs); however, scanning the road as a civilian in the United States can have a significant impact on your driving, personal safety, and the welfare of others. Another example might be that in the past following orders was automatic, whereas now you have so many decisions to make for yourself. Being able to achieve your goals successfully may require a different way of thinking, feeling, and behaving; not necessarily better or worse, but different. Our goal is not to change your personality—rather, this program will help you to learn how to cope better with stress in your life. In other words, how to "move forward."*

In addition to the face-to-face protocol, various iterations of the program have been developed and are currently under evaluation, including a program for veterans in home-based primary care (i.e., those in need of homebound care), as well as the Internet-based course (www.veterantraining.va.gov) and the smartphone app. Note that these last two resources are free and can serve as meaningful adjuncts to face-to-face treatment.

SUMMARY

This last chapter provided points for consideration when planning to conduct EC-PST with two specific populations—individuals at risk for suicide and both active and veteran members of the armed services. We also provided tips for applying EC-PST as a positive psychology approach with a specific focus on fostering hope and goal attainment.

REFERENCES

Chang, E. C. (1998). Hope, problem-solving ability, and coping in a college student population: Some implications for theory and practice. *Journal of Clinical Psychology, 54,* 953–962. doi:10.1002/(SICI)1097-4679(199811)54:7<953::AID-JCLP9>3.0.CO;2-F

Chang, E. C. (2002). Predicting suicide ideation in an adolescent population: Examining the role of social problem solving as a moderator and a mediator. *Personality and Individual Differences, 32,* 1279–1291. doi:10.1016/S0191-8869(01)00118-0

Chang, E. C., & Hirsch, J. K. (2015). Social problem solving under assault: Understanding the impact of sexual assault on the relation between social problem solving and suicidal risk in female college students. *Cognitive Therapy and Research, 39,* 403–413. doi:10.1007/s10608-014-9664-2

Choi, N. G., Marti, C. N., & Conwell, Y. (2016). Effect of problem-solving therapy on depressed low-income homebound older adults' death/suicidal ideation and hopelessness. *Suicide and Life-Threatening Behavior, 46,* 323–336. doi:10.1111/sltb.12195

Clum, G. A., & Febbraro, G. A. (1994). Stress, social support, and problem-solving appraisal/skills: Prediction of suicide severity within a college sample. *Journal of Psychopathology and Behavioral Assessment, 16,* 69–83. doi:10.1007/BF02229066

Curtin, S. C., Warner, M., & Hedegaard, H. (2016, April). Increase in suicide in the United States, 1999–2014. *NCHS Data Brief,* (241), 1–8.

Deniz, S. (2013). The relationship between emotional intelligence and problem-solving skills in prospective teachers. *Educational Research and Reviews, 8,* 2339–2345. doi:10.5897/ERR2013.1584

Erözkan, A. (2014). Analysis of social problem solving and social self-efficacy in prospective teachers. *Educational Sciences: Theory and Practice, 14,* 447–455. doi:10.12738/estp.2014.2.2014

Fitzpatrick, K. K., Witte, T. K., & Schmidt, N. B. (2005). Randomized controlled trial of a brief problem-orientation intervention for suicidal ideation. *Behavior Therapy, 36,* 323–333. doi:10.1016/S0005-7894(05)80114-5

Grover, K. E., Green, K. L., Pettit, J. W., Monteith, L. L., Garza, M. J., & Venta, A. (2009). Problem solving moderates the effects of life event stress and chronic stress on suicidal behaviors in adolescence. *Journal of Clinical Psychology, 65*, 1281–1290. doi:10.1002/jclp.20632

Gustavson, K. A., Alexopoulos, G. S., Niu, G. C., McCulloch, C., Meade, T., & Areán, P. A. (2016). Problem-solving therapy reduces suicidal ideation in depressed older adults with executive dysfunction. *American Journal of Geriatric Psychiatry, 24*, 11–17. doi:10.1016/j.jagp.2015.07.010

Hatcher, S., Sharon, C., Parag, V., & Collins, N. (2011). Problem-solving therapy for people who present to hospital with self-harm: Zelen randomised controlled trial. *British Journal of Psychiatry, 199*, 310–316. doi:10.1192/bjp.bp.110.090126

Heidari, M., & Shahbazi, S. (2016). Effect of training problem-solving skill on decision-making and critical thinking of personnel at medical emergencies. *International Journal of Critical Illness and Injury Science, 6*, 182. doi:10.4103/2229-5151.195445

Hirsch, J. K., Chang, E. C., & Jeglic, E. L. (2012). Social problem solving and suicidal behavior: Ethnic differences in the moderating effects of loneliness and life stress. *Archives of Suicide Research, 16*, 303–315. doi:10.1080/13811118.2013.722054

Hopko, D. R., Funderburk, J. S., Shorey, R. C., McIndoo, C. C., Ryba, M. M., File, A. A., … Vitulano, M. (2013). Behavioral activation and problem-solving therapy for depressed breast cancer patients: Preliminary support for decreased suicidal ideation. *Behavior Modification, 37*, 747–767. doi:10.1177/0145445513501512

Koruklu, N. (2015). Personality and social problem-solving: The mediating role of self-esteem. *Educational Sciences: Theory and Practice, 15*, 481–487. doi:10.12738/estp.2015.2.2601

Modarres, M., Mohseni, H., & Shiran-Noogi, P. (2017). The comparison of the effectiveness of problem solving skill education with two methods of workshop and educational booklet on interpersonal communication of midwives. *Research in Medical Education, 9*, 28–119. doi:10.29252/rme.9.3.28

Nezu, A. M., & Nezu, C. M. (2015, September). *Social problem-solving model of suicide prevention.* Invited address. Air Force National Suicide Prevention Summit, Andrews Joint Base, MD.

Nezu, A. M., Nezu, C. M., Stern, J. B., Greenfield, A. P., Diaz, C., & Hays, A. M. (2017). Social problem solving moderates emotion reactivity in predicting suicide ideation among U.S. Veterans. *Military Behavioral Health, 5*, 417–426. doi:10.1080/21635781.2017.1337595

Pollock, L. R., & Williams, J. M. (2004). Problem-solving in suicide attempters. *Psychological Medicine, 34*, 163–167. doi:10.1017/S0033291703008092

Shneidman, E. S. (1996). *The suicidal mind.* New York, NY: Oxford University Press.

Snyder, C. R. (2002). Hope theory: Rainbows in the mind. *Psychological Inquiry, 13*, 249–275. doi:10.1207/S15327965PLI1304_01

Snyder, C. R., Harris, C., Anderson, J. R., Holleran, S. A., Irving, L. M., Sigmon, S. T., … Harney, P. (1991). The will and the ways: Development and validation of an individual-differences measure of hope. *Journal of Personality and Social Psychology, 60*, 570–585. doi:10.1037/0022-3514.60.4.570

Srivastava, P., & Kiran, M. (2015). The relationship between perceived stress, self esteem, way of coping and problem-solving ability among school going adolescents. *Journal of Psychosocial Research, 10*, 199–209.

Stern, J. B., Nezu, A. M., Nezu, C. M., Greenfield, A. P., Diaz, C. E., & Hays, A. M. (2015, November). *Social problem solving, emotional reactivity, suicidal ideation, and self-harm among college students.* Presented at the Annual Convention of the Association of Behavioral and Cognitive Therapies, Chicago, IL.

Stewart, C. D., Quinn, A., Plever, S., & Emmerson, B. (2009). Comparing cognitive behavior therapy, problem solving therapy, and treatment as usual in a high risk population. *Suicide and Life-Threatening Behavior, 39,* 538–547. doi:10.1521/suli.2009.39.5.538

Tenhula, W. N., Nezu, A. M., Nezu, C. M., Stewart, M. O., Miller, S. A., Steele, J., & Karlin, B. E. (2014). Moving Forward: A problem-solving training program to foster veteran resilience. *Professional Psychology: Research and Practice, 45,* 416–424. doi:10.1037/a0037150

INDEX